Physics 11

A Laboratory-Based Course

2009 Edition

Author
Gordon R. Gore

Kamloops BC
Canada
Copyright, Gordon R. Gore

Published and Distributed by:
Western Campus Resources
485 Mountain Highway
North Vancouver, BC V7J 2L3
Telephone: (604)-988-1055; Toll free 1-800-995-5283
Fax: (604)-988-3309; Toll free fax 1-877-977-4539
Email: info@westerncampus.ca

ISBN: 13 - 978-0-9685526-7-4
10 – 0-9685526-7-6

Printed in Canada by Hignell Book Printers

A portion of the sale of this book will be donated to BIG Little Science Centre in Kamloops,
BC

Preface

This book may be used for an introductory course in physics, in which emphasis is placed on concrete demonstrations of physical phenomena and on *truly* 'hands-on' student laboratory activity.

The author draws on many years of teaching experience to make physics understandable and enjoyable. He earnestly believes that physics can and should be fun to learn. By 'fun', the author means 'engaging' and 'involving', as when one pursues a favorite hobby. The book provides a compromise between a traditional, highly mathematical, 'broad coverage' approach, and a purely conceptual approach. The book attempts to provide *manageable challenges* for students.

This book contains many well-known demonstrations of physics principles, and a *large* number of student investigations. Some of these are descriptive in nature, while others are more analytical. Enough emphasis is placed on measurement and graphical analysis that students should be well prepared if they take a second course in physics in high school or at a post-secondary institution.

Exercises and **Chapter Review Questions** vary in difficulty and in style. Some require non-mathematical, concept-oriented answers while others involve manipulation of formulas that students have learned in the text. *Investigations* frequently end with optional **Challenges** for students who wish to pursue topics in detail. Solutions to numerical problems are provided at the back of the book.

At the end of each chapter, a self-test called *Test Yourself!* is provided. Students may write these practice tests, then check their work using the Answer Key at the back of the book.

The author sincerely hopes that students who use this book will come away from their first physics course feeling 'glad they took physics'.

Credits

All photographs in this book are by the author. Sincere thanks to students who volunteered as subjects for photographs in the book: **Norma MacDonald** (page 21), **Steve Stanyer** (page 22), **Allison Denby** (page 44), **Simon Morris** (page 60), and **Jamie Vowles** (page 69).

Computer drawings are by **Moira Rockwell**, science laboratory assistant in Mission, B.C. Cartoon drawings are by **Ehren Stillman** of Abbotsford, B.C., one of my former physics students at **Hatzic Secondary School** in Mission. Ehren Stillman's cartoons have appeared in **The Physics Teacher (AAPT)**, **The Science Teacher (NSTA)** and in **Dr. Jim Hebden's** **Chemistry 11** and **12** books, as well as in all my science and physics books.

Contents

Chapter 1 Distance, Time and Speed

Kinematics

How far did it travel? How long did it take? How fast did it move? Did it speed up or slow down? These are typical questions one might ask about any object that moves, whether it is a car, a planet, an electron or a molecule. All of these questions fall under the heading of **kinematics:** the study of the motion of objects, without reference to the cause of the motion. In kinematics, we learn how to describe the motion of objects in terms of measurable variables such as time, distance, speed and acceleration.

1.1 Time

Any measurement of time involves some sort of event that repeats itself at regular intervals. For example, a year is the time it takes the earth to revolve around the sun; a day is the time it takes the earth to rotate on its axis; a month is approximately the time it takes the moon to revolve around the earth. (Perhaps *moonth* would be a better name for this time interval.)

All devices used to measure time contain some sort of regularly vibrating object such as a pendulum, a quartz crystal, a tuning fork, a metronome or even vibrating electrons. In *Investigation 1-1,* you will experiment with the properties of a simple pendulum that make it a useful timing device. When a pendulum undergoes regularly repeated movements, each complete movement is called a **cycle**, and the time required for each cycle is called its **period**.

Investigation 1-1   Making a Pendulum Clock

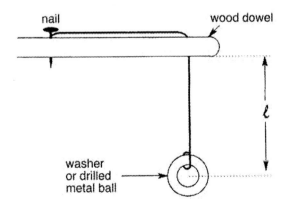

Figure 1.1

Purpose: To learn how a pendulum can be used as a clock.

Procedure

1. Prepare a simple pendulum by tying a string to a **pendulum bob** (either a large washer, as in **Figure 1.1**, or a drilled metal ball). Feed the string through the opening of the pendulum support. (Avoid winding the string *around* the support rod. If you do this, the length of the pendulum changes during a swing.)

2. Start by adjusting the length (ℓ) of the pendulum so that it is as close to being 10.00 cm as you can make it. Measure ℓ from the bottom of the pendulum clamp to the *centre* of the bob, as shown in **Figure 1.1**.

3. Push the bob a small distance (say, 2 cm) to one side and let it swing freely. To get a rough idea of how long the pendulum takes to make one swing, use a stopwatch to measure the time it takes for the bob to swing from the highest point on one side of the swing to the highest point on the other side, then back to its starting position. The time it takes the pendulum bob to complete a full swing like this is called the **period** (*T*) of the pendulum. Try measuring the period of *one* swing several times with your stopwatch. (Why do you think your measurements are so inconsistent?)

4. To obtain a more reliable measurement of the period of the pendulum, you will now measure the time for a large number of swings (50) and find the average time for one swing by dividing by 50. Set your 10.00 cm pendulum swinging through a *small* arc, as before. Start counting backward (3, 2, 1, 0, 1, 2, 3, 4, etc.) and start your stopwatch at **0**. Stop your watch after 50 swings, and record the time your pendulum took to complete 50 swings.

Table 1

Length of Pendulum	Time for 50 Swings	Time for 1 Swing
ℓ		Period, *T*
(cm)	(s)	(s)
10.00		
15.00		
20.00		
25.00		
30.00		
40.00		
50.00		
60.00		
70.00		
80.00		
90.00		
100.0		

5. To figure out the period of the pendulum, divide the time for 50 swings by 50.0. Record the period, *T*, in a table like **Table 1.** Check your result by repeating the measurement. If necessary, repeat a third time.

6. Measure the period of your pendulum for each of the lengths in **Table 1.** Record all your results in **Table 1.**

7. Prepare a graph with headings and labelling like those in **Figure 1.2**. In this experiment, the period of the pendulum depends on its length, so the period is called the **dependent variable.** The dependent variable goes on the **Y-axis.** Length is the **independent variable.** (We chose what its values would be.) Length is on the X-axis. Plot period against length using all your data from **Table 1.** Use a small dot with a circle around it to make its position more visible. (See **Figure 1.2** for a sample point.) When you have plotted all the points, draw one smooth curve through as many of the points as possible. (If one or two points are obvious errors, ignore them when drawing your curve.)

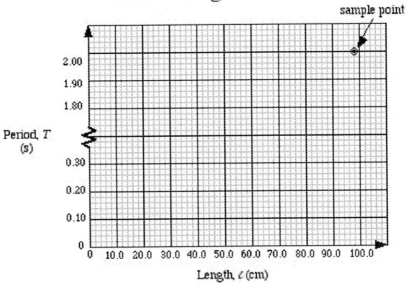

Period vs Length of a Pendulum

Figure 1.2

Concluding Questions

1. According to your graph of period vs length, how long must your pendulum be if it is to be used as (a) a 'one-second clock'? (b) a 'two-second clock'? (Such a pendulum takes one second to swing one way, and one second to swing back.)

2. To increase the period of your pendulum from one second to two, by how many times (to the nearest whole number) must you increase its length?

Follow-up

Make pendulums with the lengths you obtain from your graph for pendulums with periods of 1 s and 2 s. See if the lengths predicted by the graph actually do produce 1 s and 2 s 'clocks'.

Challenges!

1. *Predict* what length a 3.0 s pendulum clock would have to be. Test your prediction by experiment.

2. *Predict* what will happen to the period of a pendulum if you double the mass of the pendulum bob. Test your prediction.

3. Will the period of a pendulum change after it has been swinging for a while? Test your answer by experimenting!

1.2 Frequency

For objects that have a regularly repeated motion, each complete movement is called a **cycle**. The time during which the cycle is completed is called the **period** of the cycle. The number of cycles completed in one unit of time is called the **frequency** (*f*) of the moving object. You may be familiar with the frequencies of several everyday objects. For example, the turntable of an old phonograph record player may have frequencies of 33 rpm (rotations per minute), 45 rpm or 78 rpm. A pendulum 24.85 cm long has a frequency of one cycle per second. A car engine may have a frequency of several thousand 'rpm'. Tuning forks may have frequencies such as 256 vibrations per second, 510 vibrations per second, and so on.

A frequency of one cycle per second is called a **hertz (Hz)**. Higher frequencies (such as radio signal frequencies) may be expressed in **kilohertz (kHz)** or even **megahertz (MHz)**, where 1 kHz is 1 000 Hz, and 1 MHz is 1 000 000 Hz.

Figure 1.3

The Recording Timer

In *Investigation 1-2,* you will use a device called a **recording timer**. See **Figure 1.3**. The timer is a modified electric buzzer. A moving arm driven by an electromagnet vibrates with a constant frequency, and each time it vibrates, it strikes a piece of carbon paper. The carbon paper makes a small dot on a moving piece of ticker tape. The small dots are a record of both time and distance. If you know the **frequency** of vibration of the timer, you can figure out the **period** of time between the dots, because period (*T*) and frequency (*f*) are reciprocals of one another. [$T = 1/f$, and $f = 1/T$.] If you measure the distance between the dots, this will tell you how far the object attached to the tape has moved. Knowing both distance and time, you can also calculate **speed**, since the speed of an object is the distance travelled divided by the time.

Investigation 1-2   Measuring the Frequency of a Recording Timer

Purpose: To measure the frequency of a recording timer and calculate its period.

Procedure

1. Load the recording timer with a fresh piece of carbon paper. Pass a piece of ticker tape through the guiding staples, so that the carbon side of the paper faces the ticker tape. When the timer arm vibrates, it should leave a black mark on the tape.

2. To measure the frequency of the recording timer, you must determine how many times the arm swings in one second. Since it is difficult to time one second with any reasonable accuracy, let the timer run for 5 s (as precisely as you can measure it), then count the number of carbon dots made on the tape and divide by five. Practice moving the tape through the timer until you find a suitable speed that will spread the dots out for easy counting, but not waste ticker tape.

3. When you are ready, start the tape moving through the timer. Have your partner start the timer and the stopwatch simultaneously. Stop the timer when 5 s have elapsed. Count the number of dots made in 5 seconds, and then calculate the frequency of your timer in hertz (Hz).

Concluding Questions

1. What was the frequency of your recording timer, in Hz?

2. Make an estimate of the **possible error** in the timing of your experiment. (It might be 0.10 s, 0.20 s, or whatever you think is likely). Calculate the **percent possible error** in your timing. To do this, simply divide your estimate of the possible error in timing by 5.0 s, and then multiply by 100.

   Example: If you estimate your timing error to be 0.50 s, then
   $$\text{Percent Possible Error in Timing} = \frac{0.50 \text{ s}}{5.0 \text{ s}} \times 100\% = 10\%.$$

3. Your calculated **frequency** will have the same percent possible error as you calculated for your timing error. Calculate the **range** within which your timer's frequency probably falls.

   Example: If you calculate the frequency to be 57 Hz, and the possible error is 10%, then the **range** is 57 Hz ± 5.7 Hz, or between 51.3 Hz and 62.7 Hz. Rounded off, the range is between 51 Hz and 63 Hz. You might therefore conclude that the frequency of your timer is 57 ± 6 Hz.

4. If your timer operates on household voltage, its frequency (in North America) should be 60 Hz. Is 60 Hz within your estimated range for your timer?

5. (a) What is the **period** of your timer?

   (b) How many dots on the ticker tape represent
   (i) 1.0 s?
   (ii) 0.10 s?

1.3 Speed

The **speed** of an object such as a car is defined as the distance it travels in a unit of time. For highway traffic, speeds are measured in kilometres per hour (km/h). Typical highway speed limits are 80 km/h, 100 km/h and 120 km/h. Within city limits, speed limits may be 60 km/h, 50 km/h or 30 km/h (school zone or playground). The average speed of an athlete in a 100 m dash might be approximately 9.0 m/s. The speed of sound is 330 m/s, while the speed of light is approximately 300 000 000 m/s, or 300 000 km/s.

If you make a long journey by car, you might be interested in calculating your **average speed** for the trip. For example, if you travel a distance of 450 km in a time of 6.0 h, you would calculate your average speed by dividing the total distance by the total time.

$$\textbf{Average Speed} = \frac{\textbf{Total Distance}}{\textbf{Total Time}} = \frac{\textbf{450 km}}{\textbf{6.0 h}} = \textbf{75 km/h.}$$

The symbol used for speed is v, and for average speed, $\bar{v}$. The formula for calculating average speed from distance (d) and time (t) is therefore:

$$\bar{v} = \frac{d}{t}.$$

If you are driving along the highway and spot a police car parked beside the road with its radar aimed at your car, you will be less interested in your average speed and more concerned with your **instantaneous speed** (how fast your car is going at this instant in time!) Your speedometer will indicate what your instantaneous speed is.

Investigation 1-3 Measuring the Speed of a Model Car

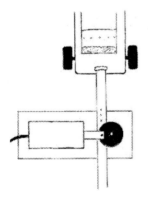

Figure 1.4

Purpose: To measure the speed of a model car, such as a radio-controlled vehicle.

Procedure

1. Remove a 5.0 m length of ticker tape from a roll. Pass one end of it through a recording timer, and then tape it to a battery-powered toy car. (**Figure 1.4**)

2. Turn on the timer and let the car travel at its full speed until all the tape has passed through the timer.

3. Mark the position on the tape of (a) the starting dot at time 0 s, (b) the 60th dot, (c) the 120th dot, (d) the 180th dot, and so on until you run out of tape.

4. Measure how far the car travelled during the first second (0 to 60 dots), second second (60 to 120 dots), third second (120 to 180 dots), and so on.

Concluding Questions

1. What was the average speed of the toy car during each of the first five one-second intervals of the trip?

2. Why might the average speed of the car during the first one-second interval perhaps be less than the average speed later in the trip?

3. Describe a way to measure the speed of vehicles passing your school. (*No! Do not use ticker tape!*)

Exercises

1. (a)   What is the difference between average speed and instantaneous speed?
   (b)   Under what condition may average speed and instantaneous speed be the same?

2. A tourist travels 320 km in 3.6 h. What is her average speed for the trip?

3. A trucker travels 65 km at an average speed of 85 km/h. How long does the trip take?

4. If your car averages 92 km/h for a 5.0 h trip, how far will you go?

5. A car moves with a steady speed of 84 km/h for 45 min, then 96 km/h for 20 min.
   (a)   What was the total distance travelled during the whole trip?
   (b)   What is its average speed for the whole trip?

6. An object is moving with uniformly increasing speed. Its speed at time zero is 0 m/s.
   (a)   If its average speed during the first second is 14 m/s, at what time will its instantaneous speed be 14 m/s?
   (b)   What is its instantaneous speed at the end of the first second?

7. The speed of light in space is 300 000 km/s. How far does light travel in:
   (a) one minute?
   (b) one hour?
   (c) one day?
   (d) one year?

1.4 Significant Digits

Imagine you are planning to paint a room in your house. To estimate how much paint you need to buy, you must know only the approximate dimensions of the walls. The rough estimate for one wall might be 8 m x 3 m. If, however, you are going to paste wallpaper on your wall and you require a neat, precise fit, you will probably make your measurements to the nearest millimetre. A proper measurement made for this purpose might look like this: 7.685 m x 2.856 m.

The **number of digits** in the written value indicates the **precision** of a measurement. In the estimate of the wall size for determining how much paint is needed to cover a wall, the measurements (8 m x 3 m) have only *one significant digit (figure)* each. They are accurate to the nearest metre. In the measurements used to install wallpaper, the measurements had *four significant digits (figures)*. They were accurate to the nearest millimetre. They were more *precise*.

If you are planning to buy a very old used car, the salesman may ask you how much you want to spend. You might reply by giving him a rough estimate of 'around six hundred dollars'. This figure of six hundred dollars has one significant digit. You might write it as $600, but the zeros in this case are used simply to place the decimal point. When you buy the car, and write a check for the full sum, you have to be more precise. For example, you might pay $589.96. This 'measurement' has *five significant digits*. Of course, if you really *did* pay exactly six hundred dollars, you would write the check for $600.00. In this case, all the zeros are measured digits, and this measurement has five significant digits!

You can see that zeros are sometimes significant digits (measured zeros) and sometimes not. The measurer should make it clear whether the zeros are significant digits or just decimal-placing zeros.

Example 1

You measure the length of a ticker tape to be seven centimetres, three millimetres and around one half a millimetre long. How do you write down this measurement? You could write it several ways, and *all* are 'correct':

7.35 cm, 73.5 mm, or 0.0735 m.

Each of these measurements is the same. Only the measuring *units* differ. Each measurement has *three significant digits*. The zeros in 0.0735 m are used only to place the decimal.

Example 2

The volume of a liquid is said to be 600 mL. How precise is this measurement? Did the measurer mean it was 'around six hundred millilitres'? Or was it six hundred to the nearest millilitre? Perhaps the volume was measured to the nearest tenth of a millilitre. Only the measurer really knows. Writing the volume as 600 mL is somewhat ambiguous. To be unambiguous, such a measurement might be expressed in **scientific notation**. To do this, the measurement is converted to the product of a number containing the intended number of significant digits (using one digit to the left of the decimal point) and a power of ten. For example, if you write 6×10^2 mL, you are estimating to the nearest hundred millilitres. If you write 6.0 x 10² mL, you are estimating to the nearest ten millilitres. A measurement to the nearest millilitre would be 6.00 x 10² mL. The zeros here are *measured zeros,* not just decimal-placing zeros. They are *significant digits.*

If it is not convenient to use scientific notation, you must indicate in some other way that a zero is a *measured zero.* For example, if the volume of a liquid is measured to the nearest mL to be '600.' mL, the decimal point will tell the reader that you measured to the nearest mL, and that both zeros are measured zeros. '600. mL' means the same as 6.00 x 10² mL.

Precision and Accuracy

The number of significant digits used to express the result of a measurement indicates how precise the measurement was. A person's height measurement of 1.895 m is more precise than a measurement of 1.9 m.

A measurement can be very precise, yet very inaccurate. In 1895, a scientist estimated the time it takes planet Venus to rotate on its axis (its period of rotation) to be 23 h, 57 min, 36.2396 s. [**George Ohring**, *Weather on the Planets* (Science Study Series, Anchor Books, Doubleday & Company, Inc., NY 1966), page 25.] This is a very precise measurement! Unfortunately, it was found out later that the period of rotation of Venus is closer to *243 days!* The latter measurement is much less precise, but probably a good deal more accurate!

There is no such thing as a 'perfectly accurate measurement'. Measurements are always subject to some **uncertainty.** Consider the following sources of experimental error:

Systematic Errors

Systematic errors may result from using an instrument that is in some way inaccurate. For example, if a wooden metre stick is worn at one end and you measure from this end, every reading will be 'too high'. If an ammeter needle is not properly 'zeroed', all the readings taken with the meter will be too high or too low. Thermometers must be regularly checked for accuracy and corrections made to eliminate systematic errors in temperature readings.

Random Errors

Random errors occur in almost any measurement. For example, imagine you make five different readings of the length of a laboratory bench. You might obtain results such as: 1.626 m, 1.628 m, 1.624 m, 1.626 m and 1.625 m. You might average these measurements and express the length of the bench in this way: 1.626 ± 0.002 m. This is a way of saying that your average measurement was 1.626 m, but the measurements, due to random errors, range between 1.624 m and 1.628 m.

Other Errors

Regardless of the accuracy and precision of the measuring instrument, errors may arise when you, the experimenter, interact with the instrument. For example, if you measure the thickness of a piece of cellophane using a micrometer caliper, your reading will be very precise but inaccurate if you tighten the caliper so much that you crush the cellophane with the caliper!

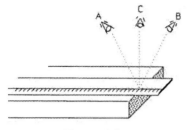

Figure 1.5

Which observer will obtain too low a reading?
Which observer will obtain too high a reading?

A common personal error made by inexperienced experimenters is failing to read scales with one's eye(s) in the proper position. In **Figure 1.5**, for example, only observer **C** will obtain the correct measurement for the length of the block.

1.5 Combining Measurements

A. Adding or Subtracting Measurements

Imagine that you have a laboratory bench that is 1.75*6* m long. The last digit (italicized) is an estimate to the nearest millimetre. You might call it an uncertain digit. Perhaps a truer measure might be 1.75*5* m or 1.75*7* m. Often you must estimate the last digit in a measurement when you guess what a reading is between the smallest divisions on the measuring scale. This is true whether you are using a metre stick, a graduated cylinder, a chemical balance or an ammeter.

Now imagine that you decide to add some thin plastic trim to the two ends of your bench. The trim has a width of 2.*2* mm, which is 0.002*2* m. What is the total length of the bench with the new trim added?

You add the widths of the two trimmed edges to the original length of the bench, like this:

$$
\begin{array}{ll}
1.756 & m \\
0.0022 & m \\
\underline{0.0022} & m \\
1.7604 & m = 1.760 \ m
\end{array}
$$

There is no point in carrying the last digit in the total. Since the *6* in 1.75*6* is uncertain, this makes the *0* in 1.760*4* also uncertain, and the *4* following it a meaningless number. The proper way to write the total width of the bench is with just one uncertain digit, 1.76*0* m.

Now imagine you have a graduated cylinder containing 12.0*0* mL of water. You carefully lower a glass marble into the graduated cylinder, and observe that the water level rises to 14.2*0* mL. What is the volume of the glass marble? To find out, you subtract the two measurements:

$$
\begin{array}{l}
14.20 \\
\underline{-12.00} \\
2.20 \quad mL.
\end{array}
$$

Notice that when the two measurements are subtracted, you lose a significant figure in this particular situation. What if the object added to the water was a small lead pellet, and the volume increased from 12.0*0* mL to 12.2*0* mL? The volume of the pellet would be 0.2*0* mL. This measurement has only two significant figures. When measurements are subtracted, there is often a loss of precision.

Here is a common sense rule for adding or subtracting measurements:

> **When adding or subtracting measurements, the sum or difference will have as many digits after the decimal point as the single measurement with the least number of digits after the decimal point.**

Example 1   Add: 4021.7 cm
                         0.089   cm
                      4021.789   cm   ≅   4021.8 cm

Example 2   Subtract: 5643.92   m
                          − 5643.7   m
                             0.22   m   ≅   0.2   m

Notice that the subtraction of two precise measurements has produced a very imprecise difference!

Exercises

Complete the following operations, using the rules for adding or subtracting measurements.

1. 12.678 mm + 0.25 mm
2. 45.987 m³ + 2.1 m³
3. 12.345 mL − 0.34 mL
4. 1.0001 mm − 0.1 mm
5. 12.5 g + 0.0005 g
6. 16.768 **kg** − 1.0 **g**

B. Multiplying or Dividing Measurements

You measure the dimensions of a wall to be 8.53 m x 2.74 m. What is the area of the wall? Imagine your calculator battery is dead, and you have to multiply the old-fashioned way. (*Disaster has struck!*) In the two measurements, the last digit is uncertain, so any product involving either of these two digits will also be uncertain.

$$8.53 \text{ m}$$
$$\times\ 2.74 \text{ m}$$
$$3412$$
$$5971$$
$$1706$$
$$23.3722 \text{ m}^2 \quad \cong\ 23.4 \text{ m}^2$$

Since the *3* following the decimal is an uncertain digit, all digits following it are meaningless. Round off the *.3722* to *.4*, and write 23.*4* m² for the area of the wall.

Use the following common sense rule when multiplying or dividing measurements:

> *When multiplying or dividing measurements, the product or quotient must have no more significant digits than the single measurement with the fewest significant digits. In other words, the least precise single measurement determines the precision of the final product or quotient.*

Example 1   Multiply 2.5*4* cm x 5.0*8* cm.

Your calculator will give you 12.9032 cm². ***DON'T YOU BELIEVE IT!*** The correct answer is 12.*9* cm², since both original measurements were accurate to only three significant digits. Notice that the *measuring units* (cm) are also multiplied.   [(cm)(cm) = cm²]

Example 2   Divide 56.*8* m² by 2.*3* m.

Your calculator says the answer is 24.695652 m. Since the divisor has only two significant digits, however, the correct answer is 2*5* m.   Only two significant digits are used, because 2.3 m has only two. The answer has been 'rounded off'. Notice that the *measuring units* are also divided. [(m²)÷(m) = m]

Exercises

Perform the following operations, using the rule for multiplying and dividing measurements. Express answers in proper measuring units.

1. 1.25 m x 0.25 m
2. 3.987654 cm x 1.3 cm
3. 14.0 cm² ÷ 2.1 cm
4. 5.646 mL x 13.6 g/mL
5. $\dfrac{98.45 \text{ g/mL x } 5.762 \text{ mL}}{1.4 \text{ mL}}$

1.6 Scientific Notation

Scientific notation is a convenient way to express numbers that are very large or very small. For example, one ampere of electric current is the same as

6 240 000 000 000 000 000 electrons passing a point in a wire in one second.

This same number can be written, in scientific notation, as 6.24×10^{18} electrons/second. This means 624 followed by 16 zeros.

Any number can be expressed in scientific notation. Here are some examples:

$$0.10 = 1.0 \times 10^{-1}$$
$$1.0 = 1.0 \times 10^{0}$$
$$10.0 = 1.00 \times 10^{1}$$
$$100.0 = 1.000 \times 10^{2}$$
$$1\,000.0 = 1.0000 \times 10^{3}$$

Review of Basic Rules for Handling Exponents

Power-of-Ten Notation

$$0.000001 = 10^{-6} \qquad 1 = 10^{0}$$
$$0.00001 = 10^{-5} \qquad 10 = 10^{1}$$
$$0.0001 = 10^{-4} \qquad 100 = 10^{2}$$
$$0.001 = 10^{-3} \qquad 1\,000 = 10^{3}$$
$$0.01 = 10^{-2} \qquad 10\,000 = 10^{4}$$
$$0.1 = 10^{-1} \qquad 100\,000 = 10^{5}$$
$$1 = 10^{0} \qquad 1\,000\,000 = 10^{6}$$

Multiplying Powers of Ten

Law of Exponents: $a^{m} \cdot a^{n} = a^{m+n}$

(When multiplying, **add** exponents.)

Examples: $100 \times 1\,000 = 10^{2} \cdot 10^{3} = 10^{5}.$

$$\frac{1}{100} \times 1\,000 = 10^{-2} \times 10^{3} = 10^{1}.$$

$$2\,500 \times 4\,000 = 2.5 \times 10^{3} \times 4.0 \times 10^{3} = 10 \times 10^{6} = 1.0 \times 10^{7}.$$

Dividing Powers of Ten

Law of Exponents: $a^{m} \div a^{n} = a^{m-n}$

(When dividing, **subtract** exponents.)

Examples: $\dfrac{10^{5}}{10} = 10^{5-1} = 10^{4}.$

$$\frac{100}{1\,000} = \frac{10^{2}}{10^{3}} = 10^{-1}.$$

$$\frac{1.00}{100\,000} = \frac{10^{0}}{10^{5}} = 10^{-5}.$$

Exercises

1. Write the following measurements in scientific notation.
   (a) 0.00572 kg
   (b) 520 000 000 000 km
   (c) 300 000 000 m/s
   (d) 0.000 000 000 000 000 000 16 C
   (e) 118.70004 g

2. Simplify.
   (a) $10^3 \times 10^7 \times 10^{12}$
   (b) $10^{23} \div 10^5$
   (c) $10^{12} \times 10^{-13}$
   (d) $10^{-8} \times 10^{-12}$
   (e) $10^5 \div 10^{-7}$
   (f) $10^{-2} \div 10^{-9}$

3. Do the following calculations, and express your answers in scientific notation with the correct number of significant digits.
   (a) $(6.25 \times 10^{-7}) \div (0.25 \times 10^4)$
   (b) $\dfrac{(93.8 \times 10^5)(6.1 \times 10^{-1})}{(7.6 \times 10^{-11})(1.22 \times 10^7)}$
   (c) $4.10 \times 10^7 + 5.9 \times 10^6$
   (d) $(4.536 \times 10^{-3}) - (0.347 \times 10^{-4})$

4. A room has dimensions 13.48 m x 8.35 m x 3.18 m. What is its volume? Express your answer in scientific notation, with the correct number of significant figures.

5. The volume of water in a graduated cylinder is 5.00 mL. A small lead sphere is gently lowered into the graduate, and the volume rises to 5.10 mL. The mass of the lead sphere is 1.10 g. What is the density of the lead? (Density = mass/volume)

Chapter Review Questions

**(Please express your answers in scientific notation, and
use an appropriate number of significant figures.)**

1. A young child on a swing completes 10.0 swings in 28.4 s.
   What is (a) the period of the swing? (b) the frequency of the swing?

2. On planet Xerox, which is a close copy of Earth, a pendulum 1.00 m long completes one
   swing in 2.00 s. What would the frequency of this pendulum be if it were only 25.00 cm long?

3. A traveller drives 568 km in 7.2 h. What is the average speed for the trip?

4. If you run with an average speed of 12.0 km/h, how far will you go in 3.2 min?

5. If the average speed of your private jet is 8.0×10^2 km/h, how long will it take you to travel a
   distance of 1.8×10^3 km?

6. The following distances and times, for consecutive parts of a trip made by a red ant, were
   recorded by different observers. There is considerable variation in the precision of their
   measurements.

   A. 4.56 m in 12 s   B. 3.4 m in 6.89 s   C. 12.8 m in 36.235 s

   (a) What total distance did the ant travel?
   (b) What was the total time for the trip?
   (c) What was the average speed of the ant?

7. Light travels with a speed of 3.00×10^5 km/s. How long will it take light from a laser to travel
   to the moon (where it is reflected by a mirror) and back to Earth? The moon is
   3.84×10^5 km from the Earth.

8. A student determines experimentally that the length of a pendulum having a period of
   1.000 s is 24.50 cm. What is the *percent difference* between her experimental result and the
   accepted value of 24.85 cm?

9. An astronaut made these observations of the period of a pendulum vibrating on the moon.

Period (T) [s]	0	0.50	0.70	0.86	1.11	1.31	1.50	1.92	2.22	2.72
Length (ℓ) [cm]	0	1.00	2.00	3.00	5.00	7.00	9.00	15.00	20.00	30.00

   (a) Plot a graph of period vs length. Draw one smooth curve through all the points.
   (b) On the moon, how long is (i) a 1.00 s pendulum? (ii) a 2.00 s pendulum?
   (c) How many times longer than a 1.00 s pendulum is a 2.00 s pendulum?
   (d) On Earth, a 1.00 s pendulum is 24.85 cm long. If you took this pendulum to the moon
       with you, how much time would it take to make one swing there? (Use your graph to
       answer this question.)

Test Yourself!

1. Perform the indicated arithmetic operations, *using the rules for significant figures.*

   (a) 11.87 cm + 4.3 cm = _____
   (b) 78.067 mL − 0.4 mL = _____
   (c) 97.2 m   x   3.479 m = _____
   (d) 36.843 g ÷ 2.1 mL   = _____

2. A fan blade rotates 3,597 times in 60.0 s. What is the **frequency** of the fan blade?

3. In 10.0 s, the arm of a recording timer vibrates 598 times. What is the **period** of vibration of the recording timer arm?

4. A jet aircraft travels a distance of 1867 km in a time of 3.0 h. What is its **average speed** for the trip?

5. A red ant travels across a driveway, which is 3.5 m wide, at an average speed of 2.6 cm/s. How long will the ant take to cross the driveway? Express your answer (a) in seconds and (b) in minutes.

6. If your car moves with a steady speed of 122 km/h for 20.0 min, then at a steady speed of 108 km/h for 30.0 min, what is the **average speed** of your car for the entire trip?

7. In a certain battery-powered circuit, an electron requires 2.0×10^5 s to travel only 2.0 m. What is the **average speed** of the electron in the circuit? Express your answer in **millimetres per second (mm/s).**

8. Light from a laser requires 1.28 s to reach the moon. If light travels with a speed of 3.00×10^5 km/s, how far is it to the moon?

9. For a pendulum 99.40 cm in length, on planet Earth, the accepted value for the **period** is 2.00 s. In your experiment, imagine you obtain a result of 1.99 s. What is the **percent difference** between your experimental result and the accepted result?

10. MORG, from MARS, made the following observations of the **periods** (T) of pendulums of different **lengths** (L) on his home planet.

T (s)	0.325	0.563	0.727	0.861	0.976	1.08	1.26	1.78	2.05	2.18
L (cm)	1.00	3.00	5.00	7.00	9.00	11.0	15.0	30.0	40.0	45.0

   (a) Plot and label a graph of period, T, vs length, L. Draw one smooth curve through the points.
   (b) According to your graph, what is the length of a pendulum that will have a period of one second (1 s) on Mars?
   (c) According to your graph, what is the length of a pendulum that will have a period of two seconds (2 s) on Mars?
   (d) On Mars, by how many times must you multiply the length of a 1 s pendulum in order to change it to a 2 s pendulum?

Chapter 2   Acceleration

Figure 2.1(a) Norma MacDonald accelerates around the barrel at a high school rodeo.

2.1 Speed and Velocity

In **Chapter 1**, you learned that **speed** is distance travelled in a unit of time. **Average speed** is total distance divided by time, and **instantaneous speed** is the speed of an object at a particular instant. If an object moves along at the same speed over an extended period of time, we say its speed is **uniform** or **constant.**

Uniform speed is uncommon, but it is possible to achieve nearly uniform speed in some situations. For example, a car with 'cruise control' may maintain fairly constant speed on the highway. Usually, however, a vehicle is making small changes in speed and direction all the time.

If an object is *not* travelling in a straight line all the time, then its direction becomes important and must be specified. When both the size and the direction of a speed are specified, we call the two properties (speed and direction) the **velocity** of the object. If you say your car is moving 80 km/h, then you are describing your car's speed. If you say your car is travelling 80 km/h in a northerly direction, then you are describing your car's velocity. The difference between speed and velocity becomes important in situations where direction changes during a trip. For example, when a ball is thrown into the air, both its speed and its direction change throughout its trajectory, therefore **velocity** is specified in this situation.

2.2 Acceleration

Whenever the velocity of an object changes, the object experiences **acceleration.** Acceleration is defined as follows:

$$\text{acceleration} = \frac{\textbf{change in velocity}}{\textbf{change in time}} \cdot$$

Figure 2.1(b) BMX trick rider **Steve Stanyer** experiences the acceleration of gravity.

The symbol for acceleration is a. Velocity has the same symbol as speed, which is v. If the velocity at the start of the time interval is v_o, and at the end of the time interval is v_f, then the change in velocity will be $v_f - v_o$. If the time at the beginning of the time interval is t_o, and the time at the end of the time interval is t_f, then the change in time (the time interval) is $t_f - t_o$. Using these symbols, acceleration can be defined as:

$$a = \frac{v_f - v_o}{t_f - t_o} \quad \text{or,} \quad a = \frac{\Delta v}{\Delta t} \, ,$$

where the Δ symbol is shorthand for 'change in...' or 'interval'.

Since velocity has two aspects to it (speed and direction), acceleration can occur (a) if speed changes, (b) if direction changes or (c) if both speed and direction change. Examples of acceleration are illustrated in **Figures 2.1(a)** and **2.1(b)**. This chapter limits the discussion of acceleration to motion in a straight line (one dimensional motion).

Examples

1. A runner racing in a 100 m dash accelerates from rest to a speed of 9.0 m/s in 4.5 s. What was his average acceleration during this time interval?

$$\text{Solution:} \quad a = \frac{\Delta v}{\Delta t} = \frac{v_f - v_o}{t_f - t_o} = \frac{9.0 \text{ m/s} - 0 \text{ m/s}}{4.5 \text{ s} - 0 \text{ s}} = 2.0 \frac{\text{m/s}}{\text{s}}.$$

This result means that the runner's speed increased, on average, 2.0 m/s every second. His average acceleration was 2.0 m/s/s, which is usually written 2.0 m/s^2.

The standard unit for expressing acceleration is m/s^2. An object is accelerating at a rate of 1 m/s^2 if its speed is increasing at a rate of 1 m/s each second.

---

2. A UFO is reported as accelerating from rest to 680 km/h in a time of 2.0 s. What is its acceleration?

$$\text{Solution:} \quad a = \frac{\Delta v}{\Delta t} = \frac{v_f - v_o}{t_f - t_o} = \frac{680 \text{ km/h} - 0 \text{ km/h}}{2.0 \text{ s} - 0 \text{ s}} = 340 \frac{\text{km/h}}{\text{s}}.$$

The speed of the UFO is increasing 340 km/h each second. This acceleration might be written in the form 3.4 x 10^2 km/h/s. Although 'km/h/s' is not the officially accepted unit for acceleration, it is often used when describing the acceleration of an automobile.

Exercises

1. What is the average acceleration if: (a) A car speeds up from 0 km/h to 60.0 km/h in 3.00 s? (b) A runner accelerates from rest to 9.00 m/s in 3.00 s?

2. What is the average acceleration of a truck that accelerates from 45.0 km/h to 60.0 km/h in 7.50 s?

3. A car travelling 120 km/h brakes hard to avoid hitting a deer on the road, slowing to 60 km/h in 4.0 s. What is its acceleration? Why is it negative?

Investigation 2-1   Measuring Acceleration

Purpose: To measure the uniform acceleration of an object.

Procedure

1. **Figure 2.2** shows one way to produce uniformly accelerated motion. Remove a 1-m piece of ticker tape from a roll. Pass the tape through a recording timer and tape it to a laboratory cart, as in the figure. A 500 g mass is attached to the cart by a 1 m string that passes over a pulley. The force of gravity on the mass accelerates both the mass and the cart to which it is attached by the string.

2. For best results in this experiment, there should be no 'slack' in the ticker tape before the cart is released. One partner should place the hanging mass over the pulley, and hold on to the cart so that it does not accelerate prematurely. When all is ready, simultaneously turn on the timer and release the cart!

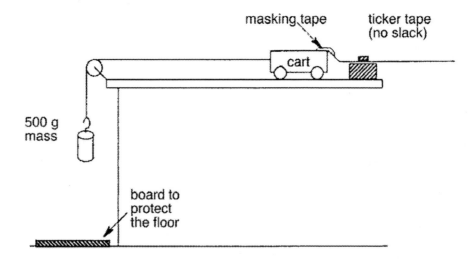

Figure 2.2

3. Your finished ticker tape record will look something like the one in **Figure 2.3**. Often there is a smudged grouping of dots at the start, so choose the first clear dot and label it the '0th' dot. (See **Figure 2.3**.) On your tape, mark clearly the 0th dot, 6th dot, 12th dot, 18th dot, 24th dot and so on until you have at least six time intervals.

The timer has a frequency of 60 Hz. This means it makes 60 vibrations each second. The time interval between dots on your tape is 1/60 s. If you use a time interval of six dots, this is 6/60 s or 1/10 s. In other words, an interval of six dots is the same as 0.10 s.

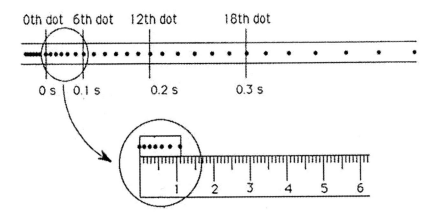

Figure 2.3

4. Carefully measure the distance the cart travelled during each successive 0.10 s time interval. For example, in the sample tape in **Figure 2.3**, the distance travelled during the interval between 0 and 0.10 s was 1.1 cm. **Figure 2.4** shows how to measure the distance travelled during the *second* 0.10 s interval (between 0.10 s and 0.20 s). In the sample tape, the distance is 1.8 cm. Prepare a table like **Table 2.1**. Record the distances travelled in *each* of the recorded intervals in your table.

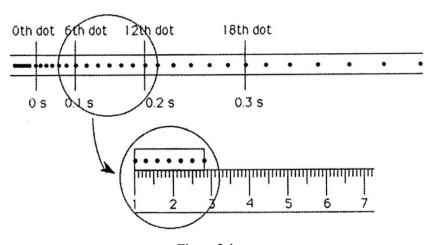

Figure 2.4

5. Your next task is to figure out the **average speed** of the cart during each of the 0.10 s time intervals. Since average speed is just the distance travelled during the time interval divided by the time interval, all you have to do is divide each measured distance by the time interval (0.10 s).

Table 2.1   Data for an Accelerating Cart

Time Interval (s)	Distance travelled (cm)	Average Speed for the Interval (cm/s)
0 to 0.10		
0.10 to 0.20		
0.20 to 0.30		
0.30 to 0.40		
0.40 to 0.50		
0.50 to 0.60		

Examples

During the first time interval on the sample tape, the cart moved a distance of 1.1 cm. The average speed of the cart during the first 0.10 s was therefore

$$\bar{v} = \frac{1.1 \text{ cm}}{0.10 \text{ s}} = 11 \text{ cm/s.}$$

During the second time interval (between 0.10 s and 0.20 s), the cart moved a distance of 1.8 cm. Its average speed during the second interval was therefore

$$\bar{v} = \frac{1.8 \text{ cm}}{0.10 \text{ s}} = 18 \text{ cm/s.}$$

Using your own tape data, calculate the average speed of the cart during each of the time intervals, and complete **Table 2.1**.

Note: You will use the data from **Table 2.1** later in this chapter, as well as to answer the following **Concluding Questions**.

Concluding Questions

1. (a) What was the average speed of the cart during the first 0.10 s time interval?
   (b) What was the average speed of the cart during the second 0.10 s interval?
   (c) By how much did the average speed of the cart *increase* between the first interval and the second interval?
   (d) Calculate the **acceleration** of the cart between the first interval and the second interval by dividing the *increase* in average speed by the time interval, which was 0.10 s.

   Example: On the sample tape, the average speed increased from 11 cm/s to 18 cm/s between the first and second time intervals. Therefore, the acceleration was:

   $$a = \frac{18 \text{ cm/s} - 11 \text{ cm/s}}{0.10 \text{ s}} = \frac{7 \text{ cm/s}}{0.10 \text{ s}} = 70 \text{ cm/s}^2.$$

2. Calculate the acceleration of the cart between the second and third intervals, third and fourth intervals, fourth and fifth intervals, and fifth and sixth intervals. Allowing for slight variations due to experimental errors, is there any pattern to your results?

Mathematical Background: The Equation for a Straight Line

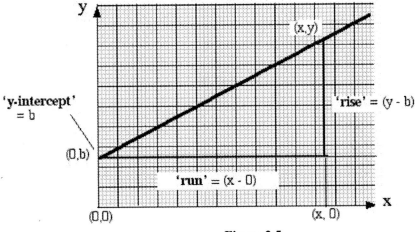

Figure 2.5

In **Figure 2.5**, a variable y is plotted against a variable x. Variable y is the *dependent* variable and variable x is the *independent variable*. In this situation, the graph is a straight line. (You might say that variable y is a **linear function** of the variable x.)

The **slope** of the graph is given the symbol k, where $k = \dfrac{\text{rise}}{\text{run}}$.

To find the value of the slope, the two points with coordinates $(0,b)$ and (x,y) will be used. The value of y where the graph intercepts the Y-axis is called the *y-intercept,* and it is given the symbol b.

$$\text{Since } k = \frac{\text{rise}}{\text{run}} = \frac{(y-b)}{(x-0)},$$

Therefore, $kx = y - b$, or

$$y = kx + b.$$

*This is a general equation for *any straight line*. The **slope** of the line is k and the **y-intercept** is b.

To write an equation for any straight line graph, you need only determine the value of the y-intercept (by inspection) and the slope (by calculation). You then substitute these values into the general equation.

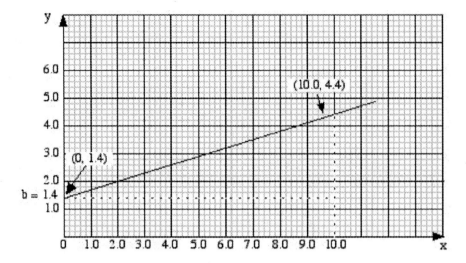

Figure 2.6

Example

For the linear graph in **Figure 2.6**, the **y-intercept**, by inspection, is 1.4. (b = 1.4) The **slope** is calculated using the two points with coordinates (0, 1.4) and (10.0, 4.4).

$$k = \frac{(4.4 - 1.4)}{(10.0 - 0)} = \frac{3.0}{10.0} = 0.30.$$

The **equation** for this straight line is therefore: $y = 0.30\,x + 1.4$.

In these examples, the units of measure of the variables have not been included, in order to simplify the explanation. In experiments, the observations you make are frequently summarized in graphical form. When graphing experimental data, always include the **measuring units** and the **specific symbols of the variables** being graphed.

In **Figure 2.7**, fictitious data is used to show how your results from *Investigation 2-1* might have been graphed. In this figure, the average speed of the cart is plotted on the Y-axis, since it is the dependent variable. Time is on the X-axis, because it is the independent variable.

Notice that in **Figure 2.7** the speeds are plotted *halfway through each time interval*. For example, the average speed of 11 cm/s, which occurs in the first time interval of the sample tape, would be plotted at 0.05 s, not at 0.10 s. This is because the *average speed* during the interval will occur *halfway* through it, not at the end of the interval. This assumes, of course, that the speed is increasing at a constant rate (therefore acceleration is constant). The average speed for each interval is the same as the *instantaneous speed* half way through the interval, if acceleration is constant.

The final graph you see in **Figure 2.7** is, in fact, a graph of the *instantaneous speed* of the cart vs *time,* although average speeds were used to obtain it. To write an **equation** describing the line in this graph, you need to know the y-intercept and the slope.

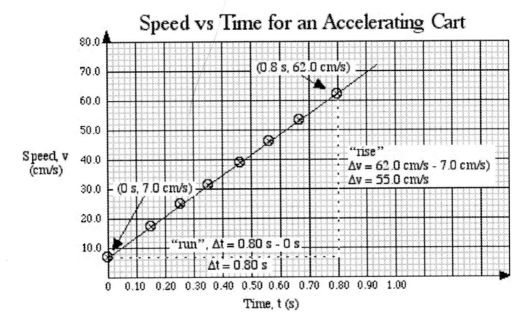

Figure 2.7

By inspection, the y-intercept, b, equals 7.0 cm/s. The slope k is found by using the points (0 s, 7.0 cm/s) and (0.80 s, 62 cm/s). Notice that the 'rise' is equal to the change in speed of the cart, Δv, and $\Delta v = v_f - v_o$. The 'run' is the change in time Δt, and $\Delta t = t_f - t_o$.

$$\text{Slope} = k = \frac{\Delta v}{\Delta t} = \frac{v_f - v_o}{t_f - t_o} = \frac{62.0 \text{ cm/s} - 7.0 \text{ cm/s}}{0.80 \text{ s} - 0 \text{ s}} = \frac{55.0 \text{ cm/s}}{0.80 \text{ s}} = 69 \text{ cm/s}^2.$$

Notice that the slope has units of *acceleration*. This is because the slope of the speed-time graph *is* acceleration! Remember that acceleration is equal to the change in speed of the cart per second. The slope $k = \Delta v / \Delta t$, which is the acceleration of the cart!

The equation for the line in **Figure 2.7** will have the same *form* as the general equation for a straight line, which is $y = kx + b$. When describing experimental results from a graph, however, we substitute the *specific symbols* for the variables used in the experiment. We also use the numerical values for the y-intercept and slope, *complete with their measuring units*. The equation for the line in **Figure 2.7** is therefore

$$v = [69 \text{ cm/s}^2]t + 7.0 \text{ cm/s},$$

where v is the speed of the cart at any time t.

Investigation 2-2
Determining Acceleration from a Speed-Time Graph

Purpose: To determine the acceleration of the cart in *Investigation 2-1*, using a graph of the speed of the cart vs time.

Procedure

1. Using your **Table of Data** *from Investigation 2-1,* plot a graph of speed vs time for the accelerating cart. Use **Figure 2.7** as a guide. Remember that the speeds in the table are *average speeds* for each interval, and should be plotted *midway* through each time interval.

2. Draw a single straight line through all the plotted points. If there are stray points due to experimental error, try to draw a line that leaves as many strays on one side of it as on the other. (If a point is an obvious gross error, ignore it when drawing your 'best line'. If in doubt, ask your instructor for advice.)

3. Determine the y-intercept of your line. Also, figure out the slope of the line using the method outlined for **Figure 2.7**.

Concluding Questions

1. What was the acceleration of your cart, according to the slope of your graph?

2. What is the equation for the speed-time graph you plotted for the cart?

3. In *Investigation 2-1,* you figured out the acceleration of your cart simply by comparing average speeds of the cart in successive time intervals. Compare the acceleration you calculated in *Investigation 2-1* with the acceleration you just obtained using the slope of your speed-time graph. Which method of finding the acceleration 'averages out' the experimental errors better? Explain.

Exercises

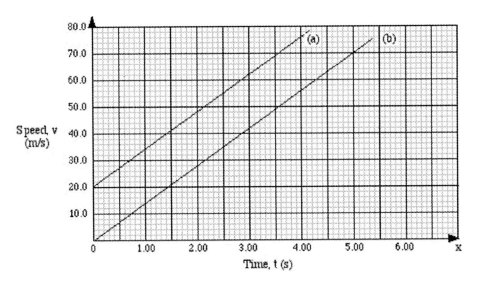

Figure 2.8

1. **Figure 2.8** shows graphs of speed vs time for an accelerating aircraft, prepared by observers at two different locations on the runway.
   (a) What is the equation for line (a)?
   (b) What is the equation for line (b)?
   (c) What is the acceleration of the aircraft according to line (a)?
   (d) What is the acceleration of the aircraft according to line (b)?
   (e) Explain why the y-intercept for line (b) is different than the intercept for line (a).

Speed, v, in m/s

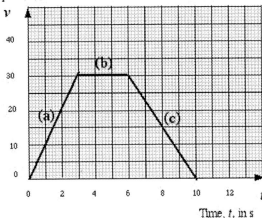

Figure 2.9

2. The graph in **Figure 2.9** describes the motion of a vehicle whose acceleration changes twice. Find the acceleration of the vehicle for the parts of the graph labelled (a), (b) and (c), by finding the slope of each part of the graph.

2.3 Uniform Acceleration

Speed, v in m/s

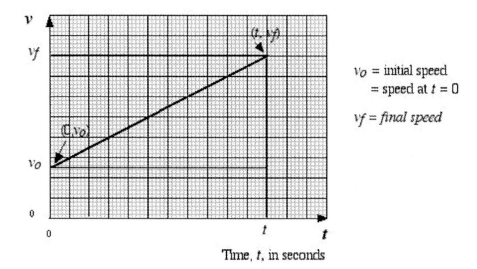

v_o = initial speed
     = speed at $t = 0$

v_f = final speed

Time, t, in seconds

Figure 2.10

In a situation where the speed of a moving body increases or decreases at a uniform rate, the graph of speed vs time will be linear (**Figure 2.10**). Since speed is the dependent variable, it is plotted on the Y-axis. Time, the independent variable, will be on the X-axis.

The y-intercept for the speed-time graph is b $= v_o$, where v_o is the speed of the object at time $t = 0$. In **Figure 2.10**, the initial time is zero and the final time is t, so the time interval is simply $\Delta t = t - 0 = t$.

The slope of the graph is k $= \dfrac{\Delta v}{\Delta t} = a$, since acceleration is change in speed divided by change in time.

$$\text{If } a = \frac{v_f - v_o}{t},$$

$$\text{Then, } at = v_f - v_o, \text{ and}$$

$$v_f = v_o + at. \qquad\qquad (I)$$

This is a general equation for any object that accelerates at a uniform rate. It says that the **final speed** of the accelerating object equals the **initial speed** plus the **change in speed** (*at*).

A Specific Example

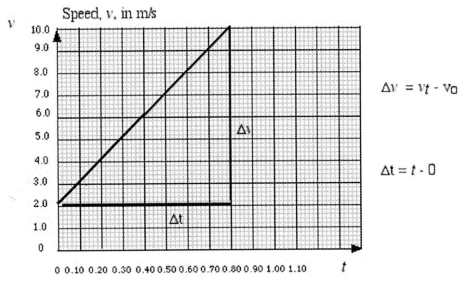

Figure 2.11

Figure 2.11 is a graph showing the uniform acceleration of an object, as it was allowed to drop off a cliff.

(a) What was the **acceleration** of the object?
(b) Write an **equation** for the graph.

Solution:

(a) The acceleration is determined by finding the slope of the speed-time graph.

$$a = \frac{\Delta v}{\Delta t} = \frac{v_f - v_o}{t_f - t_o} = \frac{10.0 \text{ m/s} - 2.0 \text{ m/s}}{0.80 \text{ s} - 0 \text{ s}} = \frac{8.0 \text{ m/s}}{0.80 \text{ s}} = 1.0 \times 10^1 \text{ m/s}^2.$$

(b) The general equation for any straight line is $y = b + kx$. For *this* line, the slope k is the acceleration. Inspection of the graph reveals that the y-intercept, b, is 2.0 m/s. Therefore the **specific equation** for this line is

$$v_f = 2.0 \text{ m/s} + [1.0 \times 10^1 \text{ m/s}^2] \cdot t.$$

Note that the final, **specific equation** for this graph includes the *actual numerical values* of the y-intercept and slope, complete with their measuring units. Once this equation is established, it can be used in place of the graph, since it describes every point on the graph.

Exercises

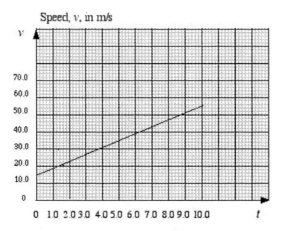

Speed, v, in m/s

Time, t, in s

Figure 2.12(a)

1. (a) What is the y-intercept (v_o) for the graph in **Figure 2.12(a)**?
   (b) What is the slope of the graph?
   (c) What property of the moving object does this slope measure?
   (d) Write the **specific equation** for the graph, using symbols v for speed and t for time.

2. The following equation describes the motion of a ball thrown straight down, by someone leaning out of the window of a tall building:

$$v_f = 5.0 \text{ m/s} + [9.8 \text{ m/s}^2] \cdot t$$

   (a) At what speed was the ball initially thrown out of the window?
   (b) What was the acceleration of the ball?
   (c) How fast was the ball moving after 1.2 s?

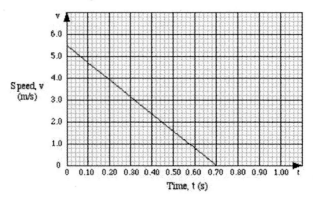

Speed, v (m/s)

Time, t (s)

Figure 2.12(b)

3. (a) What is the y-intercept (v_o) of the speed-time graph in **Figure 2.12(b)**?
   (b) What is the acceleration of the moving object?
   (c) What is the *specific equation* for this graph?

4. A cyclist coasting along a road allows her bike to come to rest with the help of a slight upslope in the road. The motion of the bike is described by the equation:

$$v_f = 6.6 \text{ m/s} - [2.2 \text{ m/s}^2] \cdot t .$$

   (a) What was the initial speed of the bike?
   (b) At what rate did the bike accelerate while coming to rest?
   (c) How long did the bike take to come to rest?

Distance Travelled by a Uniformly Accelerating Object

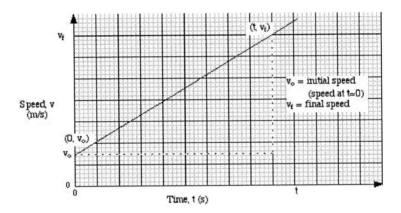

Figure 2.13

Consider an object that is accelerating uniformly from initial speed v_o to a final speed v_f in time t. How might one calculate the **distance** travelled by the object during this time? The total distance d travelled in time t will equal the **average speed** $\bar{v}$ multiplied by time t. The average speed $\bar{v}$ is just the average of the initial speed v_o and the final speed v_f, which is:

$$\bar{v} = \frac{v_o + v_f}{2} .$$

Distance travelled is $d = \bar{v}t$, or

$$d = \frac{v_o + v_f}{2} \cdot t. \qquad \text{(II)}$$

However, it has already been shown that $v_f = v_o + at$. (I)

Therefore,
$$d = \frac{v_o + v_o + at}{2} \cdot t,$$

and
$$d = \frac{2v_o + at}{2} \cdot t = \frac{2v_o t + at^2}{2}.$$

Finally,
$$d = v_o t + \tfrac{1}{2} at^2. \qquad\qquad \text{(III)}$$

Sometimes you encounter situations involving uniform acceleration where you have no information involving the time interval, t, during which the motion occurred. If you do know the initial speed v_o and the final speed v_f, you can still calculate the distance travelled if you know at what rate the object is accelerating.

For uniform acceleration, $d = \dfrac{v_o + v_f}{2} \cdot t$, and $v_f = v_o + at$,

therefore
$$t = \frac{v_f - v_o}{a}.$$

Substituting for t in the first equation, $d = \dfrac{v_o + v_f}{2} \cdot \dfrac{v_f - v_o}{a}.$

Thus,
$$2ad = v_f^2 - v_o^2,$$

therefore,
$$v_f^2 = v_o^2 + 2ad. \qquad\qquad \text{(IV)}$$

The Four Uniform Acceleration Equations

The four equations describing uniform acceleration are extremely useful in this course and in future courses you might take in physics. For your convenience, they are summarized here.

(I) $\qquad v_f = v_o + at$

(II) $\qquad d = \dfrac{v_o + v_f}{2} \cdot t$

(III) $\qquad d = v_o t + \tfrac{1}{2} at^2$

(IV) $\qquad v_f^2 = v_o^2 + 2ad$

2.4 Acceleration of Bodies in Free Fall

One of the most common situations involving uniform acceleration is the phenomenon known as **free fall**. For example, if a coin drops out of your pocket, it accelerates toward the ground. If the effects of air resistance are ignored, the acceleration of the coin toward the ground is uniform. The coin starts its downward fall with zero speed, but gains speed as it falls toward earth. Since gravity is the cause of the acceleration, we call the acceleration during free fall the **acceleration of gravity.** The acceleration of gravity is given a special symbol, g.

The magnitude of g depends on your location. At the earth's surface, g is approximately 9.81 m/s². At higher altitudes, g decreases. For our present purposes, g is assumed to be constant at the earth's surface and to be 9.81 m/s². On the moon, the magnitude of g is approximately 1/6 of what it is here on the earth's surface. A body in free fall near the moon's surface has an acceleration of gravity of only 1.60 m/s².

Of course, the four equations for uniform acceleration apply to free fall as well as other uniform acceleration situations. The symbol g may be substituted for a in the equations.

Examples

1. A golf ball is dropped from the top of the CN tower. Assuming that the ball is in true free fall (negligible air resistance), answer these questions:
   (a) How fast will the ball be falling after 1.0 s?
   (b) How far down will the ball have fallen after 1.0 s?

   Solution: The ball starts from rest, so $v_O = 0$.
   The rate of acceleration is $g = 9.8$ m/s².
   The time of fall is $t = 1.0$ s.

   The first uniform acceleration equation (I) applies to question (a).
   (a) $v_f = v_O + at = v_O + gt = 0$ m/s $+ (9.8$ m/s²$)(1.0$ s$) = 9.8$ m/s.

   The third uniform acceleration equation (III) applies to part (b).

   (b) $d = v_Ot + \frac{1}{2}at^2 = (0$ m/s$)(1.0$ s$) + \frac{1}{2}(9.8$ m/s²$)(1.0$ s$)(1.0$ s$) = 4.9$ m.

2. How fast will the golf ball in **Example 1** be moving after it has fallen a distance of 530 m, which is the height of the CN tower? (Assume free fall.)
   Solution: Since the time interval is not known, uniform acceleration equation IV must be used here.

   $$v_f^2 = v_o^2 + 2gd = (0 \text{ m/s})^2 + 2(9.8 \text{m/s}^2)(530 \text{ m}).$$
   $$v_f^2 = 10\ 388 \text{ m}^2/\text{s}^2$$
   $$v_f = \sqrt{10,388 \text{ m}^2/\text{s}^2} = 102 \text{ m/s} = 1.0 \times 10^2 \text{ m/s}$$

   Comment: The ball would be travelling approximately 100 m/s when it hit the road, if it was in true free fall. (In reality, air resistance would oppose the gravitational force pulling the ball to the ground, and the ball would eventually reach a 'peak' speed (called the **terminal velocity**), which would be less than what one would observe with true free fall.)

Exercises

1. A truck parked on a down slope slips its brakes and starts to coast downhill, accelerating from rest at a constant rate of 0.80 m/s^2.
   (a) How fast will the truck be moving after 5.0 s?
   (b) How far will the truck coast during the 5.0 s?

2. A policeman travelling 60 km/h (16.7 m/s) spots a speeder ahead, so he accelerates his vehicle at a steady rate of 2.22 m/s^2 for 4.00 s, at which time he catches up with the speeder.
   (a) How fast is the police car travelling after 4.00 s?
   (b) How far does the police car travel during the 4.00 s?

3. A motocross rider travelling 65 km/h (18.0 m/s) collides with a haystack and is brought to rest in a distance of 4.5 m. What is the average acceleration of the motorbike and rider while being brought to rest?

4. A motorbike accelerates at a constant rate from a standing start. After 1.2 s, it is travelling 6.0 m/s. How much time will have elapsed (starting from rest) before the bike is moving with a speed of 15.0 m/s?

5. An aircraft starts from rest and accelerates at a constant rate down the runway.
   (a) After 12.0 s, its speed is 36.0 m/s. What is its acceleration?
   (b) How fast is the plane moving after 15.0 s?
   (c) How far down the runway will the plane be after 15.0 s?

6. On a certain asteroid, a steel ball drops a distance of 0.80 m in 2.00 s from rest. Assuming uniform acceleration due to gravity on this asteroid, what is the value of g on the asteroid?

7. What is the rate of acceleration of a mountain bike, if it slows down from 12.0 m/s to 8.0 m/s in a time of 3.25 s?

8. A body in free fall accelerates at a rate of 9.80 m/s^2 at your latitude. How far does the body fall during (a) the first second? (b) the second second? (*Think first!*)

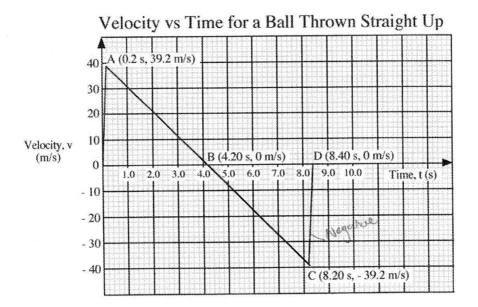

Figure 2.14

9. Figure **2.14** is a graph of the velocity of a ball thrown straight up by a strong pitcher, as a function of time. In the first part of the graph (ending at A), the ball is accelerated to 39.2 m/s in a time of 0.20 s. After the ball leaves the pitcher's hand, it experiences only the acceleration due to gravity until it is caught in a glove and brought to rest in the hand of the catcher.

(a) What is the acceleration of the ball *while it is being thrown?*

(b) What is the acceleration of the ball *after it leaves the pitcher's hand?* (**ABC**)

(c) What is the acceleration of the ball *while it is being caught?* (**CD**)

(d) What point on the graph (**A, B, C** or **D**) corresponds with the instant when the ball is at the peak of its flight? Explain your answer.

(e) Why is the slope of the graph *negative* as soon as the ball leaves the pitcher's hand?

(f) Why is the graph labelled *velocity* rather than *speed?*

(g) How far up did the ball travel?

(h) How far down did the ball fall?

(i) What is the *average velocity* of the ball for the whole trip from pitcher's hand to catcher's hand?

Chapter Review Questions

1. What is the difference between average speed and instantaneous speed?

2. What is the difference between velocity and speed?

3. What is the definition of acceleration?

4. Under what condition can acceleration be calculated simply by dividing change in speed by change in time?

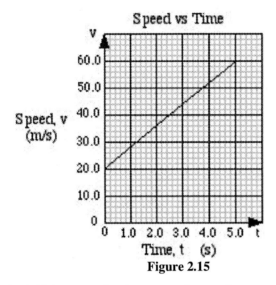

Figure 2.15

5. **Figure 2.15** is a speed-time graph for a vehicle.

   (a) What was the acceleration of the vehicle?
   (b) What was the average speed of the vehicle during its 5.00 s trip?
   (c) What distance did the vehicle travel during the 5.00 s?
   (d) Write a specific equation for this graph.

6. A high-powered racing car accelerates from rest at a rate of 7.0 m/s². How fast will it be moving after 10.0 s? Convert this speed to km/h.

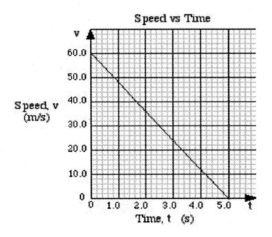

Figure 2.16

7. **Figure 2.16** is a speed-time graph for a vehicle.
   (a) What was the acceleration of the vehicle?
   (b) Write a specific equation for this graph.
   (c) What was the average speed of the vehicle during its 5.00 s trip?
   (d) What distance did the vehicle travel during the 5.00 s trip?
   (e) Calculate the *area* of the triangle formed by the line and the axes of the graph, using the units and dimensions on the axes. Why does this area equal the distance travelled by the vehicle?

8. A child on a toboggan slides down a snowy hill, accelerating uniformly at 2.8 m/s². When the toboggan passes the first observer, it is travelling with a speed of 1.4 m/s. How fast will it be moving when it passes a second observer, who is 2.5 m downhill from the first observer?

9. A space vehicle is orbiting the earth at a speed of 7.58 x 10³ m/s. In preparation for a return to earth, it fires retro-rockets, which provide a negative acceleration of 78.4 m/s². Ignoring any change in altitude that might occur, how long will it take the vehicle to slow down to 1.52 x 10³ m/s?

10. A truck is moving along at 80.0 km/h when it hits a gravel patch, which causes it to accelerate at -5.0 km/h/s. How far will the truck travel before it slows to 20.0 km/h?

11. A very frustrated physics student drops a physics textbook off the top of the CN tower. If the tower is 5.3 x 10² m high, how long will the book take to reach the ground, assuming there is negligible air resistance? (g = 9.8 m/s²)

12. If an electron inside a TV tube accelerates in a space of 5.0 cm from rest to 1/10 c, (where c is the speed of light, which is 3.0 x 10⁸ m/s), what is its acceleration?

13. Snoopy is taking off in his WW I biplane. He coasts down the runway at a speed of 40.0 m/s, then accelerates for 5.2 s at a rate of 1/2 g , where g is the acceleration due to gravity (9.81 m/s²). How fast is the plane moving after the 5.2 s?

14. A woman biker (leader of the local chapter of *Heck's Angels*) is driving along the highway at 80.0 km/h, in a 60.0 km/h speed zone. She sees a police car ahead, so she brakes so that her bike accelerates at -8.0 km/h/s. How far along the road will she travel before she is at the legal speed limit?

15. Spiderman is crawling up a building at the rate of 0.50 m/s. Seeing Spiderwoman 56 m ahead of him, he accelerates at the rate of 2.3 m/s².
    (a) How fast will he be moving when he reaches Spiderwoman?
    (b) How much time will it take to reach Spiderwoman?
    (c) When he reaches Spiderwoman, Spiderman discovers that she is a Black Widow and, as you know, Black Widows eat their mates! He is 200.00 m from the road below. How long will it take him to fall to the safety of the road, if he drops with an acceleration of g = 9.81 m/s²?
    (d) *Riddle!* Why will Spiderman not be killed by the fall?***

16. A stone is dropped from the top of a tall building. It accelerates at a rate of 9.81 m/s². How long will the stone take to pass a window that is 2.0 m high, if the top of the window is 20.0 m below the point from which the stone was dropped?

17. A glider on an air track is made to accelerate uniformly by tilting the track at a slight angle. The distance travelled by the glider was measured at the end of each 0.10 s interval, and the following data was gathered:

DISTANCE d (cm)	0	0.025	0.100	0.225	0.400	0.625
TIME t (s)	0	0.100	0.200	0.300	0.400	0.500

(a) Plot a graph with distance d on the Y-axis and time t on the X-axis.
(b) Plot a second graph with distance d on the Y-axis and t^2 on the X-axis.
(c) Use the slope of your second graph to figure out the acceleration of the glider on the air track. *HINT! Think about the third equation for uniform acceleration.*

*** Because a spider, no matter how far he falls, always has eight feet left to go!

Test Yourself!

Speed vs Time

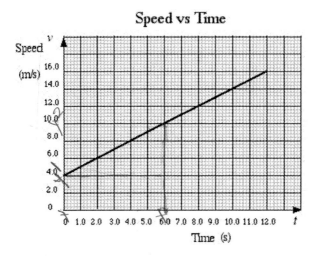

Time (s)

1. (a) What is the **y-intercept** of the above graph? (Include **units**.)
   (b) What is the **slope** of the above graph? (Include **units**.)
   (c) What is the **equation** for the above graph? (Use **symbols** *v, t,* in the equation.)

2. An aircraft, preparing for take-off, accelerates uniformly from 0 m/s to 20.0 m/s, in a time of 5.00 s.
   (a) What is the acceleration of the aircraft?
   (b) How long will the plane take to reach its take-off speed of 36.0 m/s?

3. At an air show, a jet car accelerates from rest at a rate of 3*g*, where *g* is 9.80 m/s². How far does the jet car travel down the runway in a time of 4.0 s?

4. The CN Tower in Toronto is about 530 m high. If air friction did not slow it down, how long would it take a penny to fall from the top of the tower to the ground below?
   (*g* = 9.80 m/s²)

5. A motocross rider is coasting at a speed of 2.00 m/s. He then decides to accelerate his bike at a rate of 3.00 m/s² for a distance of 100.0 m.

   (a) How fast is the bike moving, in m/s, at the end of the 100.0 m stretch?
   (b) Convert your answer to (a) from m/s to km/h.

6. A mountain bike rider, after coming down a steep hill, loses control of her bike while moving with a speed of 5.00 m/s. Fortunately, she collides with a haystack, which brings her to rest in a distance of 0.625 m. What was the acceleration of the bike and rider *while colliding with the haystack?*

7. A policeman on a mountain bike is cruising at a speed of 4.00 m/s, when he sees a wanted criminal standing on a corner, 100.0 m ahead of him. If the policeman accelerates at a rate of 2.00 m/s², how much time will he take to reach the corner?

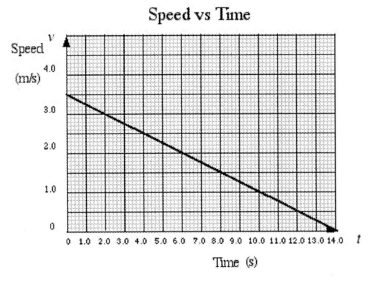

8. The graph shows how the speed of an aging physics teacher varies with time, as he tries to run up a hill.
   (a) What was the **starting speed** of the runner?
   (b) What was the **acceleration** of the runner?
   (c) What **distance** did the runner travel?
   (d) What is the *specific* **equation** for the above graph?

Chapter 3 Forces

3.1 What's a Force?

Every time you push, pull, twist or squeeze something you exert a *force* on it. Almost every time you exert a force on an object, you change something about that object: its speed, its direction or its shape.

When a soccer player 'heads' the ball (**Figure 3.1**), the speed of the ball changes, and sometimes its direction as well. When a hockey player is given a solid body check, the force changes his direction and speed. When a golf ball is struck by a golf club, the force of the impact changes the ball's shape during the collision. The force due to air friction alters the shape of a raindrop, from a perfect sphere to something more like a teardrop.

In *Investigation 3-1,* you will examine three kinds of force that affect your everyday life: gravitational, electrical and magnetic.

Figure 3.1

Investigation 3-1 Three Kinds of Force

Part 1 The Force of Gravity

Introduction

The force of gravity pulls on you all the time. The force of attraction between planet Earth and you keeps you from floating aimlessly off into space! Any two bodies in the universe exert a gravitational force on each other. The amount of force they exert depends upon how massive the bodies are, and how far apart they are. Two unique facts about the force of gravity are: (1) it cannot be 'shut it off'; and (2) it is always an *attractive* force, never *repulsive*. (In **Parts 2** and **3** you will see examples of forces that can cause bodies to either attract or repel one another.)

Purpose: To observe some interesting facts about falling bodies.

Procedure (Demonstrations)

1. Two steel balls, one more massive than the other, will be dropped from the same height at the same time. *Predict* which of the two balls will reach the floor first. Give a reason for your prediction. Now *listen* as the two balls are dropped to the floor.

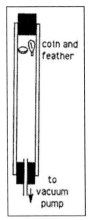

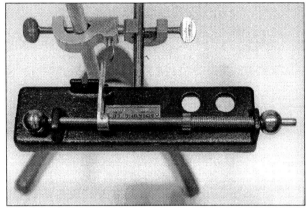

Figure 3.2   **Figure 3.3**

2. A piece of tissue paper and a steel ball will be dropped to the floor from the same height at the same time. *Predict* what will happen and explain your prediction. Observe what happens when the two objects are dropped.
3. **Figure 3.2** illustrates a long glass tube from which most of the air can be removed with a vacuum pump. Inside it are two objects: a coin and a feather. Before pumping the air out, let the coin and feather drop the length of the tube and observe which falls faster. Explain. *Predict* what will happen when the air is removed from the tube. Which will fall faster this time? Now *test your prediction!*
4. **Figure 3.3** illustrates an apparatus that can release two identical steel balls at the same time. One ball is projected straight out, while at precisely the same time an identical steel ball is dropped straight down. *Predict* which ball will hit the floor first. Give a reason for your prediction. Now test your prediction. *Listen* for the sounds of the balls hitting the floor.

Concluding Questions

1. Describe what happened when you dropped two steel balls of different mass simultaneously. Does the mass of the balls affect their rate of fall?
2. (a) Describe what happened when you dropped a piece of tissue paper and a steel ball simultaneously. Explain.
   (b) What would happen if you did this experiment in a vacuum? Explain.
3. What happened when you fired a steel ball straight out horizontally while simultaneously dropping an identical ball? Does horizontal motion affect the rate of vertical fall of a ball?
4. On the moon, the force of gravity on a given mass is only about 1/6th what it is on earth. As a result, there is no atmosphere around the moon. Explain what you would expect to observe if you did **Procedures 1** to **4** on the moon.

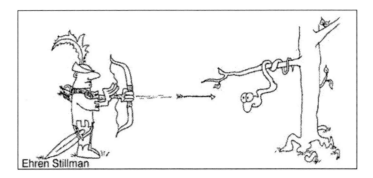

Figure 3.4

Challenges

1. An archer (**Figure 3.4**) aims his arrow at a snake hanging from a tree. At the instant the arrow leaves the bow, the snake drops from the branch. Will the arrow hit or miss the snake? Explain.
2. Design and build an apparatus for testing your prediction safely.

Part 2   Electrical Forces

Purpose: To observe some effects of electrical forces.

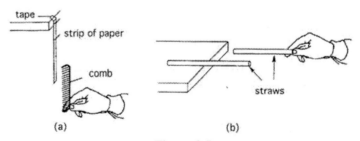

Figure 3.5

Procedure

1. Cut a strip of paper approximately 25 cm long and 1 cm wide, and tape it to the edge of your bench, as in **Figure 3.5 (a)**. Now comb your hair briskly, and bring your comb near the strip of paper, as in the figure. (A balloon rubbed on your hair or on a wool sweater will produce the same result.)
2. Rub a soda straw with wool or your hair and set it on the edge of your table [**Figure 3.5 (b)**]. Rub a second straw the same way, and then see what happens when you bring it near and parallel to the first straw. Watch what happens to the first straw.
3. Rub a soda straw with wool or hair, then dip it into a dish of very fine sawdust. Observe closely. Does any of the sawdust fly off the straw?
4. Rub a balloon on your hair or a wool sweater. See if your balloon will attract your hair. Will it stick to a wall?

Concluding Questions

1. Which appears to be the stronger force, the force of gravity between two charged objects or the electrical force? Explain your choice.

2. Were you able to observe two electrically charged objects (a) attract one another? (b) repel one another? How do electrical forces differ from gravitational forces in this respect?

Part 3   Magnetic Forces

Purpose: To observe some obvious properties of magnetism.

Procedure

1. Dip one end of a freshly magnetized bar magnet into a dish of sawdust.

2. Dip one end of a freshly magnetized bar magnet into a dish of iron filings.

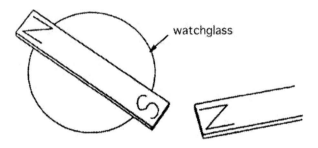

Figure 3.6

3. Arrange one freshly magnetized bar magnet on a watch glass, so that the magnet can rotate freely as in **Figure 3.6**. Bring the north end of another freshly magnetized bar magnet near (a) the south end and (b) the north end of the first magnet. Record your observations.

Concluding Questions

1. Did the bar magnet attract sawdust?

2. Did the bar magnet attract iron filings?

3. If you observed attraction in (1) or (2), could it be due to electrical forces? Explain.

4. Can magnetic forces be repulsive as well as attractive?

3.2 Measuring the Force of Gravity

Gravity causes **unsupported** objects to fall toward earth. The usual way to measure the force of gravity is to balance it with another force acting upward. For example, when you stand on a bathroom scale, gravity pulls you *downward*. A coiled spring inside the scale pushes *upward* and balances the force of gravity.

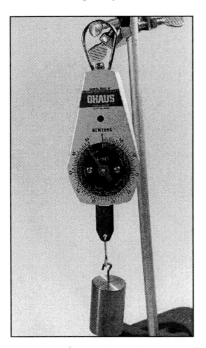

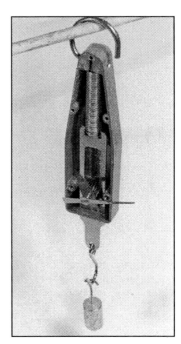

Figure 3.7(a)   **Figure 3.7(b)**

The common laboratory spring balance (**Figure 3.7**) uses a spring that is stretched by the force of gravity acting on the object that is being 'weighed'. If the spring is of good quality, the amount it stretches will depend directly on the force of gravity. That is, if the force of gravity doubles, the stretch will double. If the force of gravity triples, the stretch will triple. In other words, the amount of stretch is *directly proportional* to the force of gravity on the object.

Forces are measured in a unit called the **newton (N)**, named after **Sir Isaac Newton**.

Hooke's Law

Figure 3.8 is a graph showing how the stretch of a certain spring varies with the force of gravity acting on it. This is not only a linear graph, but also a direct proportion. When the force of gravity on the spring is 1.0 N, the stretch is 0.75 cm. When the force is doubled to 2.0 N, the stretch doubles to 1.50 cm. If the force is tripled to 3.0 N, the stretch is also tripled to 2.25 cm.

If a force is exerted on an object, such as a spring or a block of metal, the object will be stretched or compressed. If the amount of 'stretch' or 'compression', ΔL (change in length), is small compared with the length of the object, then ΔL is proportional to the force, F, exerted on the object. **Figure 3.8** illustrates this proportionality. In **Figure 3.8**, stretch is given the symbol y, and the straight-line graph through (0,0) suggests that $y \propto F_g$, or that $y = kF_g$. The slope of the graph is the **constant of proportionality**, k.

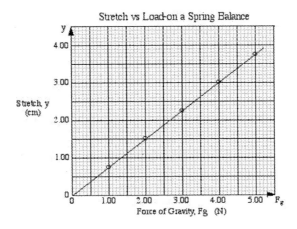

Figure 3.8

Robert Hooke (1635-1703) first noticed the direct proportion between the force exerted on a solid object and the change in length of the object, caused by the force. If too much force is applied, and an object is stretched or compressed excessively, the direct proportion breaks down, and the object may be permanently stretched or compressed. **Hooke's Law** is sometimes written with *force* the subject of the equation:

$$F = k\Delta L,$$

where F is the applied force, ΔL is the change in length, and k is the constant of proportionality.

Exercises

1. What is the slope of the graph in **Figure 3.8**?
2. Using symbols 'y' for stretch and 'F' for force of gravity, write a specific equation for the line in **Figure 3.8.**
3. (a) Use your equation to solve for the stretch of the spring when a force of gravity of 4.0 N acts on it. Check your solution by inspection of the graph.
   (b) Use your equation to solve for the force of gravity needed to stretch the spring 2.0 cm. Check your solution by inspection of the graph.
4. In a direct proportion graph, the slope of the graph is called the **constant of proportionality.** At any point on the line, the ratio of the stretch to the force of gravity will equal the constant of proportionality. By inspection of the graph, find the constant of proportionality when $F = 5.0$ N.

Investigation 3-2   Another Way to Weigh

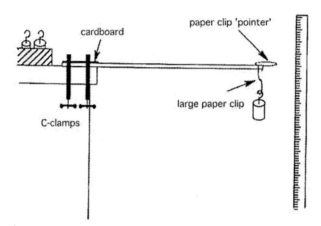

Figure 3.9

Purpose: To make a 'gravity measurer' out of a metre stick.

Introduction

In an earlier course, you may have done an experiment where you added known masses to a spring, and graphed the stretch of the spring against the force of gravity on the masses. In *Investigation 3-2,* you will learn how you can measure the force of gravity using a metre stick.

Procedure

1. Set up the apparatus in **Figure 3.9**. Clamp a metre stick horizontally so that 80.0 cm overhangs the edge of your bench. (Use a piece of cardboard to protect the metre stick from damage by the clamp.) Tape a large paper clip to the end of the metre stick, and bend the clip so that masses can be hung from it.
2. Mount another metre stick or ruler vertically so that the depression of the horizontal metre stick can be measured. Align the top edge of the horizontal metre stick with a convenient point on the vertical metre stick, such as 0.0 cm. (Another paper clip might be used as a pointer.)
3. Hang a 50.0 g mass on the paper clip, and measure the depression (vertical drop) of the end of the horizontal metre stick, estimating to the nearest one tenth of a millimetre. The force of gravity on a 50.0 g mass is 0.490 N. Record the force of gravity and the depression in a table like **Table 3.1**.
4. Measure the depression caused by each of the forces of gravity listed in **Table 3.1**. When you finish reading the depression for 4.90 N, remove the masses and see whether the depression returns to 0.00 cm. (If it does not, check that the metre stick is securely clamped. If it is not, tighten the clamps and repeat your measurements.) Do not dismantle your set-up yet!

Table 3.1 Data for *Investigation 3-2*

Mass (g)	Depression (y) (cm)	Force of Gravity (F_g) (N)
0		0
50		0.49
100		0.98
150		1.47
200		1.96
250		2.45
300		2.94
350		3.43
400		3.92
450		4.41
500		4.90

5. Prepare a graph of **depression** (Y-axis) vs **force of gravity** (X-axis). Find the slope, and write a *specific equation* for the line you obtain.
6. Hang an 'unknown object' (such as a small C-clamp) from the metre stick and measure the depression it causes. Find out what the force of gravity on it is (a) by direct reading of your graph and (b) by calculation using the equation for the line.
7. Measure the force of gravity on the unknown object using a commercial laboratory spring balance.

Concluding Questions

1. (a) What is the equation for the graph you prepared of y vs F ? Remember to include the numerical value of your slope, with proper units.
   (b) Is the graph linear? Is the relationship between the two variables a direct proportion? Explain.
2. Calculate the percent difference between the force of gravity on the unknown as determined from the graph and as measured with a laboratory spring balance.

Challenge: Make a 'letter weigher' using a strip of hacksaw blade instead of a metre stick. Calibrate it in grams instead of newtons. (The gram is a mass unit, but most postal rate scales are based on mass instead of force of gravity.)

3.3 Science Friction

When a body moves, there is almost always a resisting force exerted on it by materials in contact with it. An aircraft moving through the air must overcome the resistance of the air. A submarine encounters resistance from the water. A car experiences resistance from the road surface and from the air. In all cases like this, the force opposing the motion of the body is called **friction**. Engineers attempt to design aircraft, ships and automobiles so that friction is minimized.

Friction is not always a 'bad' thing, of course. You need friction to bring your bike or car (or yourself) to a stop. Walking on a frictionless floor would be a major challenge. Friction is desirable when you wish to strike a match or write with a pencil. If you ever have to use a parachute, you will appreciate the resisting force of the air on your parachute!

If you want to push a book along your bench, you know that you have to keep on pushing to keep it moving. This is true in many everyday situations. A skateboarder cannot coast along a level road indefinitely without some force being applied to counter the friction force. Friction is such a normal phenomenon, that for centuries it was believed impossible for an object to keep moving without a constant force being applied. Approximately 400 years ago, **Galileo Galilei (1546-1642)** suggested that if friction was eliminated, a body, once moving, and in the absence of any other unbalanced forces, would continue moving at the same speed and in the same direction indefinitely. Why is this a difficult idea to verify experimentally?

In *Investigation 3-3,* you will examine one type of friction, called **sliding** friction. Sliding friction is the friction force between two flat surfaces that exists when one surface slides over the other. In this two-part experiment, you will investigate the effects of two variables on sliding friction: (1) **the force of gravity** on the sliding object and (2) **the surface area** of the sliding object.

Investigation 3-3 Friction Can Be a Real Drag!

Part 1

Problem: **When an object slides over a 'smooth' horizontal surface, how does the force of friction (F_f) depend on the force of gravity (F_g) on the object?**

Procedure

1. Use a spring balance to measure the force of gravity on each of four nearly identical wood blocks provided, and write their weights (in N) in pencil on each block.
2. Prepare a data table like **Table 3.2**.

Table 3.2   Data For *Investigation 3-3,* Part 1

Number of Blocks	Total Force of Gravity (N)	Force of Friction (N)
1		
2		
3		
4		

3. Adjust your spring balance so that it reads '0 N' when it is held in a *horizontal* position (parallel to the bench top). Attach it to the hook on one of the four blocks. See **Figure 3.10**. Set the wide side of the block on a smooth, clean bench top. To measure the force of sliding friction, measure the smallest force needed to keep the block sliding at a *slow, steady speed* along the bench top. You will have to give the block a small extra nudge to get it moving. Once it is moving, however, a steady force equal to the **force of sliding friction** should keep it moving at a steady speed. Do several trials until you are satisfied you have a meaningful

average friction force. Record the force of gravity and the force of sliding friction in your copy of **Table 3.2**.

4. Place a second block on top of the first. The total force of gravity will now be the *sum* of the weights of the two blocks. Measure the force of friction with two blocks.

5. Repeat with three, then four blocks. Record the total force of gravity and force of friction each time in **Table 3.2**.

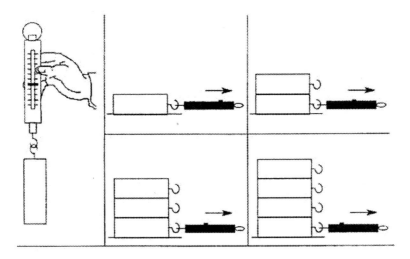

Figure 3.10

6. Plot a graph with force of sliding friction F_f on the Y-axis and force of gravity F_g on the X-axis. Determine the **slope** of the graph and write a *specific equation* for your graph. Include the units for the slope, if any.

Concluding Questions

1. When you doubled the force of gravity on the object sliding over your bench, what happened to the force of friction? What happened to the force of friction when the force of gravity was tripled? quadrupled?
2. What is the equation for your graph? (Please remember to use the proper symbols and units.)
3. The slope of your graph is called the **coefficient of kinetic friction,** and the coefficient is given the special symbol μ, which is the Greek letter *mu*. What is the coefficient of kinetic friction between the block and the tabletop you used?
4. Name three situations where you need to have
   (a) a *low* coefficient of friction, and
   (b) a *high* coefficient of friction.

Challenge: Measure the coefficient of kinetic friction between your blocks and a different horizontal surface.

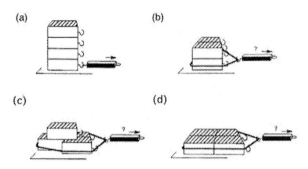

Figure 3.11

Part 2

Problem: **How does the force of sliding friction vary with the area of contact between two smooth, flat surfaces, when all other factors are controlled?**

Procedure

1. Make a *prediction!* If you double the area of contact between two smooth, flat objects, will the force of friction (a) stay the same, (b) double, (c) be cut in half or (d) change in some other way?
2. Pile four blocks on top of one another as in **Figure 3.11 (a)**. Loop a string around the blocks, attach a spring balance (properly 'zeroed') and measure the force of friction as in **Part 1**. Prepare a table of data like **Table 3.3**. Record your results.

Table 3.3 Data for *Investigation 3-3*, Part 2

Number of Blocks	Area	Total Force of Gravity (N)	Force of Friction (N)
4	1 x A	(constant)	
4	2 x A	(constant)	
4	3 x A	(constant)	
4	4 x A	(constant)	

3. Double the surface area by arranging the blocks as in **Figure 3.11 (b)**. Notice that the force of gravity is still the same; only the area has changed. Measure and record the force of friction. (Measure it several times until you are satisfied that you have an acceptable average.)
4. Arrange the blocks so that the surface area is tripled, then quadrupled without changing the force of gravity. See **Figure 3.11**. Measure and record the force of friction each time.

Concluding Questions

1. After comparing your results for **Part 2** with several other groups doing the same experiment, write a conclusion regarding the effect that varying the surface area has on the amount of friction between a smooth flat object of constant force of gravity and another smooth surface.

2. Discuss sources of error in this experiment.

Coefficients of Friction

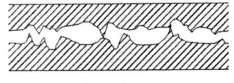

Figure 3.12

Even the smoothest-looking piece of metal, if viewed under a microscope, will have irregular bumps and hollows. Where the bumps come in contact, the electrical attraction between the atoms of the two surfaces produces a small-scale 'welding' of the materials at the points of contact. (**Figure 3.12**)

When one surface is moved over the other, the welded regions must be broken apart. Friction arises from the breaking of these welded regions and from the 'plowing' effect as the harder surface moves through the softer one.

Static friction acts when you have two objects at rest relative to one another. Static friction, for example, keeps a car with its parking brakes on from sliding down a hill. A block of wood will remain stationary on a sloped table until you increase the angle sufficiently that it begins to slide. The force required to overcome static friction is always greater than the force needed to balance sliding friction (also called **kinetic friction**). Presumably this is because to overcome static friction, you have to 'break the welds' before the objects can move relative to one another. When you did *Investigation 3-3,* you no doubt noticed that the force needed to get the blocks of wood moving was slightly greater than the force needed to keep them moving at steady speed.

Your results from *Investigation 3-3* probably convinced you that the force of friction F_f is proportional to the force of gravity F_g on the object sliding over a smooth surface. A more general truth about sliding friction is that the force of friction is proportional to the **normal force** F_n (which is the force acting perpendicular to the surfaces).

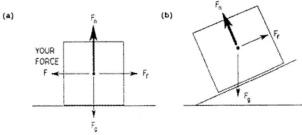

Figure 3.13

If a block slides horizontally across a table as in **Figure 3.13 (a)**, the force of gravity is equal in magnitude to the normal force, but if the surfaces are at an angle to the horizontal as in **Figure 3.13 (b)**, the normal force does *not* equal the force of gravity. You will encounter situations like this in future physics courses.

In general, for two objects with smooth flat surfaces sliding over one another, it can be said that the force of friction is proportional to the normal force. The constant of proportionality is called the **coefficient of kinetic friction**, μ. Written symbolically,

$$F_f = \mu F_n.$$

Table 3.4 lists some coefficients of kinetic friction.

Table 3.4	Coefficients of Kinetic Friction*
Surfaces in Contact	**Coefficient μ***
wood on wood	0.25
steel on steel	0.50
steel on steel (lubricated)	0.10
rubber on dry asphalt	0.40
rubber on wet asphalt	0.20
rubber on ice	0.005
steel on ice	0.01

* All values are approximate. Precise values vary with conditions such as degree of smoothness.

As you observed in **Investigation 3-3**, surface area does not affect the force of friction appreciably. For example, it will require the same force to slide a building brick on its edge, as it will on its broad side. The two factors that have the greatest effect on friction are (1) the normal force pushing the surfaces together, and (2) the nature of the surfaces.

Example

The coefficient of kinetic friction between a wooden box and a concrete floor is 0.30. With what force must you push to slide the box across the floor at steady speed if the force of gravity on the box is 450 N?
Solution: In this situation, the normal force equals the force of gravity on the box, so

$$Ff = \mu Fg = (0.30)(450 \text{ N}) = 135 \text{ N} = 1.4 \times 10^2 \text{ N}.$$

To slide the box across the floor at a steady speed you must exert a force equal to the friction force, which is 1.4×10^2 N.

Exercises

1. (a) Where on a bicycle do you want to *reduce* friction? How is this done?
   (b) Where on a bicycle do you want friction?
2. (a) What is meant by the **coefficient of kinetic friction**?
   (b) Why are there no units attached to values of μ?
   (c) A force of 120 N is needed to push a box along a level road at a steady speed. If the force of gravity on the box is 250 N, what is the coefficient of kinetic friction between the box and the road?
3. The coefficient of kinetic friction between a steel block and an ice rink surface is 0.0100. If a force of 24.5 N keeps the steel block moving at steady speed, what is the force of gravity on the block?
4. A copper block has dimensions 1 cm x 2 cm x 4 cm. A force of 0.10 N will pull the block along a table surface at steady speed if the 1 cm x 4 cm side is face down on the table. What force will be needed to pull the same block along when its 2 cm x 4 cm side is face down?

3.4 Gravity and Isaac Newton

One of **Sir Isaac Newton's** many valuable contributions to science is his **Law of Universal Gravitation**. Newton (1642-1727) realized that the force of gravity, which affects you and everything around you, is a *universal* force. Any two masses in the universe exert a gravitational force on each other. How strong the force is depends on how massive the bodies are. It also depends on the distance between the two bodies. In *Investigation 3-4,* you will be supplied with some 'manufactured' data to work with, so that you can understand the nature of the relationship between gravitational force and the distance between two masses.

Investigation 3-4 How Gravitational Force Depends on Distance

---

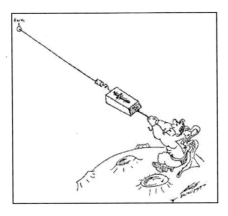

Figure 3.14

Purpose: To use space age data to discover the nature of the relationship between gravitational force and distance.

Table 3.5 The Force of Gravity on a Kilogram Mass

Force of Gravity (N)	Distance from Centre of Earth (Mm*)
9.81	6.37
2.45	12.74
1.09	19.11
0.61	25.48
0.39	31.85

(*1 Mm = 1 megametre = 10^6 m)

58

Procedure

1. In an imaginary experiment, Superman was hired to measure the force of gravity on a 1 kg mass at different distances from the centre of the earth. See **Figure 3.14**. He used a precise spring balance to obtain the data in **Table 3.5**. Make a graph with force of gravity (F_g) on the Y-axis and distance from the centre of the earth (d) on the X- axis.

Graphs of Various Power Law Relations

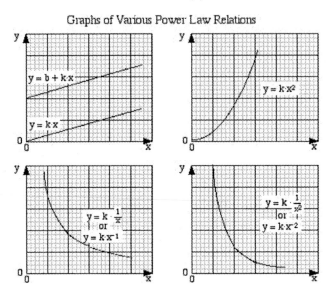

Figure 3.15

2. Your first graph will not be a straight line, because the relationship between F_g and d is not linear ($y \neq kx + b$) and is not a direct proportion ($y \neq kx$). The relationship is a **power law** ($y = k \cdot x^n$) where the power n is neither 1 nor 0. How can you find out what the value of n is? If you look at **Figure 3.15**, you will see the shapes of the graphs of several power law relationships. Which of these graphs does your graph most resemble? To find out if your graph is a particular type of relationship, plot force of gravity (F_g) on the Y-axis, as before, and your chosen d^n on the X-axis. Plot the following graphs and see which one gives a straight line: (a) F_g vs d^{-1} (b) F_g vs d^{-2}

Concluding Questions

1. (a) What variables must you plot to obtain a straight line (through the origin)?
   (b) What is the specific equation for your final straight line?

2. From your equation, calculate:
   (a) at what distance the force of gravity on the kilogram mass is half of what it is at the earth's surface;
   (b) the force of gravity on the 1 kg mass at a distance of 10 earth radii (63.7 Mm).

3.5   Kinds of Force

The three kinds of force that you are most likely to encounter in everyday life are **gravity**, **electrostatic** and **magnetic**. **Strong** and **weak nuclear forces** exist within the atom, and you may study these later. The **Law of Universal Gravitation** may be investigated in more detail in a later course, as will the force law governing electrically charged bodies and laws governing magnetic forces.

As a matter of interest, *Investigation 3-5* takes a descriptive look at two types of force (both of them electrical in nature), which you encounter often but perhaps take for granted. These are **cohesive forces** and **adhesive forces**.

Cohesive and Adhesive Forces

Cohesive forces are forces that exist between molecules of the *same* type. Cohesive forces between water molecules make the water form spherical droplets, as in **Figure 3.16 (a)**.

Adhesive forces exist between molecules of *different* materials. The adhesive force between the water molecules and the glass molecules causes the **meniscus**, formed at the edge of a glass container. See **Figure 3.16 (b)**.

Figure 3.16 (c) shows how the cohesive forces between molecules can be used to form extremely large soap bubbles. The bubbles consist mostly of water, but soap molecules are needed to *reduce* the cohesive force between the water molecules, so that the water forms a thin film.

Investigation 3-5   Cohesion and Adhesion

Purpose: To observe examples of situations where cohesive and adhesive forces between molecules exist.

Procedure

1. Place a square of waxed paper (30 cm x 30 cm) on your bench. Use a medicine dropper to see how large a drop of water you can make on the waxed surface. Now add a single drop of soapy water to the large drop on the waxed paper.
2. Place a drop of water on a small square of paper towel or tissue paper. Compare the result with what happened when you used waxed paper.
3. Punch three holes about 3 mm apart near the bottom of an empty milk carton. Cover the holes with one strip of masking tape. Fill the carton with water, and place it beside the sink. Strip off the tape and let the water stream out. See if you can bring the three streams of water together into one by pinching them with your fingers.
4. Place a penny in the bottom of a large test tube. Note the size of the coin. *Partially* fill the test tube with water. Look down into the test tube and note the apparent size of the coin now. Next fill the test tube until it is *overflowing*. Clamp it vertically, and use a medicine dropper to form a convex bulge on the top of the test tube. Note the apparent size of the coin when you look down at it now.

(a)

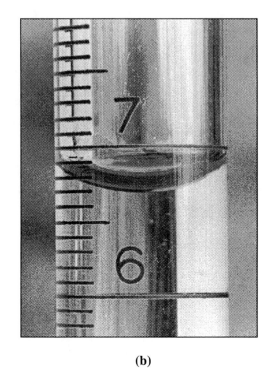

(b)

(c)

Figure 3.16

5. Examine the **meniscus** formed by water in a graduated cylinder. Also look at the meniscus formed by mercury in a thermometer or in a thermostat switch.

> **Caution! Mercury is toxic. Do not remove it from a sealed container.**

6. Moisten two *thick* flat glass plates. Place one above the other, and try to pull them apart without sliding one over the other.
7. Your instructor will provide you with three lengths of glass tubing, each with a different hole diameter. Place the three tubes vertically in a dish of coloured water, and observe how far the water travels up each tube.
8. Make a needle or a paper clip float on water. Now add a single drop of soap to the water.
9. Use a giant soap bubble device to make the largest soap bubble you can. See **Figure 3.16 (c)**. Do this outdoors!

> **Note!** One recommended bubble mix is: 400 mL Ultra **Ivory**™ (Dawn) dishwashing detergent, 4 L water, and 50 mL (or more) of either glycerin or clear corn syrup. On a dry day, use more water, since it will evaporate quickly.

Challenges!

1. Take a picture of water coming from a tap using (a) a high speed electronic flash and (b) room light and no flash. (When taking the picture in room light, place your camera on a tripod and use a slow shutter speed such as 1/15 s.) Compare the two pictures.
2. Obtain some **Magic Sand**™ and figure out what it does and how it works.

Concluding Questions

1. Which is stronger — the cohesive force between water molecules or the adhesive force between water molecules and wax molecules? Explain.

2. Why can you not form a drop of water on a paper towel?

3. Why can you bring the streams of water together into one stream in **Procedure 3**?

4. Why do the images of the coin change in **Procedure 4**?

5. Why does water form a **concave** meniscus and mercury a **convex** meniscus?

6. What makes two pieces of wet glass stick together?

7. Why does water rise further up a narrow bore tube than a wide bore tube?

8. Why can a dense steel needle float on water? Why does soap make the needle sink?

9. Do soap bubbles illustrate cohesive forces or adhesive forces, or both? Explain.

10. What does water really look like when it comes out of a tap?

Chapter Review Questions

1. What are two kinds of force that can be either attractive or repulsive?

2. A student added masses to the end of a hanging spring, then measured the amount of extension (stretch) caused by the force of gravity on each mass. The following readings were obtained:

Mass (kg)	0.200	0.400	0.600	0.800	1.000
Force of Gravity (N)	1.96	3.92	5.88	7.84	9.80
Extension (cm)	0.47	0.93	1.41	1.89	2.35

   (a) Plot a graph with Force of Gravity (F_g) on the Y-axis and Extension (x) on the X-axis. Determine the slope of the graph (in appropriate units), and write an equation describing how the force of gravity varies with the extension.

   (b) Use both your graph and your equation to figure out the force of gravity that would stretch the spring 1.50 cm.

   (c) Use both your graph and your equation to figure out how much stretch would occur in the spring when the force of gravity is 6.50 N.

3. To slide a metal puck across a greased sheet of metal at constant speed requires a force of 0.525 N. If the force of gravity on the puck is 5.00 N, what is the coefficient of friction between the puck and the greased metal?

4. The force of gravity on a wooden crate is 560 N. It can be pushed along a certain floor at steady speed if a horizontal force of 224 N is applied to it. How much horizontal force will be needed to move a stack of two crates at the same steady speed? What force will be needed if the two crates are not stacked but tied to one another side by side?

5. The force of gravity on a black bear is 2500 N on the earth's surface. The animal becomes so 'unbearable' that it is transported four earth radii from the *surface* of the earth. What is the force of gravity on it now?

6. **Newton's Law of Universal Gravitation** is written as follows: $F_g = \dfrac{GMm}{d^2}$, where F_g is the force of gravity between mass M and mass m, and d is the distance between the centres of mass. G is called the **universal gravitation constant**.

   (a) Given two small, chocolate-centred candies of masses M and m, what will happen to the force of gravity F_g between them if
   (i) d is doubled?
   (ii) d is tripled?
   (iii) d is reduced to 1/2 d ?
   (iv) d is reduced to 1/3 d ?

   (b) Given two candies with masses M and m a distance d apart, what will the force of gravity F_g between them become, if
   (i)   only M is doubled?
   (ii)   only m is doubled?
   (iii)   both M and m are doubled?
   (iv) $M, m,$ and d are *all* doubled?

(c) The constant G in the Law of Universal Gravitation has a value of 6.67 x 10^{-11} Nm^2/kg^2. Calculate the force of gravity between

  (i)   a 100.0 kg person and the earth. Earth's mass is 5.98 x 10^{24} kg, and its radius is 6.38 x 10^6 m.

  (ii)   a 100.0 kg person and the moon. The moon's mass is 7.35 x 10^{22} kg, and its radius is 1.74 x 10^6 m.

  (iii) two 46 g golf balls whose centres of mass are 10 cm apart.

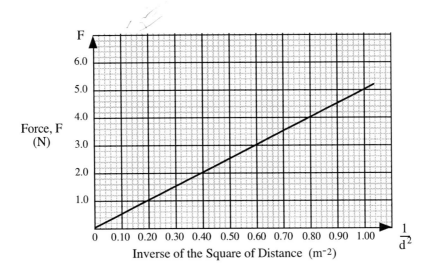

Figure 3.17

7. **Figure 3.17** is a graph of force vs the *inverse of the square of the distance* between two small, electrically charged spheres.

  (a) What is the slope of this graph, expressed in proper units?
  (b) What is the equation of the graph?
  (c) How would you describe how the electrical force between the two small charged spheres varies with the distance between them?

8. When doing a routine filtration, a chemist pours his solution from a beaker down a glass stirring rod into the filter. Why does this procedure reduce the possibility of spilling the solution?

9. Try pouring water down (a) a dry string and (b) a wet string. Which is easier, and why?

Test Yourself!

Depression, in cm

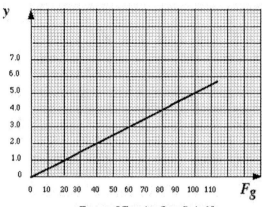

Force of Gravity (Load), in N

1. A wooden beam was clamped horizontally, so that masses could be hung from its free end. The **depression** y (in cm) caused by the **force of gravity** F_g (in N) on the masses was measured, for loads up to 100.0 N. The above graph summarizes all the data.
   (a) What is the **slope** of the graph, expressed in appropriate units?
   (b) Write an equation for this graph, specifically.
   (c) According to the above graph, how much will the beam be depressed by a load of 80.0 N?
   (d) According to the above graph, what load will cause the beam to be depressed by 3.0 cm?
2. The coefficient of sliding friction between a rubber disc and the ice is 0.0050. If the force of friction is 0.25 N, what is the force of gravity on the rubber disc?
3. Planet Mars has a mass of 6.4 x 10²³ kg, and you have a mass of 5.0 x 10¹ kg. What force of gravity is exerted between you and Mars, if you are standing on its surface? The radius of planet Mars is 3.4 x 10⁶ m. Calculate this using Newton's Law of Universal Gravitation,
   $F = G \dfrac{Mm}{d^2}$, where G = 6.67 x 10⁻¹¹ Nm²/kg².

Multiple Choice Questions

1. Which forces can be either *attractive* or *repulsive?*
   (A) gravity and electric
   (B) gravity and magnetic
   (C) electric and magnetic
   (D) gravity and friction

2. What instrument is used to measure force of gravity?
   (A) spring balance
   (B) chemical balance
   (C) wheel balance
   (D) bank balance

3. In what metric unit is mass measured?
   (A) pound
   (B) ounce
   (C) newton
   (D) kilogram

4. Metre is to distance as newton is to
   (A) inertia.
   (B) momentum.
   (C) acceleration.
   (D) force.

5. On the moon, two stowaways on a moon probe vehicle ran from the vehicle on landing, and fell off a moon cliff at the same instant. One had a parachute, and the other did not. Which stowaway hit the ground at the base of the moon cliff first?
   (A) The stowaway with the parachute will hit the ground first.
   (B) The stowaway without a parachute will hit the ground first.
   (C) Both stowaways will remain 'floating' above the ground, at the top of the cliff.
   (D) Both stowaways will hit the ground at the same time.

6. To slide a 40 N box at steady speed along a smooth bench top, a pulling force of 2.5 N is needed. This force is equal in magnitude to the force of friction. Now, an 80 N box is placed on top of the 40 N box. What force must be exerted to slide the *combined* boxes at steady speed across the same bench surface?
   (A) 2.5 N   (B) 5.0 N   (C) 7.5 N   (D) 10.0 N

7. If the friction force is 2.5 N, when a 40 N object is pulled across a bench, then what is the **coefficient of sliding friction?**
   (A) 0.063   (B) 16   (C) 100   (D) 0.630

8. What happens to the coefficient of friction between a load and the floor, if the load is tripled?
   (A) The coefficient of friction is tripled.
   (B) The coefficient is reduced to one third of what it was.
   (C) The coefficient stays the same as before.
   (D) The coefficient increases nine times.

9. What single factor has the *least effect* on the amount of friction between two surfaces sliding over one another?
   (A) Increasing the mass of the object that is on top.
   (B) Roughening the surfaces facing each other.
   (C) Using a lubricant between the surfaces.
   (D) Changing the surface area of contact.

10. At the earth's surface, a package is a distance of one earth radius from the centre of earth. The force of gravity on a particular space payload is 1440 N. If this package is moved to an orbit that is four earth radii from the centre of earth, what will the force of gravity on the package be?
    (A) 1440 N   (B) 720 N   (C) 360 N   .(D) 160 N   (E) 90 N

Chapter 4 Newton's Laws of Motion

4.1 Inertia

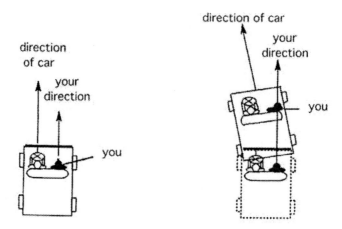

Figure 4.1

Imagine you are a passenger in a car, and the driver makes a sudden left turn. What sensation do you feel during the left turn? From your own experience, you might recall that you *feel* as if you are being pushed to the right.

Contrary to what your 'common sense' might tell you, *you are not being pushed to the right at all!* **Figure 4.1** will help you understand what really happens. The driver steers the car to the left. Your body wants to carry on in a straight line, but the door of the car is moving left with the rest of the car. You *feel* as if you are being pushed against the door by a force aimed toward the right door, but in fact *your body is trying to continue along its original path (straight ahead)* while the car is turning left.

As a general rule, any object tends to continue moving with whatever speed and direction it presently has. This can include zero speed, of course. When your driver accelerates the car, your body tends to stay where it was, and you *feel* as if you are being pushed back into your seat.

Galileo was possibly the first person to realize that the speed and direction of an object will stay the same *unless* some kind of **unbalanced force** acts on the body. If you pull a block of wood along a tabletop with a force just equal to friction, the block will move with *steady* speed, because the forces are balanced. If you pull a bit harder, the block will no longer move with a steady speed; it will *accelerate!*

The tendency that all massive bodies have to resist change in their states of motion is given a special name: **inertia.** Every object in the universe that has mass has this property of inertia.

Some objects have more inertia than others. A logging truck has much more inertia than a BMX bike. Because it has so much more inertia, the logging truck is (a) more difficult to get moving, (b) more difficult to stop, and (c) more difficult to turn at a corner.

Is there a way to measure inertia? Actually, you have measured it many times in science class. The way to measure inertia is to measure the object's **mass**. What you measure when you determine the mass of an object on a chemical balance is equal to the object's **inertial mass,** which is the measure of inertia. Strictly speaking, what the chemical balance measures is called **gravitational mass**. This is because the unknown object is placed on one pan, and the standard mass on the other. The masses are assumed equal when the force of gravity on the unknown mass balances the force of gravity on the standard mass. *Gravitational mass is numerically equal to inertial mass,* however, so a chemical balance can be used to measure inertial mass as well.

Investigation 4-1   Inertia Demonstrations

Figure 4.2

Problem 1: How does a seatbelt work?

Procedure

1. Place a small toy human figure on a toy car or truck. (See **Figure 4.2**.) Do not fasten the figure to the vehicle. Let the vehicle move toward a suitable obstruction (another toy vehicle or a brick) and collide with it. Observe what happens to the unattached passenger.

2. Repeat **Procedure 1**, but this time give the toy human figure a 'seat belt'. (Tape it to the vehicle.)

Question: How does this demonstration illustrate inertia? Why are you more likely to survive a collision with a seatbelt than without one?

Problem 2: Where will the string break? (Getting the 'Hang' of Inertia)

Figure 4.3

Procedure

1. Attach two equal masses (500 g or 1 kg) to a supporting rod, as in **Figure 4.3**. Use string that is strong enough to support the hanging masses, but not so strong that you cannot break it with a moderate pull with your hand. Add a 50 cm length of the same kind of string to the bottom of each mass.
2. *Predict* where the string will break (*above* or *below* the mass) if you pull (a) *gently*, and (b) *abruptly*, on the string. *Test* your predictions by experiment.

Question: Explain what happened, in terms of inertia.

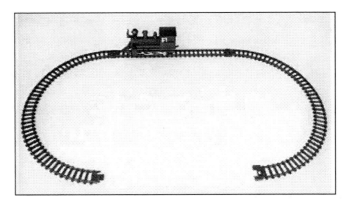

Figure 4.4

Problem 3:   Getting Off on the Right Track

Procedure

1. Place a battery-powered toy train on a circular track, and let it run a few full circles. (**Figure 4.4**)
2. *Predict* which way the train will go if one of the sections of curved track is removed. Will the train
   (a) continue to move in a circle? (b) move off along a radius of the circle? (c) move off in a straight line tangent to the circle? or (d) follow some other path? (Describe.)
3. Now test your prediction by experiment.

Question: What happens to the toy train when it leaves the track? Explain this in terms of inertia.

Problem 4: Taking a Well-Calculated Wrist

Procedure: Have a friend hold a coin in the middle of his or her open palm as in **Figure 4.5**. Your challenge is to get the coin out of his or her palm faster than he or she can take the hand away. *Think inertia!*

Question: Explain how you used inertia to snatch the coin.

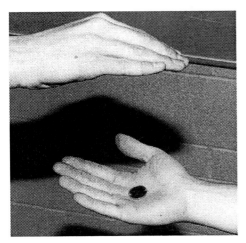

Figure 4.5

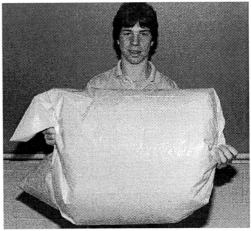

Figure 4.6

Problem 5: Does Air Have Inertia?

Procedure: Fill a large garbage bag with air, and hold it as in **Figure 4.6**. Quickly jerk the bag to one side. What happens to the air in the bag (a) when you start moving the bag? and (b) when you stop the bag?

Question: Does air have inertia? How does a grocery clerk use inertia to open a paper bag, before filling it with groceries?

Problem 6: Inertia on an Air Track

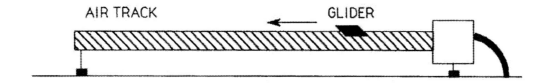

Figure 4.7

Procedure

1. Place a glider on an air track. See **Figure 4.7**. Turn on the compressed air supply and check that the track is absolutely level. (The glider should have no tendency to move one direction or the other.)
2. Place the glider at one end of the track. Give it a slight nudge, and then let go. Observe the motion of the glider.

Question: Are there any unbalanced forces on the glider? Describe its motion. (Is it moving at a constant speed or is it accelerating?) How does this demonstration illustrate inertia?

Problem 7: The Pop-Up Coaster

(a)   (b)

Figure 4.8

Procedure

The cart in **Figure 4.8** contains a spring that can fire a steel ball straight up in the air. The cart is given a steady horizontal speed by pulling on it with a string, which also activates the trigger for the spring-loaded cannon. When the cart is moving with a steady speed, the string is given a sudden pull, which releases the spring and fires the ball up in the air. *Predict* whether the ball will land ahead of the cannon, behind the cannon or in the cannon. Explain your prediction. Now, test your prediction!

Question: How does this demonstration illustrate inertia?

4.2 Unbalanced Forces

If there are no forces acting on an object, or if there are two or more forces that balance each other, the object will continue on its way with the same speed and in the same direction. That is how things work in nature. The label scientists attach to this property of matter is **inertia. Galileo Galilei (1564-1642)** was aware of this property of nature, which is sometimes called the **Law of Inertia.**

Isaac Newton (1642-1727) incorporated Galileo's results into his **Laws of Motion,** which are the topic of this chapter.

The First Law of Motion (**Law of Inertia**) might be stated this way:

A body will continue to move at the same speed and in the same direction for as long as there are no unbalanced forces acting on it.

What happens to a body if the forces acting on it are *not* balanced? For example, what happens to the speed of a cart if the force you exert to pull it or push it is *greater* than the force of friction? Now you have an **unbalanced force** acting on the cart.

In *Investigation 4-2,* you will experiment with the effects of two variables on the motion of a cart: (1) the **unbalanced force** and (2) the **mass** of the cart.

Investigation 4-2   Newton's Second Law of Motion

Note! This experiment can be a team effort by various groups in a class. It is best that all groups use the same set of apparatus to obtain their speed-time tapes, so that variables such as cart mass, timer frequency and unbalanced forces are better controlled.

Purpose: To investigate how the change in speed of a cart is affected by
(a) the amount of **unbalanced force** and
(b) the amount of **mass** in the cart.

Procedure:

1. Set up the apparatus in **Figure 4.9(a)**. Suspend a mass of 200 g from the end of a string, which passes over a pulley at the end of the bench. The force of gravity on this mass is 1.96 N, or approximately 2.0 N.

2. Lift one end of your laboratory table so that the cart rolls toward the pulley at a *steady speed.* (This can be checked with a ticker tape and your recording timer.) If your bench cannot be lifted, do the experiment on a length of board, which can be raised at one end. (What this does is balance friction with a little help from gravity.)

3. The class will now share the task of preparing and analyzing ticker-tape records of speed vs time for each of the situations in **Figure 4.9**. Note that the *whole system* of *cart plus string plus hanging mass* moves as one unit. It is the *whole system* whose mass must be kept constant, if you are varying the unbalanced force. It is the *whole system* whose mass must be doubled, tripled, etc., if you are varying the mass while keeping the unbalanced force constant.

Each lab group of two students will choose one of the eight set-ups and prepare *two* tapes (one for each partner). If necessary, adjust the slope of the bench or board for each set-up to compensate for different amounts of friction with different loads on the cart. The class as a team will prepare and analyze tapes for each of the situations in **Figure 4.9**. If your class is large enough, some duplication of data is advisable so that data can be double-checked.

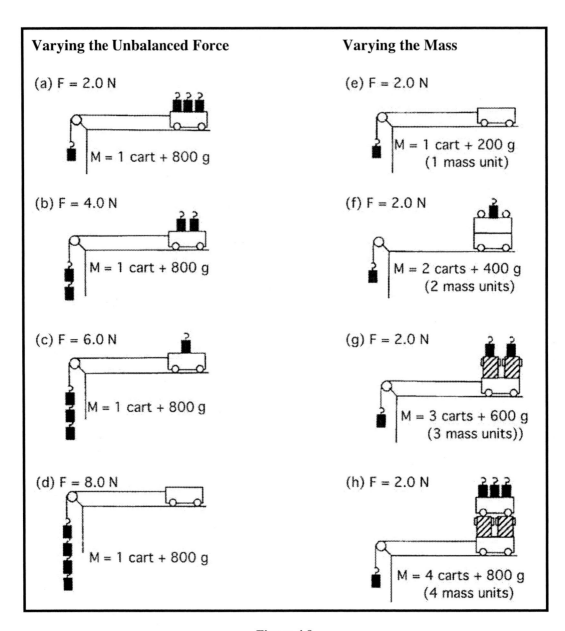

Figure 4.9

(a) Preparing Your Own Tape:

Use the technique you employed to measure acceleration in an earlier chapter. Remember that a group of six dots represents 0.10 s and that the average speeds for each interval are plotted mid-way through each time interval (not at the end of the interval). Prepare your graph. Label it carefully with the unbalanced force used (2.0 N, 4.0 N, 6.0 N or 8.0 N) and the mass of the cart *system*. The most important measurement you need is the **acceleration** of the cart, which you get from the slope of the graph. Express the acceleration in cm/s². You will share this information with the rest of the class.

(b) Analysis of Class Data:

(i) Prepare the following tables of data, summarizing class results.

Table 4.1 Acceleration vs Unbalanced Force (Mass constant)

Unbalanced Force, F (N)	Acceleration, a (cm/s²)
0	0
2.0	
4.0	
6.0	
8.0	

Table 4.2 Acceleration vs Mass (Unbalanced Force constant)

Mass, m 'mass units'	Acceleration, a cm/s²	$\dfrac{1}{\text{mass}}, \dfrac{1}{m}$ (mass units⁻¹)
1.0		1.0
2.0		0.50
3.0		0.33
4.0		0.25

(ii) Plot a graph of acceleration (Y-axis) against unbalanced force (X-axis).
(iii) Plot a graph of acceleration against mass.
(iv) Plot a graph of acceleration against the reciprocal of mass ($1/m$).

Concluding Questions

1. Describe how the speed of a cart changes when a constant unbalanced force pulls it.
2. According to your first graph (a vs F), how does acceleration depend upon unbalanced force? Does your graph suggest that acceleration is directly proportional to unbalanced force? Discuss.
3. According to your second and third graphs, how does the acceleration of the cart vary when the mass is doubled, tripled and quadrupled? Write an equation for the third graph, complete with the numerical value and units for the slope.
4. What were some of the experimental difficulties encountered in this investigation, which would make it difficult to obtain ideal results?

Challenge! Try a similar experiment, using an air track and glider for the apparatus. Use strobe photography or photo gates for measuring speeds and accelerations.

4.3 Newton's Second Law of Motion

Newton's Second Law deals with the problem of what happens if an **unbalanced force** acts on a body. Isaac Newton's conclusions regarding the motion of bodies acted on by unbalanced forces are expressed in his second law of motion.

Newton's Second Law

If an unbalanced force acts upon a body, it will accelerate.
The rate at which it accelerates depends directly on the unbalanced force and inversely on the mass of the body.

If appropriate measuring units are used, we can write:

$$\textbf{acceleration} = \frac{\textbf{unbalanced force}}{\textbf{mass}}, \text{ or } a = \frac{F}{m}.$$

Newton's Second Law is often written,

$$F = ma.$$

The direction in which the body accelerates will be the same direction as the unbalanced force. The measuring unit for force is the **newton (N)**.

One **newton** is the force needed to accelerate one kilogram (1 kg)
at a rate of one metre per second per second (1 m/s²).

Whenever Newton's Second Law is used, it is *understood* that the force F in the equation $F = ma$ is the **unbalanced force** (also called the **net force**) acting on the body. A few sample questions will serve to illustrate the Second Law.

Examples

1. A one-kilogram mass falls under the influence of gravity. The earth pulls down on the mass with a force of 9.80 N. At what rate does the mass accelerate?

   Solution: $a = \dfrac{F}{m} = \dfrac{9.80 \text{ N}}{1.0 \text{ kg}} = \dfrac{9.8 \text{ kg}\cdot\text{m/s}^2}{1.0 \text{ kg}} = 9.80 \text{ m/s}^2.$

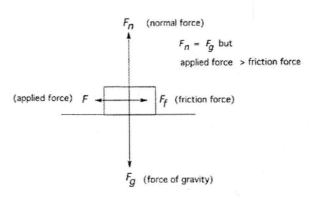

Figure 4.10

2. A 45.0 N block is being pushed along a floor, where the coefficient of kinetic friction is 0.333. If a force of 25.0 N is applied, at what rate will the block accelerate? The mass of the block is 4.60 kg.

Solution: Acceleration depends on the **unbalanced force**. **Figure 4.10** shows four different forces acting on the block. The two vertical forces balance each other, because the **force of gravity** and the **normal force** (the force exerted on the block by the floor) equal each other in size, and act in opposite directions. The **unbalanced force** will be the difference between the 25.0 N **applied force** and the **friction force** opposing the applied force.

Friction force $\quad F_f \;=\; \mu F_n \;=\; \mu F_g \;=\; (0.333)(45.0 \text{ N}) \;=\; 15.0 \text{ N}.$
Unbalanced force = Applied Force - Friction Force

$$F \;=\; 25.0 \text{ N} - 15.0 \text{ N} \;=\; 10.0 \text{ N}$$

Acceleration $\quad a = \dfrac{F}{m} = \dfrac{10.0 \text{ N}}{4.60 \text{ kg}} = 2.17 \text{ m/s}^2$

Exercises

1. What unbalanced force is needed to accelerate a 5.0 kg cart at 5.0 m/s²?

2. A net force of 7.5×10^4 N acts on a spacecraft of mass 3.0×10^4 kg.
   (a) At what rate will the spacecraft accelerate?
   (b) Assuming constant acceleration is maintained, how fast will the spacecraft be moving after 25 s, if its initial speed was 5.0×10^3 m/s?

3. What is the mass of a rock if a force of 2.4×10^3 N makes it accelerate at a rate of 4.0×10^1 m/s²?

4. A model rocket has a mass of 0.12 kg. It accelerates vertically to 60.0 m/s in 1.2 s.
   (a) What is its average acceleration?
   (b) What is the unbalanced force on the rocket?
   (c) If the force of gravity on the rocket is 1.2 N, what is the total thrust of its engine?

5. A fully loaded military rocket has a mass of 3.0 x 10^6 kg, and the force of gravity on it at ground level is 2.9 x 10^7 N.
   (a) At what rate will the rocket accelerate during lift-off, if the engines provide a thrust of 3.3 x 10^7 N?
   (b) Why will this acceleration not remain constant?

6. A boy and his skateboard have a combined mass of 60.0 kg. After an initial shove, the boy starts coasting at 5.5 m/s along a level driveway. Friction brings him to rest in 5.0 s. If the combined force of gravity on the boy and skateboard is 5.9 x 10^2 N, what is the average coefficient of (rolling) friction between the driveway and the skateboard wheels?

4.4 Gravity and Newton's Second Law

Any unsupported body in the presence of another massive body (usually the earth) will experience an **unbalanced gravitational force,** and be accelerated toward the other body. Newton's Second Law allows us to calculate the rate of acceleration:

$$a = \frac{F}{m}.$$

In the special case where the unbalanced force is entirely due to gravity, the value of the acceleration, *a,* is called the **gravitational field strength**, and is given the symbol, *g.* Therefore, in a gravitational field, $g = \frac{F_g}{m}$, or $F_g = mg$.

You will notice that gravitational field strength could be measured either in **N/kg** or in **m/s²** (acceleration units). The local value of *g* tells you (a) what the force of gravity on a kilogram of mass is in that locality and (b) the rate at which an object in free fall will accelerate toward the earth.

Examples

1. A student measures the force of gravity on a 0.500 kg mass and finds it to be 4.91 N. What is the local gravitational field strength?

   Solution: $\qquad g = \frac{F_g}{m} = \frac{4.91 \text{ N}}{0.500 \text{ kg}} = 9.82 \text{ N/kg.}$

2. What is the force of gravity on a 60.0 kg astronaut:
   (a) While she is standing on the surface of the earth, where $g = 9.81$ N/kg?
   (b) While she is standing on the moon, where $g = 1.63$ N/kg?

   Solution: $\qquad$ (a) On earth, $F_g = mg = (60.0 \text{ kg})(9.81 \text{N/kg}) = 589$ N.

   $\qquad\qquad\qquad$ (b) On the moon, $F_g = mg = (60.0 \text{ kg})(1.63 \text{ N/kg}) = 98$ N.

Exercises

1. What is the force of gravity on a 1.0 g mass here on earth, where the gravitational field strength is 9.8 N/kg?

2. What is the gravitational field strength in a location where the force of gravity on a 14.67 kg mass is 143.62 N?

3. If the force of gravity on a football player is 789.5 N in Vancouver, where the gravitational field strength is 9.80 N/kg, what is the mass of the player?

4. The force of gravity on a 5.0 kg mass on Mars is 18.05 N. At what rate will the mass accelerate toward Mars if it is in free fall? What fraction is this acceleration of what the same mass would have in free fall on earth?

5. At the North Pole of the earth, the gravitational field strength is 9.832 N/kg. At the equator it is 9.782 N/kg.
   (a) What is the **percent difference** between the force of gravity on a 1 kg mass at the equator and the force of gravity on the same mass at the North Pole?
   (b) The force of gravity on a girl is 600.0 N at the equator. What will it be at the North Pole?
   (c) How much change will occur in the girl's **mass** if she is transported from the equator to the North Pole?

4.5 Mass and Weight

Weight is one of the most *misused* words in the English vocabulary. Very often, the word weight is used where one really means mass. The weight of an object is the **force of gravity** on the object. The force of gravity is measured in **newtons**. Grocery stores often refer to the weight of an object in kilograms, when they really mean the mass of the object.

The **mass** of a body is the quantity of matter in the body. Moving a body from one location to another does not change its mass. A 1 kg mass here on earth is a 1 kg mass on the moon or anywhere else in the universe. **Mass** is also a measure of a body's resistance to change in motion; that is, its **inertia**.

The **weight** of a body is the force of gravity on the body, and weight may change from place to place. The force of gravity depends on (a) the mass of the body in question, (b) the mass of the body attracting it and (c) the distance between the two masses. A body can have a huge mass, yet very little weight if it is very far from the earth and other massive bodies. This follows from Newton's Law of Gravitation:

$$F_g = G\frac{Mm}{d^2}.$$

Every body in the universe has mass. An object has weight only if there is another massive object to exert a gravitational force on it.

4.6 Newton's Third Law of Motion

☞ If you wish to climb stairs, in which direction do *you* push?

☞ If you wish to swim forward, in which direction must your arms push?

☞ If you are rowing a boat, which way must your oars push if the boat is to move forward?

☞ When a car is moving forward, in which direction do the *wheels* push on the road?

Isaac Newton observed that whenever forces exist between two bodies, the forces are *mutual*. If one body pushes on another, the other body exerts an equal force on the first body, but in the opposite direction. To do push-ups, for example, you push *down* on the floor. The floor exerts an equal force up on you. It is the floor that lifts you up! The earth exerts a force of gravity on the moon. What evidence is there that the moon exerts an equal force on earth?

Situations involving forces between pairs of bodies were studied by Newton, and his conclusions regarding mutual forces between pairs of bodies are stated in **Newton's Third Law of Motion.** (This Law is often called the **Law of Action and Reaction.**)

Newton's Third Law

If two bodies interact, the force the first body exerts on the second body will equal the force the second body exerts on the first body. The two forces will be opposite in direction and will act simultaneously (over the same interval of time).

Sometimes the first force is called the **action** force, and the second force the **reaction** force. If we call the first body **A** and the second body **B**, then the Law of Action and Reaction can be expressed mathematically like this:

$$F_{A \text{ on } B} = -F_{B \text{ on } A}.$$

where the minus sign indicates *opposite direction*.

Investigation 4-3   Newton's Third Law

Purpose: To observe demonstrations of Newton's Third Law.

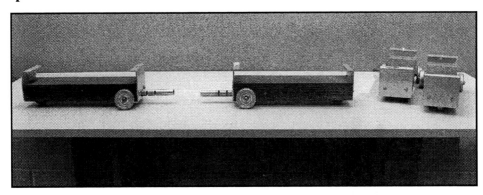

Figure 4.11

Procedure:

1. (a) Push two identical laboratory carts together so that their spring bumpers are compressed.
    (**Figure 4.11**) Release the carts on a flat table or floor. Observe as they accelerate away
    from each other. What force makes the carts accelerate? Why do the two carts, of identical
    mass, accelerate at the same rate? How does this demonstration illustrate Newton's Third
    Law?
  (b) *Predict* what will happen if you double the mass of one of the carts (by placing an extra
    cart on top of it). Test your prediction. Has the force repelling the carts changed? What
    has changed?
  (c) Try making the mass of one of the carts much greater than the mass of the other. Is the
    force changed? What has changed?

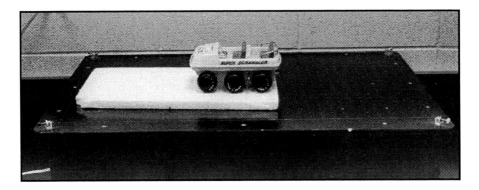

Figure 4.12

2. Place a piece of light plastic insulating Styrofoam™ board (50 cm x 25 cm x 2.5 cm) at one end of an air table. See **Figure 4.13**. Place a wind-up toy car or a radio-controlled car at one end of the board. Turn on the air table, and then start the car moving. Observe what happens (a) to the car and (b) to the 'road' under the car. How does this demonstration illustrate Newton's Third Law?

Figure 4.13

3. Tie a string between two 20 N spring balances. Have two students stretch the string between them. See **Figure 4.13**. What do the two spring balances read? Try pulling with different forces. Compare the forces on each spring balance each time you pull on the string with a different force. Does it matter who does the pulling? Try adding a third spring balance in the middle of the string? How does this demonstration illustrate Newton's Third Law?

Concluding Questions

1. When a car moves forward, in which direction do the wheels of the car push on the road? What force actually makes the car move forward?

2. List and discuss three examples of situations from your own everyday experience, that involve Newton's Third Law.

Challenges

1. Strictly speaking, your **weight** is the **force of gravity** exerted on you by the earth. Debate this 'outrageous' statement: "You weigh the same as planet earth!"

2. Fire a water-propelled model rocket. (Do this outdoors!)

3. Build and launch a model rocket using commercially available kits and engines.

4. Find out why space rockets use multiple stages.

4.7 Momentum

One of the most important concepts in physics is the idea of **momentum.** Isaac Newton first used the idea when he phrased his Second Law of Motion. In his original version, the Second Law looks like this:

$$F = \frac{\Delta(mv)}{\Delta t}$$

Newton called the product of mass and velocity (*mv*) **quantity of motion.** Thus, his Second Law said that the unbalanced force on an object is equal to the rate of change of quantity of motion with respect to time. We now call the product (mass x velocity) **momentum,** and we give it the special symbol, *p*.

$$p = mv$$

Newton's Second Law can be written this way:

$$F = \frac{\Delta p}{\Delta t}$$

Thus, the **unbalanced force** equals the **rate of change of momentum with respect to time.**

Any moving body has momentum equal to the product of the body's mass and its velocity. What makes momentum such an important quantity in nature is the fact that it is **conserved.** In a **closed system** (that is, a system upon which no outside forces act), **momentum is neither created nor destroyed.** Total momentum is therefore constant. This is the **Law of Conservation of Momentum.**

Newton's Third Law is a special case of the Law of Conservation of Momentum. Consider two bodies interacting such that body A exerts a force on body B, and body B exerts an equal force on body A, but in the opposite direction.

$$F_{A \text{ on } B} = -F_{B \text{ on } A}$$

(Action Force) $= -$ **(Reaction Force)**

The minus sign indicates that the direction of the reaction force is opposite to that of the action force. Using Newton's Second Law, written in terms of momentum,

$$\frac{\Delta(m_B v_B)}{\Delta t} = -\frac{\Delta(m_A v_A)}{\Delta t}.$$

Since the time intervals on both sides of the equation are the same, because both forces act over the same interval of time, the equation can be simplified to:

$$\Delta(m_B v_B) \;=\; -\,\Delta(m_A v_A).$$

Therefore, $$\Delta(m_A v_A) \;+\; \Delta(m_B v_B) \;=\; 0$$

or $$\Delta p_A \;+\; \Delta p_B \;=\; 0.$$

In other words, the total change in momentum within the closed, two-body system is zero. This means that the total momentum is constant, or that momentum is conserved.

Scientists have done many, many experiments with momentum, and are convinced that momentum truly is a conserved quantity in nature. At the subatomic level (in experiments done with high energy particle accelerators), physicists rely heavily on the Law of Conservation of Momentum in interpreting the results of collisions of particles.

Impulse

According to Newton's Second Law, in its original form, $F = \dfrac{\Delta(mv)}{\Delta t}$. This can be rearranged to:

$$F\,\Delta t = \Delta(mv).$$

The product of the force and the time interval during which it acts is called the **impulse** of the force. The last equation shows that the **impulse** is equal to the **change in momentum** it produces.

Units for Momentum and Impulse

Momentum is measured in **kg·m/s**, because these units have the dimensions of [mass x velocity]. Impulse is measured in **N·s**, because these units have the dimensions of [force x time]. Since impulse is equal to change in momentum, these units must be equivalent. It can easily be shown that this is true:

$$[\text{N·s}] \;=\; [\text{kg·m/s}^2] \cdot [\text{s}] \;=\; [\text{kg·m/s}].$$

(**Momentum** and **impulse** may be expressed in *either* unit.)

Examples of Momentum and Impulse Situations

1. (a) What is the momentum of a 112 kg football player running with a speed of 3.6 m/s?

   Solution: $p = mv = (112 \text{ kg})(3.6 \text{ m/s}) = 4.0 \times 10^2$ kg·m/s.

   (b) What impulse must a tackler impart to the football player to bring him to a stop?

   Solution: Impulse $= F\Delta t = \Delta(mv) = 0 - 4.0 \times 10^2$ N·s $= -4.0 \times 10^2$ N·s.

(c) If the tackle was completed in 0.80 s, what average force did the tackler exert on the other player?

Solution: $\quad F \;=\; \dfrac{\text{Impulse}}{\Delta t} \;=\; \dfrac{-4.0 \times 10^2 \text{ N}\cdot\text{s}}{0.80 \text{ s}} \;=\; -5.0 \times 10^2 \text{ N}.$

(The force is *negative,* because it opposes the motion of the player.)

2. A railway car of mass 6.0×10^3 kg is coasting along a track with a velocity of 5.5 m/s, when suddenly a 3.0×10^3 kg load of sulfur is dumped into the car. What is its new velocity?

Solution:

The momentum of the railway car will not change. Let its initial mass be m_1 and its initial velocity be v_1. The final mass of the railway car will be m_2 and the final velocity v_2.

$$\text{Since} \quad m_1 v_1 \;=\; m_2 v_2 \, ,$$

$$(6.0 \times 10^3 \text{ kg})(5.5 \text{ m/s}) \;=\; (6.0 \times 10^3 \text{ kg} + 3.0 \times 10^3 \text{ kg})(v_2)$$

$$33 \times 10^3 \text{ kg·m/s} \;=\; (9.0 \times 10^3 \text{ kg})(v_2)$$

$$v_2 \;=\; \dfrac{33 \times 10^3 \text{ kg m/s}}{9.0 \times 10^3 \text{ kg}} \;=\; 3.7 \text{ m/s}.$$

Exercises

1. What is the momentum of a 75 g mouse running across the floor with a speed of 2.6 m/s?
2. What is the impulse of a 55 N force exerted over a time interval of 1.0 ms?
3. A 0.060 kg rifle bullet leaves the muzzle with a velocity of 6.0×10^2 m/s. If the 3.0 kg rifle is held very loosely, with what velocity will it recoil?

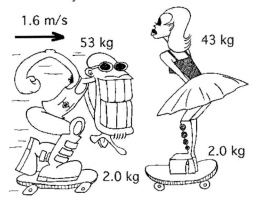

Figure 4.14

4. A 53 kg skateboarder on a 2.0 kg skateboard is coasting along at 1.6 m/s. (See **Figure 4.14**.) If he collides with a stationary skateboarder of mass 43 kg (also on a 2.0 kg skateboard), and the two skateboarders coast off in the same direction that the first skateboarder was travelling, what velocity will the combined skateboarders now have?

5. What impulse is needed to change the speed of a 10.0 kg object from 12.6 m/s to 25.5 m/s in a time of 5.00 s? How much force is needed?

6. A 1.5×10^3 kg car travelling 44 m/s collides 'head-on' with a 1.0×10^3 kg car travelling 22 m/s in the opposite direction. If the cars stick together on impact, what is the velocity of the wreckage immediately after impact? (Hint: Let the velocity of the second car be -22 m/s, since it is moving in a direction opposite to the first car.)

7. (a) What impulse must be imparted by a baseball bat to a 145 g ball to change its velocity from 40.0 m/s to -50.0 m/s? (Why is there a minus sign here?)

   (b) If the collision between the baseball and the bat lasts 1.00 ms, what force was exerted on the ball? (1 ms = 10^{-3} s)

Chapter Review Questions

1. A person who does not wear a seatbelt may crash through the windshield if a car makes a sudden stop. Explain what happens to such a person in terms of Newton's First Law of Motion. Also, explain why it is wise to wear a seatbelt.

2. In a frame of reference where there are no external, unbalanced forces, show that Newton's Second Law *includes* the Law of Inertia.

3. What unbalanced force is needed to accelerate a 2.0×10^3 kg vehicle at 1.5 m/s²?

4. What is the acceleration of a 5.8×10^3 kg vehicle if an unbalanced force of 1.16×10^2 N acts on it?

5. What is the mass of a space satellite if a thrust of 2.0×10^2 N accelerates it at a rate of 0.40 m/s² during a small steering adjustment?

6. At what rate will a 5.0 kg object accelerate if a 12.8 N force is applied to it, and the friction force opposing its motion is 2.8 N?

7. (a) What is the force of gravity on a 45.2 kg girl, here on earth where the gravitational field strength is 9.80 N/kg?

   (b) At what rate will she accelerate if she falls off a diving board?

8. What is the difference between the mass of a body and its weight? Does your grocer use these terms correctly? Discuss.

9. A rope is strong enough to withstand a 750 N force without breaking. If two people pull on opposite ends of the rope, each with a force of 500 N, will it break? Explain.

10. State Newton's Third Law of Motion. Describe an example of a situation involving the Law of Action and Reaction that you have not already used.

11. (a) Define momentum.

    (b) Why is momentum considered a very important quantity in physics?

12. (a) Define impulse.

    (b) What is the impulse due to a force that causes the speed of a 46 g golf ball to change from 0 to 60.0 m/s in 0.50 ms?

    (c) What force was applied to the ball?

13. A 0.250 kg ball of Plasticine™ moving 5.0 m/s overtakes and collides with a 0.300 kg ball of Plasticine™, travelling in the same direction at 2.0 m/s. The two balls of Plasticine™ stick together on collision. What is their speed after the collision?

14. Imagine you are in a space shuttle. In the orbiting shuttle, you *feel* as if you are *weightless,* because both you and the shuttle are 'falling' toward the earth at the same rate. A spring balance cannot be used to measure the weight of anything under these conditions. Is there any way you might use the spring balance to compare the 'heaviness' of twin babies born on the shuttle? Discuss.

15. Two tug-of-war teams are at opposite ends of a rope. Newton's Third Law says that the force exerted by team A will equal the force that team B exerts on team A. How can either team win the tug-of-war?

16. A hunter who fails to hold his/her rifle firmly against his shoulder may be injured when he or she shoots. Explain, in terms of Newton's Third Law.

17. A 4.2 kg rifle shoots a 0.050 kg bullet at a speed of 3.00×10^2 m/s. At what speed does the rifle recoil?

18. A railroad car of mass 12 000 kg is travelling at a speed of 6.0 m/s when it collides with an identical car at rest. The two cars lock together. What is their common speed after the collision?

Test Yourself!

1. Write a few sentences explaining, in terms of Newton's Laws of Motion, why it is considered wise to wear a seatbelt when travelling in a car or truck.

2. If an unbalanced force of 125 N acts on an object of mass 6.25 kg, at what rate will the object accelerate?

3. What unbalanced force is needed to accelerate a 15.0 kg object at 9.80 m/s^2?

4. What is the mass of a rock, if an unbalanced force of 96.0 N causes it to accelerate at a rate of 8.00 m/s^2?

5. (a) What is the force of gravity on a 0.40 kg model rocket, sitting on the launch pad?
   (b) If the 0.40 kg rocket accelerates at a rate of 30.0 m/s^2 when launched, what is the unbalanced upward force on the model rocket?
   (c) What is the total upward force (**thrust**) on the rocket?

6. (a) You are pushing a wooden box across a floor, with a force of 95.0 N. If the friction force is 35.0 N, what is the **unbalanced force** on the box?
   (b) If the box has a mass of 120.0 kg, at what rate will it accelerate?

7. What is the **momentum** of a 0.046 kg golf ball, travelling at 22 m/s?

8. If an **impulse** of 2.0 Ns is applied to a 0.046 kg golf ball, what speed will it have immediately after the impulse is applied?

9. A 5.0 g air pellet is fired into a 495 g sandbag, which is suspended by a string to form a pendulum. If the sandbag plus the imbedded pellet move off at 2.0 m/s immediately after the pellet hits the sandbag, what was the speed of the pellet just before it hit the sandbag?

10. A 6.0 kg rifle, held very loosely, recoils when a 0.0060 kg bullet is fired at 360 m/s. At what velocity does the loosely held rifle recoil?

11. A boy and his skateboard have a combined mass of 64 kg. If he is moving with a speed of 3.2 m/s, and collides with a stationary skateboarder whose mass (including his skateboard) is 96 kg, with what speed will the two skateboarders move immediately after the collision? Assume they are hopelessly entangled, but their wheels point in the same direction.

12. State Newton's Third Law, and describe two examples of situations in your everyday life that illustrate Newton's Third Law.

Multiple Choice Questions

1. On Earth, your mass is 72 kg. What would your mass be on the moon?
A. 0 kg   B. 12 kg   C. 36 kg   D. 72 kg   E. 432 kg

2. Near the moon's surface, why is the gravitational acceleration less than it is near the earth's surface?
    A. There is no air on the moon.
    B. There is no gravity on the moon.
    C. The moon's radius is smaller than the earth's radius.
    D. The moon has less mass than the earth.

3. What are the dimensions of a **newton**, the unit of force?
    A. kg   B. kg m/s   C. kg m/s^2 D. kg m^2/s^2

4. Little Johnny fires his paper airplane across the classroom. If *all* the forces on the airplane are balanced, and there is no unbalanced force acting on the airplane, what will the plane do?
    A. It will continue at steady speed in a straight line.
    B. It will immediately fall to the floor.
    C. It will accelerate and hit the wall.
    D. It will stop moving and hover in the air in one spot.

5. The acceleration of a body depends
    A. directly on mass and directly on unbalanced force.
    B. directly on mass and inversely on the unbalanced force.
    C. inversely on mass and directly on unbalanced force.
    D. inversely on mass and inversely on unbalanced force.

6. Newton's First Law of Motion is sometimes called the Law of Inertia. It was first stated by
    A. Joseph Inertia   B. Galileo   C. Copernicus D. Aristotle

7. What force is directly responsible for making a car move forward?
    A. The force exerted by exploding gases on the pistons in the engine.
    B. The force the driver exerts on the gas pedal.
    C. The force exerted by the wheels on the road.
    D. The force exerted by the road on the wheels.

8. On Earth, a scale says your mass is 60 kg. If you were transported to a place that is an infinite distance from Earth, what would your mass be there?
    A. 60 kg   B. 0 kg   C. It would approach zero. D. It would approach infinity

9. In a tug-of-war, why does team A defeat team B?
    A. Team A exerts a greater force on the rope than team B.
    B. Team A exerts a greater force on the floor than team B.
    C. Team B exerts a greater force on the floor than it does on the rope.
    D. The floor exerts a greater force on team A than it does on team B.

10. The force of gravity on Judy here on Earth is 720 N. What would the force of gravity be on the moon?

A. 0 N   B. 120 N   C. 360 N   D. 720 N   E. 4320 N

11. If you wished to have a measure of the **inertia** of a body, what would you measure?

A. its size
B. its speed
C. its momentum
D. its mass

12. The force of friction between a cart and the floor is 25 N. If you push the cart with a force of 35 N, and you wish to calculate its acceleration, what force would you use in Newton's Law, $F = ma$?

A. 25 N   B. 10 N   C. 35 N   D. 60 N

13. An 80 kg hockey player exerts a force of 200 N on a 160 kg hockey player (during a body check). What force does the 160 kg hockey player exert on the 80 kg player?

A. 100 N   B. 200 N   C. 400 N   D. 240 N

14. Which one of these equations is an **incorrect** way of stating Newton's Second Law?

A. $F = ma$ B. $F = \dfrac{\Delta p}{\Delta t}$ C. $F = \Delta(mv)$ D. $F\Delta t = \Delta(mv)$

15. Momentum is an important property in science, because

A. it is easily measured.
B. it can be precisely measured.
C. anything that moves has momentum.
D. it is a conserved quantity.

16. In an unauthorized physics experiment during an art class, two balls of modelling clay approach each other at high speed, collide head-on, and stop dead. What has happened to the total momentum of the system containing the two spheres?

A. It is converted to heat.
B. It stays the same.
C. It decreases.
D. It increases.

17. A certain rope will break if a force of 500 N is exerted through it. A group of physics students (who like their experiments with lots of strings attached) tried these ways of breaking the rope.

Student 1 tied one end of the rope to a post and pulled on the other end with a force of 250 N.
Student 2 tied one end of the rope to a post and pulled on the other end with a force of 500 N.
Student 3 gave one end to a partner, and they both pulled on opposite ends of the rope, each with a force of 250 N.
Student 4 gave one end to a partner, and they both pulled on opposite ends of the rope, each with a force of 500 N.

Which student(s) succeeded in breaking the rope?

A. 1, 2, 3 and 4
B. 2 only
C. 4 only
D. 2 and 4 only

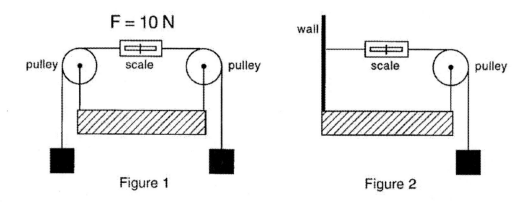

Figure 1   Figure 2

18. The scale in **Figure 1** reads 10 N. The two hanging masses are identical. In **Figure 2**, one of the hanging masses is replaced by a hook in the wall. What will the scale in **Figure 2** read?

A. 0 N
B. 5 N
C. 10 N
D. 20 N

Chapter 5 Vectors

5.1 Introduction to Vectors

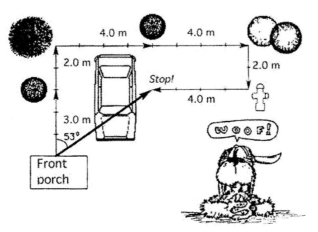

Figure 5.1

In **Figure 5.1**, notice a series of arrows drawn on the map of a physics teacher's front lawn. Each arrow shows the **magnitude** (size) and **direction** of a series of successive trips made by Buddy, the teacher's dog. Buddy was 'doing his thing' before getting into the car for a trip to school. These arrows, showing both magnitude and direction of each of Buddy's **displacements**, are called **vectors**.

When Buddy reaches his final spot near the car door, how far has he walked since he left the front porch? This question has two answers, depending on what one means by 'How far?' The **distance** Buddy has travelled is the *arithmetic sum* of all the short distances he has travelled between the shrubs, trees and fire hydrant while he 'visited' them. This is simple to calculate.

Total distance = 3.0 m + 2.0 m + 4.0 m + 4.0 m + 2.0 m + 4.0 m = 19.0 m

If, however, you want to know how far Buddy has travelled from the porch (the **extra-bold** line in **Figure 5.1**), then you want to know Buddy's **displacement**. It turns out that Buddy's displacement from the front porch is 5.0 m. The extra-bold arrow represents the magnitude (5.0 m) and the direction (53° to the right of his starting direction) of Buddy's displacement, and is called the **resultant displacement**. The resultant displacement is not the arithmetic sum, but the *vector sum* of the individual displacement vectors shown on the diagram.

> **Note!** There are two ways to indicate that a quantity is a **vector quantity**. In diagrams, or in handwritten notes, a small arrow may be drawn above the symbol for the vector quantity. For example, $\vec{D}$ symbolizes a displacement **vector**. In a textbook like this, the symbol for a vector quantity may be typed in ***bold italics***. ***D*** also symbolizes a displacement **vector**. If only the *magnitude* of the vector is of importance, the symbol '*D*' (*plain italics*) is used.

The vector sum of the displacements Buddy had during his trip might be written like this:

$$D_R = D_1 + D_2 + D_3 + D_4 + D_5 + D_6$$

The bold italics indicate that the quantity (displacement) is a **vector quantity**; therefore it has both **magnitude** and **direction.**

Adding Vectors

Draw the first vector to scale, and in the proper direction. Draw the second vector to scale, beginning at the tip of the first vector, and in the proper direction. Add the third vector (if there is one), beginning at the tip of the second vector. Repeat this procedure until all the vectors have been 'added'. The **vector sum** or **resultant** of all the vectors is the vector that starts at the tail of the first vector and ends at the tip of the last vector.

This is what was done in **Figure 5.1**. The resultant displacement of Buddy is correctly written as 5.0 m, 53° to the right of his starting direction.

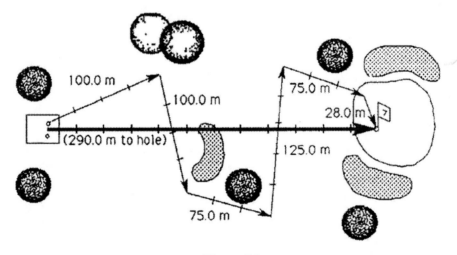

Figure 5.2

Exercise

Figure 5.2 shows the 'displacements' of a golf ball caused by a rookie golfer attempting to reach hole number 7 on Ocean View Golf and Country Club. The golfer, Arnold Sniffle, requires six shots to put the ball in the hole. The diagram shows the six 'displacements' of the ball.

(a) What is the total distance the golf ball travelled while Arnold was playing the seventh hole?

(b) What is the resultant displacement of the ball?

5.2 Scalars and Vectors

If you add 3 kg of sugar to 2 kg of sugar, you will have 5 kg of sugar. If you add 3 L of water to 2 L of water, you will have 5 L of water. **Masses** and **volumes** are added together by the rules of ordinary arithmetic. Mass and volume are **scalar quantities**. Scalar quantities have magnitude but no direction. Other scalar quantities include: distance, speed, time, energy and density.

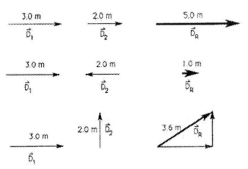

Figure 5.3

If you add a 3 m displacement to a 2 m displacement, the two displacements together *may* add up to 5 m, but they may also add up to 1 m or any magnitude between 1 m and 5 m! **Figure 5.3** shows some of the ways these displacements might 'add up'. In **Figure 5.3**, the two displacement vectors are added by the rule for vector addition. As you can see, the resultant displacement depends on the *directions* of the two vectors as well as their magnitudes. In addition to displacements, other vector quantities include **force, velocity, acceleration** and **momentum.**

> When you describe a displacement, a force, a velocity, an acceleration or a momentum, you must specify not only the magnitude of the quantity but also its direction.

5.3 Velocity Vectors

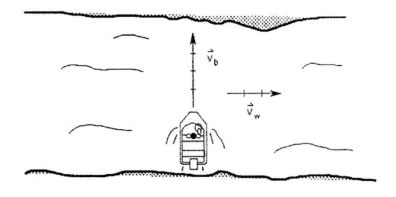

Figure 5.4

A small motorboat is aimed directly across a river. It travels 4.0 m/s relative to the water. The river water is flowing to the right with a velocity of 3.0 m/s relative to the ground. See **Figure 5.4**. What will the **resultant velocity** of the boat be relative to the ground?

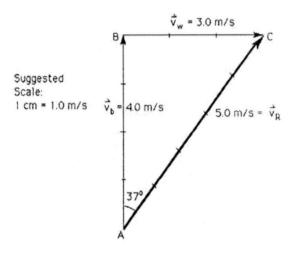

Figure 5.5

To find resultant velocity, the two velocity vectors must be added using the rule for vector addition. See **Figure 5.5**. A suitable scale is chosen, and then vector v_b (boat velocity) is drawn to this scale, and in the proper direction. (In the drawing, 1 cm represents 1 m/s.) Vector v_w (water velocity) is then drawn using the same scale. Its tail is at the tip of vector v_b, and its tip points to the right. The **resultant velocity** v_R is the vector that starts at the tail of vector v_b and ends at the tip of vector v_w.

If the scale diagram is carefully drawn, then the length of the resultant vector provides an answer of 5.0 m/s for the resultant velocity. Measuring angle **A** gives an angle of 37°. Therefore the **resultant velocity** of the boat is 5.0 m/s, in a direction 37° to the right of the boat's intended direction.

A problem like this one, where the two velocities form a right angle, can also be solved using **Pythagoras' Theorem**. Since the three sides form a right-angled triangle, and the resultant velocity vector is the hypotenuse of the right-angled triangle, then

$$v_R{}^2 = v_b{}^2 + v_w{}^2 = (4.0 \text{ m/s})^2 + (3.0 \text{ m/s})^2 = 16 \text{ m}^2/\text{s}^2 + 9.0 \text{ m}^2/\text{s}^2 = 25 \text{ m}^2/\text{s}^2.$$

$$\therefore \quad v_R = \sqrt{25 \text{ m}^2/\text{s}^2} = 5.0 \text{ m/s} .$$

Since we are dealing with a vector, we must specify direction as well as magnitude. Measuring angle A with a protractor gives an angle of 37°.

Exercises

1. The boat operator in **Figure 5.4** finds that it takes 25 s to cross the river.
   (a) What is the shortest distance across the river?
   (b) How far down the bank from its starting point will the boat land (measured from the point to which the boat was aiming when it started to cross the river)?
   (c) How far does the boat actually travel while crossing the river?

2. The boat operator again crosses the river, which still has a water speed of 3.0 m/s, but this time he doubles the boat speed to 8.0 m/s.
   (a) What is the resultant velocity of the boat this time?
   (b) How long will the boat take to cross the same river?
   (c) How far down the bank from its starting point will it land?
   (d) How far will the boat actually travel while crossing the river?

Brain Buster

3. If the boat travels 8.0 m/s relative to the water, the river water speed is 3.0 m/s, and the boat operator *must* land his boat directly opposite to the point from which he embarks on his trip, in what direction must he aim his boat throughout the trip? How long will it take to cross the river?

5.4 Force Vectors

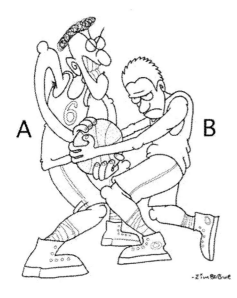

Figure 5.6

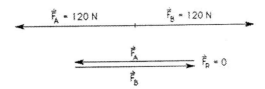

Figure 5.7

In **Figure 5.6,** two basketball players, **A** and **B**, are having a tug-of-war for possession of the ball. Neither is winning. What is the resultant of the forces exerted by **A** and **B** on the ball? **A** is pulling with a force of 120.0 N to the left, and **B** is pulling with a force of 120.0 N to the right. If the two force vectors F_A and F_B are added by the rule for vector addition, the resultant is zero. (See **Figure 5.7.**) This should not surprise anyone, because if there is no acceleration of the ball in either direction, the net force on the ball *should* be zero! (Newton's Law!)

250.0 N

600.0 N

In **Figure 5.8**, a football player is being pushed by one opponent with a force of 250.0 N, and by another opponent with a force of 600.0 N. Both forces are exerted horizontally, and the player being tackled has his feet momentarily off the ground. If the two force vectors form an angle of 90°, what is the resultant of the two forces exerted on the ball carrier?

Figure 5.8

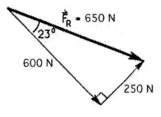

$\vec{F}_R$ = 650 N

23°

600 N

250 N

Figure 5.9

Figure 5.9 shows how to add the force vectors. Since the two forces exerted on the hapless football player form a right angle, and the resultant force vector forms the hypotenuse of a right-angled triangle, F_R can be determined using **Phythagoras' Theorem**.

$$F_R^2 = (250.0 \text{ N})^2 + (600.0 \text{ N})^2 = 62500 \text{ N}^2 + 360000 \text{ N}^2 = 422500 \text{ N}^2.$$

$$F_R = \sqrt{422500 \text{ N}^2} = 650.0 \text{ N}.$$

Since forces are vectors, we must specify the direction of the resultant force. From a carefully drawn scale diagram, the angle between the resultant force and one of the two forces exerted on the ball carrier can be measured. In **Figure 5.9**, the angle between the resultant force and the 600.0 N force has been measured to be 23°. The resultant force exerted on the ball carrier is therefore 650.0 N in a direction that is 23° from the direction of the 600.0 N force exerted by one of the tacklers.

Exercises

1. What is the resultant force if these three forces act on the same point?

    100.0 N to the north; 50.0 N to the east; and 220.0 N to the south.

2. Two horses on opposite sides of a narrow stream are pulling a barge along the stream. Each horse pulls with a force of 720 N. The ropes from the horses meet at a common point on the front of the barge. What is the resultant force exerted by the two horses if the angle between the ropes is:

    (a) 60°?
    (b) 30°?
    (c) 120°?

Trigonometric Ratios

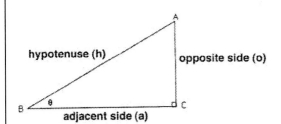

Three trigonometric ratios are particularly useful for solving vector problems. In the right-angled triangle **ABC**, consider the angle labelled θ. With reference to θ, **AC** is the **opposite side (o)**, **BC** is the **adjacent side (a)**, and **AB** is the **hypotenuse (h)**. In any right-angled triangle, the hypotenuse is always the side opposite to the right angle.

The three most commonly used trigonometric ratios are defined as follows:

$$\text{sine } \theta = \frac{\textbf{opposite side}}{\textbf{hypotenuse}} = \frac{o}{h}$$

$$\text{cosine } \theta = \frac{\textbf{adjacent side}}{\textbf{hypotenuse}} = \frac{a}{h}$$

$$\text{tangent } \theta = \frac{\textbf{opposite side}}{\textbf{adjacent side}} = \frac{o}{a}$$

Trigonometric ratios can help you solve vector problems quickly and accurately. Scientific calculators can provide you with the ratios for any angle.

Investigation 5-1 Force Vectors

Purpose: **To experiment with forces acting at a common point.**

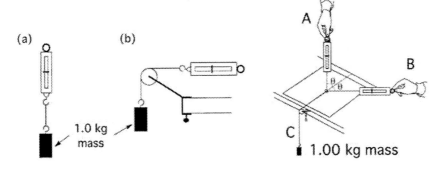

Figure 5.10   **Figure 5.11**

Procedure

1. Use a spring balance with a newton scale to measure the force of gravity on a 1.00 kg mass. If the scale is accurate, it should read 9.80 N. See **Figure 5.10(a)**.

2. Arrange the scale so it sits horizontally, and adjust the scale so that it reads 'zero' when no force is exerted on it. (When the scale is used horizontally, the force of gravity on the hook does not come into play, and the balance must be 're-zeroed' for horizontal use.)

3. Attach a string approximately 50 cm long between the 1.00 kg mass and the spring balance. Arrange the string so that it passes over a bench-mounted pulley as in **Figure 5.10 (b)**. Now measure the force exerted on the spring balance. Check whether using a pulley to change the *direction* of the force changes the *magnitude* of the force. Is it still 9.80 N?

4. Set up the arrangement in **Figure 5.11**. Attach a string from the hanging mass to a metal ring (or washer). Attach two other strings to the ring, and attach each of these to a spring balance. Centre the ring over a piece of *polar coordinate graph paper* (or, if you prefer, a standard plastic protractor).

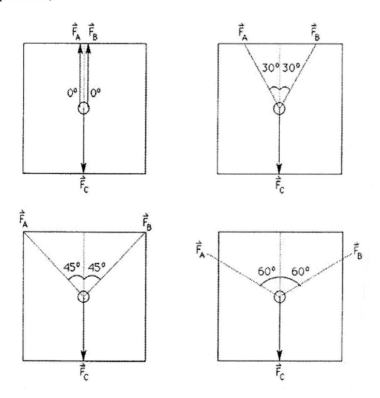

Figure 5.12

5. Arrange the two spring balances at each of the angles shown in **Figure 5.12**, and in each case measure the forces exerted on spring balances **A** and **B**.

6. When you have completed taking all the measurements required in **Procedure 5**, do this: Gradually increase the angle θ for each balance and measure (if you can) (a) the angle and (b) the force on each balance at the instant the string breaks! *Protect the floor from the falling mass! Place a sheet of wood or thick cardboard where the kilogram mass will fall.*

Record your measurements in a table like **Table 5.1**.

Table 5.1

Angle θ	Force A	Force B	Force C	Resultant of Forces A and B
0°			9.80 N	
30°			9.80 N	
45°			9.80 N	
60°			9.80 N	

7. Choose a suitable scale (perhaps 1.0 cm = 1.0 N), and for each of the four situations in **Procedure 5**, add the **force vectors** for forces **A** and **B**. What is the direction of their **resultant force** in each case?

Concluding Questions

1. According to your data, how does the magnitude of the resultant of forces **A** and **B** compare with the magnitude of the force **C** (the force of gravity on the hanging mass)?

2. How does the direction of the resultant of forces **A** and **B** compare with the direction of force **C**?

3. What would be the resultant of forces **A**, **B** and **C** all together?

4. At what angle did your string break? What was the magnitude of the force in either **A** or **B** when the string broke? Was this breaking force less than, equal to or greater than the force of gravity (**C**) on the hanging mass?

5. If you had a stronger string, could you ever support the hanging mass at angles of 90° on each side? (That is, is it possible to have the two strings in a straight line and support a hanging mass?) Explain.

Exercises

1. What is the resultant force on a falling skydiver at an instant when the force of gravity on the skydiver is 720 N, and the force of friction is 480 N?

2. Three ants are struggling to move the remains of a bee. (Three uncles refuse to help.) One ant pushes north with a force of 35 mN (millinewtons). A second ant pushes east with a force of 12 mN. The third ant, an uncooperative little bug, exerts a force that exactly cancels the effects of the other two. What is the magnitude of the force exerted by the third ant, and in what direction does it push?

3. Two girls are fighting over a boyfriend. Mary pulls John toward the north with a force of 80.0 N, while Gertrude pulls him toward the west with a force of 150.0 N. What is the resultant of the two forces acting on John? Assume John has been 'swept off his feet' and can offer no effective resistance by pushing against the ground.

5.5   Vector Components

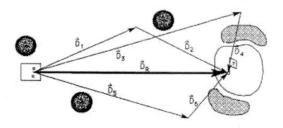

Figure 5.13

Figure 5.13 shows three different ways a golfer might score a 'two' on a hole.   All three combinations of two displacements give the same resultant D_R.   In terms of vector addition:

$$D_1 + D_2 = D_R,$$
$$D_3 + D_4 = D_R, \text{ and}$$
$$D_5 + D_6 = D_R.$$

Any two or more vectors that have a resultant such as D_R are called **components** of the resultant vector. A vector such as D_R can be **resolved** into an endless number of component combinations. **Figure 5.13** shows just three possible combinations of components of D_R.

In many problems, the most useful way to resolve a vector into components is to use the components that are **perpendicular** to each other.   Three examples will be given of situations where it is convenient to use the *components* of a vector rather than the vector itself.

Example 1   Components of a Force

Figure 5.14

In **Figure 5.14**, a father is pulling his son along on a toboggan with a force of 141 N. The rope makes an angle of 45^0 with the pathway. What is the magnitude of the horizontal component of the force exerted by the father?

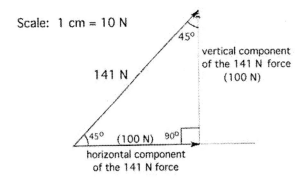

Scale: 1 cm = 10 N

45°

141 N

vertical component
of the 141 N force
(100 N)

45°   (100 N)   90°

horizontal component
of the 141 N force

Figure 5.15

Solution: To find the horizontal component of the 141 N force, a vector representing the 141 N force is drawn at 45° to the horizontal, as in **Figure 5.15**. A vertical line is then drawn from the tip of the 141 N vector, in a direction perpendicular to a horizontal reference line.

Where this vertical line intersects the horizontal determines what the horizontal component of the 141 N force is. If the 141 N force has been drawn to a suitable scale (say, 1 cm = 10 N), then the magnitude of the horizontal component can be determined using the same scale.

The scale drawing shows that the horizontal component is 1.00×10^2 N. Therefore, the force that actually tends to make the toboggan move horizontally to the right is 1.00×10^2 N.

The nature of the motion of the toboggan will depend on the force of friction between the toboggan and the pathway on which it is moving. The force of friction acts horizontally to the left (in the direction opposite to the motion). If the friction force were 1.00×10^2 N, the toboggan would move at steady speed, since forces in a horizontal direction would be balanced. If the force of friction were, say, 80.0 N, there would be a resultant force to the right of 20.0 N, and the toboggan would accelerate to the right.

If the boy and his toboggan have a combined mass of 50.0 kg, the toboggan would accelerate at a rate determined by Newton's Law.

$$a = \frac{F}{m} = \frac{20.0 \text{ N}}{50.0 \text{ kg}} = 0.40 \text{ m/s}^2.$$

Example 2   Projectile Motion

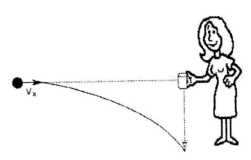

v_x

Figure 5.16

In **Figure 5.16**, a boy fires a baseball horizontally at a pop can held by his girlfriend. His girlfriend has second thoughts about the safety of the situation, and she drops the pop can at the same instant that the baseball leaves her boyfriend's hand. Will the baseball hit the can? (The ball and the can are at the same height above the ground at the instant the ball is thrown and the can is dropped.)

Solution: This situation is an example of **projectile motion**. To answer the question, consider the *components* of the baseball's displacements during its trip toward the can. Once the baseball leaves the hand of the thrower, it also becomes a falling body. It just happens that this falling body has a horizontal displacement (and velocity) as well as a vertical displacement.

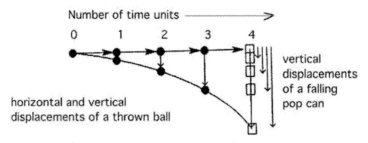

Figure 5.17

Imagine that the illustration in **Figure 5.17** is a multiple exposure photograph of the baseball and the falling can. Each image is taken the same time interval (perhaps 1/10th s) after the previous image.

First, look at the successive horizontal displacements of the baseball. In each time interval, the baseball travels the same distance horizontally. Its horizontal velocity is obviously constant. This makes sense, since (if we ignore air friction) there is no horizontal force to change the horizontal velocity of the ball.

The vertical displacement of the ball increases throughout the trip in exactly the same way as the vertical displacement of the falling can. If one looks at the vertical component of the baseball's displacement, it behaves in exactly the same way as the displacement of the falling can.

The vertical displacement, and therefore the vertical velocity and vertical acceleration of the baseball, are identical with the displacement, velocity and acceleration of the falling pop can. Assuming the baseball was correctly aimed at the can before the girl dropped it, and assuming the baseball was thrown fast enough to travel the distance to the girl in the time it takes the can to fall to the ground, the baseball will hit the can on its way to the ground!

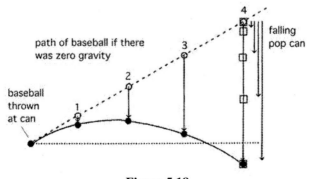

Figure 5.18

Figure 5.18 shows a modified version of the situation in Figure 5.17. This time, the pop can is higher up than the baseball thrower. If the baseball is thrown at the same instant the can is dropped, and aimed directly at the starting position of the can, will it *still* hit the can?

The rising dashed line shows the path the baseball would take *if there were no gravity*. Again, imagine the illustration is a multiple exposure photograph with equal time intervals (perhaps 1/10 s) between images. Imagine the baseball (dark circles) is 'falling' from the position on the dashed line where it would have been had there been no gravity (empty circle). Notice that the vertical displacement of the baseball at the end of each time interval (relative to the 'no gravity' line) is the same as the vertical displacement of the falling pop can. The horizontal displacement of the baseball is the same during each time interval, since the horizontal velocity remains constant in the absence of friction. Assuming the baseball was correctly aimed at the pop can before it was dropped, and assuming the baseball was thrown fast enough to reach the can in the time it takes to drop, the baseball will arrive at the same position as the can at the end of the fourth time unit.

Example 3   Components of Acceleration

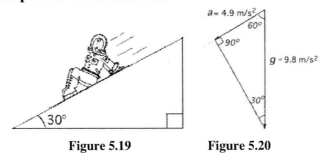

Figure 5.19   Figure 5.20

In Figure 5.19, Marcia is sliding down an icy slope on a plastic sheet. Friction is small enough that it can be ignored. At what rate will she accelerate down the hill, the surface of which makes an angle of 30^0 with the horizontal?

Solution: Marcia's acceleration down the slope will be the component of g in the direction of the slope. In Figure 5.20, a vector representing g (9.80 m/s²) has been drawn to scale. A perpendicular has been dropped to a line down the direction of the slope. Her acceleration down the slope will have the magnitude and direction of the component of g in the direction down the slope.

The magnitude of Marcia's acceleration down the icy slope can be determined by using the scale diagram, or by Pythagoras' Theorem. In a right-angled triangle, if the angles are 30°, 60° and 90°, the sides have dimensions that have a ratio of 2:1:$\sqrt{3}$.

The side opposite the 30° angle is [1/2 x the hypotenuse], or [1/2 (9.8 m/s²)], or 4.9 m/s². Marcia will accelerate down the slope at a rate of 4.9 m/s².

If you prefer to use trigonometry to solve for *a*, then $\dfrac{a}{g}$ = sin θ.

Therefore, a = g sin θ = (9.80 m/s²)(sin 30°) = (9.80 m/s²)(0.500) = 4.90 m/s².

Exercises

Use scale diagrams, Pythagoras' Theorem, or trigonometry to solve these problems.

1. A girl walks 1.41 km directly northeast. What is the component of her displacement in a north direction?

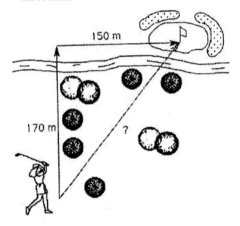

Figure 5.21

2. A golfer can get to a green by hitting a 170 m shot to the corner of the fairway in **Figure 5.21**, then hitting a 150 m shot to the centre of the green. However, there is a gap in the trees, which permits her to make a direct shot to the green if she dares risk ending up in the ditch beside the green. The edge of the ditch next to the green is 8.0 m from the centre of the green. The golfer knows she can hit a three-wood shot 220 m on the fly. She can win the tournament if she makes it to the green in one shot. Should she 'go for it?' Back up your answer with data!

3. A helium balloon is rising in the air with a resultant velocity of 6.1 m/s. If the vertical component of its velocity is 6.0 m/s, what is the horizontal component of its velocity (caused by a side wind)?

4. A boat is crossing a river. The boat's velocity is 5.6 m/s (in a direction directly across the stream). The flowing water carries the boat downstream at a rate such that the resultant velocity of the boat is 6.5 m/s. What is the velocity of the water in the river? Use a scale diagram or trigonometry to determine the angle the boat's resultant velocity makes with its intended velocity, which was directly across the stream.

5. A man is plowing snow from his driveway. He pushed down the handle of the plow with a force of 48 N, with the handle forming an angle of 60° with the horizontal driveway. What is the useful (horizontal) component of the force he exerts down the handle?

6. If the snow gets heavy, should the man in **Exercise 5** increase or decrease the angle the handle of the plow makes with the horizontal? Explain with the help of vector diagrams.

Chapter Review Questions

1. (a) What is a 'vector' quantity?
   (b) Name four examples of vector quantities.

2. (a) What is a scalar quantity?
   (b) Why are speed and distance considered scalars rather than vectors?
   (c) Name four other scalar quantities.

3. An airplane is heading directly north at 120 m/s, but a wind from the west is giving the plane a velocity component of 20.0 m/s relative to the air. What is the resultant velocity of the plane relative to the ground? Give the direction of the plane in 'degrees east of north'.

4. An aircraft is travelling southwest with a speed of 1410 km/h. What is the west component of this velocity?

5. A dandelion seed floats to the ground in a mild wind with a resultant velocity of 26.0 cm/s. If the horizontal component velocity due to the wind is 10.0 cm/s, what is the vertical component velocity?

6. Two dogs are pulling on the same bone. A poodle is pulling toward the south with a force of 7.0 N. A spaniel is pulling toward the east with a force of 24.0 N. With what force and in what direction must a collie pull on the same bone, if the bone is to have a net force of zero on it? Express your answer in degrees relative to north.

7. At what rate will a skier on a 45° frictionless slope accelerate down the slope? [g = 9.80 m/s².]

Brain Busters

8. '**Big Bird**' has a force of gravity on him of 720 N. He is perched on a clothesline such that the clothesline forms a symmetrical 'V' with the angle within the 'V' being 150°. What is the tension force in the rope on each side of '**Big Bird**'?

9. The handle on a certain lawn mower forms an angle of 30° with the surface over which it runs. Is it easier to push the mower up a hill or to pull it up the hill? Explain with the help of vector diagrams.

Challenge

Build or obtain a small ramp to launch a marble or ball bearing along your workbench. Use a stopwatch to measure the speed of the ball as it leaves the ramp. Now imagine the ball is going to come off the ramp and travel over the edge of your bench and fall to the floor. *Calculate* the time of fall of the ball from d = 1/2 gt^2, then *predict* exactly where the ball will hit the floor. (Place a plastic cup where you say it will hit.) Test your prediction by experiment.

Test Yourself!

Multiple Choice Questions

1. Which one of the following is a **vector** quantity?

   A. temperature   B. mass   C. density   D. weight

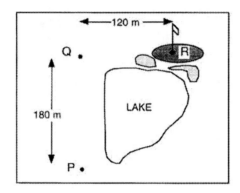

2. Golfer 'Tiger' Smith (at point P) wants to reach the green (at R) with a single golf shot. He knows he is 180 m to point Q, and that Q is 120 m from R. Which golf club should he select, to hit his shot safely from P to R?
   A. A driver, which he can hit 250 m
   B. A 3-wood, which he can hit 220 m
   C. A 1-iron, which he can hit 210 m
   D. A 2-iron, which he can hit 200 m
   E. A 3-iron, which he can hit 190 m

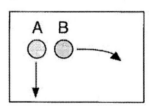

3. Steel balls A and B are released at the same instant, so that ball A falls vertically, and ball B is projected horizontally. Which statement describes what will happen?

   A. Ball A will hit the ground first.
   B. Ball B will hit the ground first.
   C. The ball with more mass will hit the ground first.
   D. Both balls will hit the ground at the same time.

Word Problems

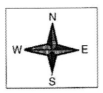

1. A lady walking her dog travels 200 m North, then 400 m West, then 500 m South.
   (a) What was the total **distance** she travelled?
   (b) What was the magnitude of her **displacement** for the entire trip?

2. A dandelion seed is falling down at a steady (terminal) velocity of 0.80 m/s, but a slight breeze is also pushing it toward the East at a steady velocity of 0.60 m/s.
   (a) Draw a vector diagram, and show how to calculate the **resultant velocity** of the seed.
   (b) What is the **magnitude** of the resultant velocity of the seed?
   (c) What is the **direction** (in degrees east of the vertical) of the resultant velocity?

3. An airplane is travelling northeast with a velocity of 1600 km/h. What is the East **component** of its velocity?

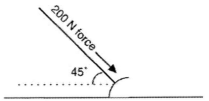

4. (a) What is the **horizontal component** of the 200 N force applied straight down the handle of the snow plow in the above figure, if the handle makes an angle of 45° with the horizontal road?
   (b) To what angle must you change the handle in order to increase the horizontal component of the force exerted down the handle by 25%?

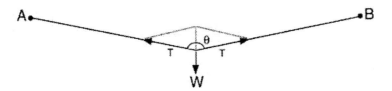

5. Vector **W** represents the force of gravity on a cable, which is stretched between two poles, A and B. Vectors **T** represent the **tension force** exerted along the cable due to the weight of the cable. Angle θ is 150°. A worker decides to tighten the cable between A and B, so that the cable forms a 'dead straight line' (180°) between A and B. Explain why the worker will never achieve his goal to straighten the cable. Use a vector diagram to help your explanation.

Chapter 6   Mechanical Energy

Energy appears in a variety of forms. Some forms you are familiar with include: light, sound, thermal energy, electrical energy, elastic potential energy, gravitational potential energy, chemical potential energy, nuclear energy and mechanical energy. What is energy? Your experience tells you it is associated with movement, or with the potential for motion. Energy is what makes things move. The usual definition of energy says that *energy is the capacity to do work*.

6.1 Do You Know the Meaning of Work?

In physics, **work** has a specific meaning. If work is to be done on an object, two things must happen: (1) a **force** must act on the object and (2) the object must move through a **distance** *in the direction of the force*.

The amount of work done is equal to the product of the force exerted and the distance the force causes the object to move, *measured in the direction of the force*.

Work = Force x Distance

$$W = Fd$$

Since force is measured in newtons (N) and distance in metres (m), work can be measured in **N·m**. One **newton·metre** is called a **joule (J)** after **James Joule (1818-1889)**.

$$1 \text{ J} = 1 \text{ N·m}$$

Example

How much work does a golfer do lifting a 46 g golf ball out of the hole and up to his pocket (0.95 m above the ground)?

Solution: The amount of work done will equal the force used to lift the ball up to the golfer's pocket multiplied by the distance to his pocket. The force needed to lift the ball at a steady speed up to his pocket will just equal the force of gravity on the ball.

$$F = mg = (0.046 \text{ kg})(9.8 \text{ N/kg}) = 0.45 \text{ N}.$$

The work done is therefore

$$W = Fd = (0.45 \text{ N})(0.95 \text{ m}) = 0.43 \text{ J}.$$

Exercises

1. How much work will you do if you push a block of concrete 4.3 m along a floor, with a steady force of 25 N?

2. If your mass is 70.0 kg, how much work will you do climbing a flight of stairs 25.0 m high, moving at a steady pace? (Use g = 9.80 N/kg)

3. Your car is stuck in the mud. You push on it with a force of 300.0 N for 10.0 s, but it will not budge. How much work have you done in the 10.0 s?

4. How much work is done on a 10.0 kg mass by Earth's gravitational field, when the mass drops a distance of 5.0 m?

5. A girl uses a 3.0 m long ramp to push her 110 kg motorbike up to a trailer, the floor of which is 1.2 m above the ground. How much work is done on the motorbike?

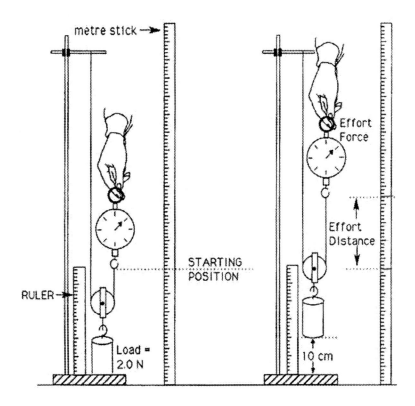

Figure 6.1

Investigation 6-1 Getting Work Done with Pulleys

Problem: Machines such as pulleys are used to get work done. But *you* must do some work to operate these simple machines. How does the amount of work that *you* do using a pulley system compare with the amount of work the pulley does for you?

Procedure

1. Set up the pulley system in **Figure 6.1**. The pulley system will be used to lift a 200 g mass up to a height of 10.0 cm (0.100 m). The force of gravity on the mass is approximately 2.0 N. The work that the pulley system will get done is therefore:

$$W \ = \ Fd \ = \ (2.0 \text{ N})(0.10 \text{ m}) \ = \ 0.20 \text{ J}.$$

2. Your task is to see how much work *you* have to do when you operate the pulley system to get the 0.20 J of work done.

   (a) Pull gently on the spring balance until the string is tight and the load is just about to lift. Mark the position of the bottom of the spring balance hook. Pull up on the spring balance until the load has been raised 10.0 cm. Write down the force *you* had to exert (**Effort Force**) and the distance through which *you* had to exert it (**Effort Distance**).

   (b) Calculate how much work *you* did by multiplying your effort force by your effort distance. Express your answer in joules (J).

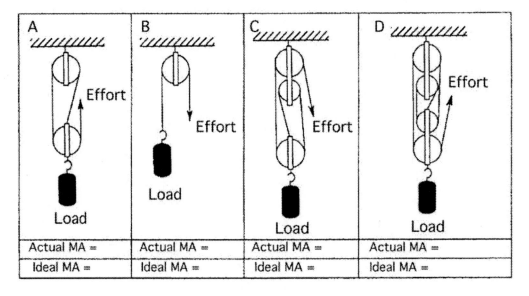

A	B	C	D
Actual MA =	Actual MA =	Actual MA =	Actual MA =
Ideal MA =	Ideal MA =	Ideal MA =	Ideal MA =

Figure 6.2

3. Repeat **Procedure 2** using each of the pulley arrangements in **Figure 6.2**. In each trial, use the pulley system to lift a 2.0 N **load** a distance of 10.0 cm (0.100 m), so that the work done by each pulley system is 0.20 J. Measure your effort force and your effort distance with each system. Record all your data in a copy of **Table 6.1**.

Table 6.1 Data for *Investigation 6.1*

System used	Load lifted	Load lifted this distance	Work done by pulley system	*Your* Effort Force	*Your* Effort distance	Work done by *You*
	(N)	(m)	(J)	(N)	(m)	(J)
6.1	2.0	0.10	0.20			
6.2A	2.0	0.10	0.20			
6.2B	2.0	0.10	0.20			
6.2C	2.0	0.10	0.20			
6.2D	2.0	0.10	0.20			

Concluding Questions

1. According to your results and those of your classmates, is the work that *you* do operating the pulley systems greater than, equal to or less than the work that is done by the pulley systems?

2. Does a pulley system 'save you work'? Explain. Why are pulley systems used to lift heavy loads?

3. If a pulley system allows you to lift a load that is twice your effort force, we say that it has a **mechanical advantage (MA)** of 2. Mechanical advantage is equal to the load divided by the effort force:

$$MA = \frac{Load}{Effort\ Force}$$

Calculate the mechanical advantage of each of the five pulley systems you used.

4. Examine the diagrams in **Figures 6.1** and **6.2**. Note the number of sections of rope that are exerting an *upward* force on the load. Considering that these sections of rope share the load equally, can you figure out a quick, easy way to predict the **ideal mechanical advantage** of each system? Test your prediction against the **actual MA**'s you calculated for each pulley system.

5. How might the effort distance and the load distance be used to calculate the **ideal MA** of a pulley system? Write a formula for calculating MA from effort distance and load distance.

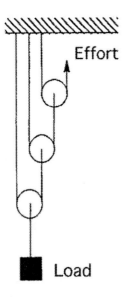

Figure 6.3

Challenges

1. *Predict* what the mechanical advantage of the pulley system in **Figure 6.3** will be. Test your prediction by experimenting. Hint! Is it really just *one* pulley system?

2. Draw a pulley system that has a mechanical advantage of less than one. For what purpose might it be used?

6.2 Power

A machine is **powerful** if it can do a lot of work in a short time. **Power** *is the measure of the amount of work a machine can do in one second.*

$$\textbf{Power} = \frac{\textbf{Work}}{\textbf{Time}}$$

Power could be measured in **joules per second (J/s)**, but one joule per second is called one **watt (W)**, after **James Watt (1736-1819)**.

$$\textbf{1 W} = \textbf{1 J/s}$$

Power can be measured in **kilowatts (kW)** or **megawatts (MW)**.

$$\textbf{1 kW} = \textbf{1 000 W} \ (\textbf{10}^3 \ \textbf{W})$$

$$\textbf{1 MW} = \textbf{1 000 000 W} \ (\textbf{10}^6 \ \textbf{W})$$

Examples

1. An electric motor is used, with a pulley and a rope, to lift a 650 N load from the road up to a height of 12 m. This job is done in a time of 11 s. What is the power output of the motor?

Solution: $$\textbf{Power} = \frac{\textbf{Work}}{\textbf{Time}}$$

$$P = \frac{Fd}{t} = \frac{(650 \text{ N})(12 \text{ m})}{11 \text{ s}} = 7.1 \times 10^2 \text{ W}.$$

Note: The often-used unit of power, 1 **horsepower**, is equivalent to 7.5×10^2 W.

The motor in this question would have a 'horsepower' of $\dfrac{7.1 \times 10^2 \text{W}}{7.5 \times 10^2 \text{W/HP}} = 0.95$ HP.

2. The power of a light bulb is the amount of electrical energy it consumes in one second. A 40 W bulb, for example, uses 40 J of electrical energy in 1 s. What is the power rating of a light bulb that consumes 4 200 J of electrical energy in 70.0 s?

Solution: $$P = \frac{\text{Energy}}{t} = \frac{4200 \text{ J}}{70.0 \text{ s}} = 60.0 \text{ W}.$$

Exercises   [Use $g = 9.80 \text{ m/s}^2$.]

1. An airport baggage handler lifts 42 pieces of luggage, averaging 24 kg each, through a height of 1.6 m onto a baggage cart, in a time of 3.6 min. In this situation, what is the power of the baggage handler?
2. How much energy (in J) does a 150 W light bulb convert to heat and light in 1.0 h?
3. An incandescent light bulb is approximately 5% efficient. This means that only 5% of the electrical energy used to operate the bulb is converted into light. If a 150 W bulb is used for 2.0 h, how much light energy (in J) does it produce in that time? How much heat does it produce?
4. If you use a pulley system of MA = 8 to lift a load, which of these variables will *improve in your favour* compared with the results you would get using a pulley system of MA = 2? Discuss reasons for your answer.
   (a) effort distance
   (b) effort force
   (c) work done by you
   (d) your power
   (e) work done by the machine
5. Draw a pulley system that has a mechanical advantage of 1/2. For what purpose might you use such a system?

Investigation 6-2   Measuring the Power of a Small Motor

Problem: **To measure the rate at which a small electric motor does work, and thus determine its power output.**

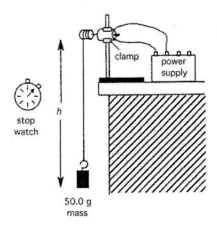

Figure 6.4

Procedure

1. Clamp a small electric motor, which is equipped with a special shaft upon which a 2.0 m length of string can be wound, to a ring stand. See **Figure 6.4**.
2. Try different source voltages applied to the motor, to see what you need to have the motor lift a mass of 50.0 g up from the floor in a time of approximately 2.0 - 3.0 s.
3. To measure the useful power of the motor, you will need to know the force of gravity on the mass, the height through which the mass will be raised, and the time it takes to lift the mass through that height. (Remember that one kilogram of mass has a force of gravity on it of 9.8 N.)
4. Calculate the power of the motor for at least three different sets of conditions, using

    $\text{Power} = \dfrac{\text{work done}}{\text{time}}$. Try different loads and/or different source voltages to vary the conditions.)

Concluding Questions

1. What is the maximum power output you measured for your motor?
2. What was the maximum power achieved by a motor by a member of your class?

Challenge

Measure the current and the voltage used to run your motor, and calculate the electrical power used to run it ($P = IV$). How efficient is your motor?

6.3 What's Watt? Historical Notes on Horsepower

Power is commonly measured in **horsepower.** Eventually, horsepower may be replaced by the **kilowatt**, which is a metric unit, but the horsepower (non-metric) will persist for some time because it is firmly entrenched in our vocabulary.

A Scottish instrument-maker named **James Watt (1736-1819)** is famous for his improved design of a steam engine, invented earlier by **Thomas Newcomen.** At a time when Watt's new engine was finding increased use for pumping water out of coal mines, work that previously had been done by horses, customers wanted to know how many horses Watt's new engines would replace. So that he could answer their questions, Watt did the following:

(1) He measured the force, in pounds, exerted by the 'average' horse over a distance, measured in feet.
(2) He calculated the amount of work the horse did, in 'foot-pounds'.
(3) He measured the time it took the horse to do the work.
(4) He calculated how much work the horse would do in one second, which is the average **power** of the horse. He found this to be 550 foot-pounds per second. This was taken to be the average power of one horse, or 'one horsepower'.

$$\text{One horsepower } = 550 \, \frac{\text{foot-pounds}}{\text{second}} \, .$$

The modern unit for power is the **watt (W)**, after James Watt. One horsepower is equivalent to 746 W, which is very nearly 3/4 kW.

6.4 Mechanical Energy

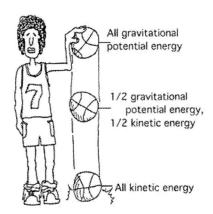

All gravitational potential energy

1/2 gravitational potential energy, 1/2 kinetic energy

All kinetic energy

Figure 6.5

Figure 6.5 shows an extremely simple mechanical system. A basketball player lifts a basketball straight up to a height h. The ball has mass m, so the force of gravity on the ball is mg. In lifting the ball, the basketball player has done work equal to mgh on the ball. He has *transferred energy* to the ball. Chemical energy in his cell molecules has been changed, because of the work the player did, into **gravitational potential energy**.

Work is always a measure of energy transferred to a body. When the basketball is held aloft at height h, it has gravitational potential energy (E_p) equal to mgh.

$$E_p = mgh$$

Now consider what happens when the ball is allowed to fall under the influence of the force of gravity. The unbalanced force (ignoring air friction) is equal to the force of gravity on the ball. For any situation where an object of mass m is pulled by an unbalanced force F, there will be an acceleration, a. Newton's Second Law of Motion tells us that: $F = ma$.

In this situation, the basketball is a free-falling body, and $a = g$. As the ball falls through height h, its speed increases from 0 to v_f. For uniform acceleration,

$$v_f{}^2 = 2ad.$$

For *this* situation, $v_f{}^2 = 2gh$. Since the unbalanced force pulling the ball down is mg, the **work** done on the ball by the earth's gravitational field is mgh.

$$\text{If } v_f{}^2 = 2gh, \text{ then } gh = \frac{v_f{}^2}{2}.$$

$$\text{Therefore, } mgh = m\frac{v_f{}^2}{2} = \tfrac{1}{2}mv_f^2.$$

When the ball is at the top of its path, all its energy is **gravitational potential_energy.** The ball is not moving. It has energy only because of its position above the floor from which it was lifted. As the ball falls, it loses its potential energy and gains energy of motion, which is called **kinetic energy.** Just before it collides with the floor, all the energy of the ball is kinetic energy, and the potential energy is zero. The amount of kinetic energy (E_k) at the bottom of its fall is given by:

$$E_k = \tfrac{1}{2}mv_f^2.$$

On the way down, the kinetic energy of the ball at any time depends on the speed the ball has reached. For any speed v, kinetic energy $E_k = \tfrac{1}{2}mv^2$. As the ball gains kinetic energy, it loses gravitational potential energy, but at all times the *sum of the gravitational potential energy and the kinetic energy is constant.*

$$E_p + E_k = \text{constant}$$

This is an example of the **Law of Conservation of Mechanical Energy.**

The total energy of a mechanical system is constant. Energy may be transformed from one form into another, but the total amount of energy is unchanged.

As the ball falls through positions 1, 2, 3, etc., the sum of the potential energy and the kinetic energy remains constant:

$$mgh_1 + \tfrac{1}{2}mv_1^2 = mgh_2 + \tfrac{1}{2}mv_2^2 = mgh_3 + \tfrac{1}{2}mv_3^2 = \ldots.$$

Notice that mechanical energy can be either potential or kinetic. For a mechanical system, the *total* mechanical energy is constant.

Example

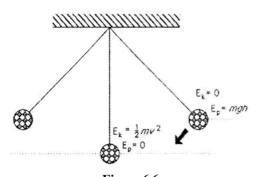

Figure 6.6

The pendulum bob in **Figure 6.6** is pulled back far enough that it is raised 0.36 m above its original level. When it is released, how fast will it be moving at the bottom of its swing?

Solution: When the pendulum is pulled back, it is also lifted through a height h, and work mgh is done in lifting the bob against the force of gravity. The bob gains gravitational potential energy equal to the work done on it, so $E_p = mgh$.

When the bob is released, its gravitational potential energy is transformed into kinetic energy. At the bottom of the swing, $E_p = 0$, and $E_k = \frac{1}{2}mv^2$, but the kinetic energy at the bottom of the swing must equal the gravitational potential energy at the top (according to the **Law of Conservation of Mechanical Energy**).

Thus, $\qquad\qquad\qquad\qquad\qquad \frac{1}{2}mv^2 = mgh.$

Therefore, $\qquad\qquad\qquad\qquad v^2 = 2gh,$

and $\qquad\qquad v = \sqrt{2gh} = \sqrt{2(9.8\text{m/s}^2)(0.36\text{m})} = 2.7 \text{ m/s}.$

Exercises

1. A physics student lifts his 2.0 kg pet rock 2.8 m straight up. He then lets it drop to the ground. Use the Law of Conservation of Mechanical Energy to calculate how fast the rock will be moving (a) half way down and (b) just before it hits the ground.

2. A 65 kg girl is running with a speed of 2.5 m/s. How much kinetic energy does she have? She grabs on to a rope that is hanging from the ceiling, and swings from the end of the rope. How high off the ground will she swing?

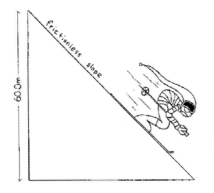

3. How much kinetic energy does the 80.0 kg skier sliding down the frictionless slope in **Figure 6.7** have when he is two-thirds of the way down the ramp? The vertical height of the ramp is 60.0 m.

Figure 6.7

4. A golfer wishes to hit his drives further by increasing the kinetic energy of the golf club when it strikes the ball. Which would have the greater effect on the energy transferred to the ball by the driver — doubling the mass of the club head or doubling the speed of the club head? Explain.

5. A rubber ball falls from a height of 2.0 m, bounces off the floor and goes back up to a height of 1.6 m. What percentage of its initial gravitational potential energy has been lost? Where does this energy go? Has the Law of Conservation of Energy been 'violated'?

6. How much work must be done to increase the speed of a 12 kg bicycle ridden by a 68 kg rider from 8.2 m/s to 12.7 m/s?

7. A vehicle moving with a speed of 90 km/h (25 m/s) loses its brakes but sees a 'runaway' hill near the highway. If the driver steers his vehicle into the runaway hill, how far up the hill (vertically) will the vehicle travel before it comes to a stop? (Ignore friction.) If friction is taken into account, will the vertical distance the vehicle moves be less or greater than the 'ideal' distance you just solved for, neglecting friction? Explain.

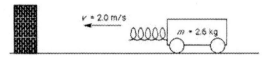

Figure 6.8

8. A 2.6 kg laboratory cart is given a push and moves with a speed of 2.0 m/s toward a solid barrier, where it is momentarily brought to rest by its spring bumper. (**Figure 6.8**) How much **elastic potential energy** will be stored in the spring at the moment when the spring is fully compressed? What is the *average* force exerted by the spring if it is compressed 0.12 m? (Why is it necessary to specify *average* force in this situation?)

Chapter Review Questions

1. (a) How much work will you do if you lift a 0.67 kg book from a table top up a distance of 1.5 m to a shelf?
   (b) How much work will be done on the book if you lift it and move it 1.5 m sideways to a spot on the same shelf?

2. If you push a 75 N block along a floor a distance of 4.2 m at a steady speed, and the coefficient of kinetic friction is 0.40, how much work will you do on the block?

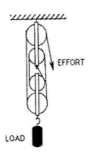

Figure 6.10   **Figure 6.9**

3. (a) What is the ideal mechanical advantage of the pulley system in **Figure 6.9?**
   (b) If the load is 240 N, what will the effort force be, ignoring friction?
   (c) If the load is lifted 2.8 m, how far will you have to pull down on the rope?
   (d) If the load is lifted 2.8 m in 1.6 s, what is the power rating of the pulley system?

4. *Predict* which of the two students will move when the rope in **Figure 6.10** is pulled. Give a reason for your prediction. Be sure to test your prediction!

5. How much work will a 4.0 HP (3 kW) motor do in half an hour?

6. One watt is equivalent to one joule per second, so a joule is the same as a watt·second. How many joules are there in 1 kilowatt·hour (kW·h)?

7. A 75 kg girl runs up a 3.0 m flight of stairs in 2.5 s. What is her 'horsepower' in this situation?

8. A pendulum bob is moving 1.8 m/s at the bottom of its swing. To what height above the bottom of the swing will the bob travel?

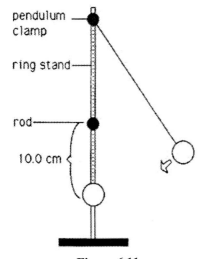

Figure 6.11

9. The pendulum bob in **Figure 6.11** must circle the rod interrupting its swing, and the string must remain taut at the top of the swing. How far up must the bob be raised before releasing it to accomplish these goals?

10. A pendulum is started swinging from a height of 0.3000 m above its rest position, and allowed to swing freely back and forth. If 1.00% of the bob's energy is lost due to friction each swing, to what maximum height will the bob swing at the end of its fourth swing?

11. The initial speed of a golf ball, struck with a driver by professional golfer Tiger Woods, has been measured to be 285 km/h. From what vertical height would you have to drop a golf ball, if it is to reach this same speed as it hits the ground? Assume that air friction can be ignored.

Test Yourself!

1. The force of gravity on a box of apples is 98.0 N. How much work will you do
   (a) if you lift the box from the floor to a height of 1.2 m?
   (b) if you carry the box horizontally a distance of 2.0 m?

2. A hiker carries a 25 kg load up a hill, at a steady speed, through a vertical height of 350 m. How much work does she do on the load?

3. The force of gravity on a box is 100.0 N. The coefficient of friction between the floor and the box is 0.250. How much work is done when the box is pushed along the floor, at a steady speed, for a distance of 15.0 m?

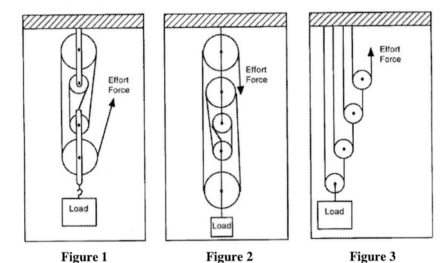

Figure 1   **Figure 2**   **Figure 3**

4. The pulley system in **Figure 1** may be considered 'frictionless'.
   (a) What is the **mechanical advantage** of this system?
   (b) If the **load** is 600.0 N, what **effort force** is needed?
   (c) If the load is lifted up a distance of 1.2 m, how much **work** will be done on the load by the pulley system?
   (d) If the load is lifted up 1.2 m, how much rope must you pull? (What is the **effort distance**?)
   (e) How much **work** will *you* do?
5. (a) What is the **mechanical advantage** of the pulley system in **Figure 2**? (Assume no friction.)
   (b) If someone pulls on the rope for a distance of 3.5 m, to what height will the load be lifted?
6. (a) What is the ideal **mechanical advantage** of the pulley system in **Figure 3**?
   (b) How heavy a load could you lift with the pulley system in **Figure 3**, if your effort force is 300 N?

7. How powerful is a motor that can lift a 500.0 kg load through a height of 12.0 m, in a time of 12 s?
8. How much energy is consumed by a 100.0 W light bulb, if it is 'left on' for 12.0 h?
9. A motor does 25 MJ (megajoules) of work in one hour.
   (a) What is the power rating of the motor?
   (b) How many horsepower is this motor, if 1 HP = 750 W?
10. Discuss the scientific accuracy of this statement:
   "I used a ramp to get my motorbike up on my truck, and the ramp saved me a lot of work!"
11. Tarzan grabs a vine 12 m long and swings on the end of it, like a pendulum. His starting point is 5.0 m above the lowest point in his swing. How fast is Tarzan moving as he passes through the bottom of the swing?
12. With a pulley system, a mechanic can lift an 840 N engine using an effort force of only 70.0 N.
   (a) What is the mechanical advantage of the pulley system?
   (b) To lift the engine up 20.0 cm, how far down on the rope will the mechanic pull?
   (c) How much work is done on the 840 N engine when it is lifted a height of 20.0 cm?
   (d) What is the minimum amount of work the mechanic will have to do to lift the engine 20.0 cm?

Multiple Choice Questions

1. Pulleys and other simple machines can help you in several ways. Which of these goals can they *not* help you achieve?
    A. Reduce the amount of work you do.
    B. Reduce the effort force you must exert.
    C. Apply a force from a more convenient direction
    D. Lift a load that you might otherwise not be able to lift.

2. A motor is more powerful than another motor if
    A. it is bigger.
    B. it draws more current.
    C. it lifts heavier loads.
    D. it does more work in the same time.
    E. it operates on a higher voltage.

3. Power is measured in
    A. joules.   B. newtons.   C. watts.   D. volts.

4. An appliance that consumes electrical energy at the rate of 1500 J/s, accomplishes 1200 J/s of useful work. How efficient is the appliance?
    A. 80%   B. 125%   C. 75%   D. 120%

5. A skier has 60 kJ of **gravitational potential energy** when at the top of the hill. Assuming no friction, how much kinetic energy does she have when she is one-third of the way down the hill?
    A. 60 kJ   B. 40 kJ   C. 20 kJ   D. 0 kJ

6.   The head of a golf club imparts a certain amount of kinetic energy to the ball upon impact. Let this be E_k. If the golfer lightens the mass of the club head by 1/3, and increases the club head speed so that it is 3 times it previous speed, how much kinetic energy will be imparted to the ball now?

A. E_k B. $3E_k$ C. $6E_k$ D. $9E_k$ E. $\frac{1}{3}E_k$

Ehren Stillman Cartoon

Ehren Stillman Cartoon

Chapter 7 Thermal Energy

7.1 Temperature, Heat and Thermal Energy

According to the **kinetic molecular theory,** all matter is made up of tiny particles, which are constantly moving. The particles — molecules or atoms — attract each other to some extent. The particles can move in a number of ways: they can move in straight lines (between collisions); they can rotate; and they can vibrate. **Figure 7.1** illustrates ways in which a molecule can move.

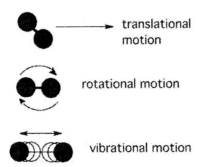

translational motion

rotational motion

vibrational motion

Molecules may have **translational kinetic energy** (energy due to motion in straight lines), **rotational kinetic energy** and **vibrational kinetic energy**. They may also have **potential energy**, which arises from attractions between molecules (or repulsions at very close range).

Figure 7.1

The **total energy** of all the molecules in a certain amount of material is called the **thermal energy** of the material. When thermal energy is transferred from one material to another material, *the amount of energy transferred is called* **heat.** Heat is transferred from a hotter body to a cooler body. For a transfer of energy to occur, there must be a *difference in temperature* between the body from which the thermal energy is being transferred and the body to which the thermal energy is being transferred.

The way we describe how hot or cold a body is, relative to some well-chosen standard, is to use a number we call the body's **temperature.** On the **Celsius** scale, named after **Anders Celsius (1704-1744)** (a Swedish astronomer who first suggested its use), 0°C is assigned to the temperature at which ice melts (or water freezes), and 100°C is assigned to the temperature at which water boils at standard sea level air pressure. On a typical mercury or alcohol thermometer, the space between 0°C and 100°C is divided into 100 equal divisions called **degrees.**

What does temperature really measure? Temperature depends on the *average translational kinetic energy of all the molecules in a material*. Imagine a drop of boiling hot water spilled from a large bucket of boiling water. The bucket of boiling water has far more thermal energy in it, and its **total kinetic energy** is far greater than the total kinetic energy in the drop of boiling water. The molecules in the bucket of water and those in the drop of water, however, have the same **average translational kinetic energy**, so both have the same **temperature.**

Absolute Zero

What would happen if a substance were cooled so much that the average translational kinetic energy of its molecules was zero? The substance would have virtually no energy to transfer to any other body. If its average translational kinetic energy were zero, its temperature would be the lowest it could possibly be. On the Celsius scale, this temperature would be approximately –273°C. This temperature is called **absolute zero**. On another temperature scale called the **Kelvin** scale, after British physicist **Lord Kelvin (1824-1907)**, absolute zero is assigned a value of **0 K**. On this scale, the unit for temperature is not called a degree, but instead a **kelvin (K)**. Therefore, **0 K = –273°C**. A kelvin is the same size as a Celsius degree. This means that a temperature of 0°C would be equal to 273 K. Water boils at 100°C, or 373 K. To scientists, the Kelvin scale is useful because on this scale, *the temperature of an 'ideal' gas in kelvins is directly proportional to the average translational kinetic energy of the molecules in the gas.* (Helium is a gas that behaves like an ideal gas. It is monatomic, which means that its smallest particles consist of just one atom.)

Exercises

1. (a) Explain the difference between **temperature, thermal energy** and **heat.**

   (b) Why is it strictly incorrect to say that a body 'contains heat'?

2. A sample of helium gas has a temperature of 20°C.

   (a) What is its temperature in kelvins (K)?

   (b) In another helium sample, the atoms have *twice* the average translational kinetic energy. What is the temperature of this sample in (i) kelvins? (ii) °C?

3. A large pot of near-boiling water has a small, red-hot nail dropped into it.

   (a) Which has more thermal energy to begin with — the pot of water or the nail?

   (b) Which has the higher average kinetic energy to begin with?

   (c) Which will lose heat, and which will gain heat when the nail is dropped into the pot of boiling water?

   (d) After five minutes, which will have (i) more thermal energy? (ii) higher average kinetic energy?

7.2 How Heat Is Transferred

(1) Conduction

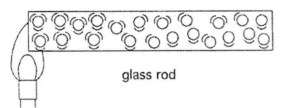

glass rod

Figure 7.2

Imagine that you hold one end of a glass rod in your hand and heat the other end with the flame of a Bunsen burner. See **Figure 7.2**. Molecules near the heated end have thermal energy transferred to them from the flame.

These glass molecules gain kinetic energy, collide with their neighbours, and pass the increased kinetic energy on. Eventually, the whole rod will be warmed up, and the end you are holding may in time become too hot to hold.

Heat is transferred through the glass rod slowly by **conduction.** Conduction is the transfer of heat energy from molecule to molecule or atom to atom through a material. Glass is not a particularly good conductor. The best **conductors** are metals. **Metals** conduct heat and electricity well, because atoms of metals have loosely attached electrons, called **free electrons,** which can move easily throughout the length of the metal. When these free electrons gain kinetic energy, they can transfer their energy easily to other electrons and atoms with which they collide.

Investigation 7-1 Heat Transfer by Conduction

Purpose: To demonstrate conduction and conductors.

Procedure

Part 1 (Demonstration)

1. (a) Obtain a conduction apparatus, as in **Figure 7.3**, and clamp it above an alcohol burner. Drops of candle wax have been used to attach small nails or paper clips to the ends of each of the metal rods. ***Predict*** which of the metals will conduct heat fastest. Which will be the poorest conductor?
   (b) Test your prediction by heating the rods at the junction. Record the order in which the rods drop their nails. Was your prediction correct?

2. Touch the surface of your wooden workbench with the flat of your hand. Now touch the base of a metal ring stand or a sheet of aluminum foil. Which feels warmer to the touch? Is either surface at a different temperature than the other? Why does one surface *feel* cooler than the other?

Figure 7.3

Part 2 (Demonstration)

Place some crushed ice in a *large* test tube, and use a few marbles to keep the ice at the bottom of the test tube. Add water (**Figure 7.4**), and use a Bunsen burner to *carefully* heat the test tube near the *top*. Can you make the water at the top of the test tube boil while the ice remains frozen at the bottom? Do your observations suggest that water is a good conductor or a poor conductor?

Figure 7.4

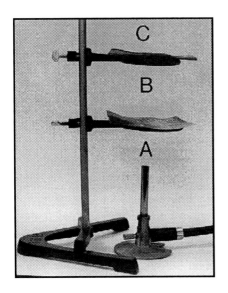

Figure 7.5

Part 3 (Demonstration)

Set up the arrangement in **Figure 7.5.** Attach two rings to the same ring stand. Ring **A** is approximately 15 cm above the top of the Bunsen burner. Cover each ring with a sheet of **copper gauze.**

(a) Turn on the gas, and use a match to light the gas at **A**. Observe what happens. Does the gas initially burn at **B** and/or **C**? Turn off the gas.

(b) Turn on the gas, and light the gas at **B**. Observe what happens. Turn off the gas.

(c) Turn on the gas, and light the gas at **C**. Observe what happens. Turn off the gas.

(d) Turn on the gas, and light the gas at **A** and **C**. Observe, then turn off the gas.

Concluding Questions

1. Of the metals you tested for conductivity, list the order in which they conduct heat, from best to worst.
2. List three metals that are used in cooking utensils because they conduct well.
3. Materials that slow down conduction are called **insulators**. Name at least five good insulators.
4. Is water a good conductor? Is water a good insulator? Explain your answer.
5. Explain the results you observed in **Part 3**.

Challenges

1. Have a contest to see who can design a container that will keep an ice cube solid for the longest time.
2. Explain why fur, wool and feathers are so warm to the touch. Why are these materials often used to line winter jackets?

(2) Convection

Thermal energy is not easily transferred by conduction through gases and liquids. In conduction, the energy is transferred through collisions of atoms or molecules or electrons with neighbouring particles.

In **fluids** (that is, gases or liquids), thermal energy can be transferred very efficiently by **convection.** In convection, the thermal energy 'flows' with the molecules from one place to another. In convection, the substance being warmed moves, carrying the thermal energy with it. *Investigation 7-2* demonstrates the nature of convection.

Investigation 7-2   Convection

Purpose: To observe convection currents in fluids. (Demonstrations)

Part 1   Convection in a Liquid (water)

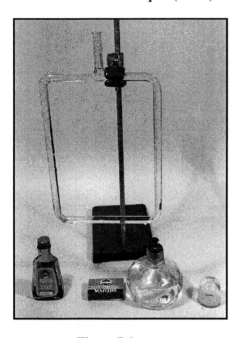

Figure 7.6

Procedure

1. Your instructor has filled the ring-shaped glass tube (**Figure 7.6**) with water. An alcohol burner or candle is arranged so that its flame will warm a bottom corner of the tube.
2. *Predict* which way the water in the tube will circulate when the flame is lit and the water is warmed.
3. Your instructor will light the flame. After allowing the water to warm up slightly, your instructor will add one drop of food colouring to the opening at the top of the tube. Sketch the tube, and show the direction in which the water flows.

The flow you observe is called a **convection current**.

Part 2   Convection in a Gas (Air)

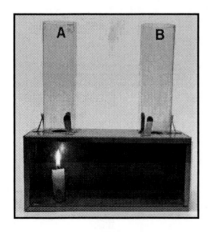

Figure 7.7

Figure 7.7 shows a **convection box**, which has a sliding front window and two glass chimneys. Light the candle, and close the front window. Allow the candle to burn for a minute, then light a piece of **touch paper** (or other source of smoke), and hold the smoking source above each of the two chimneys in turn. Observe the pattern of motion of the air, as shown by the visible smoke carried by the air.

Concluding Questions

1. Explain, in terms of **molecular motion** and **density** (Density = Mass/Volume), why a convection current in water or air moves in the direction that it does.

2. In *Investigation 7-1*, you were able to boil water at the top of a test tube while ice at the bottom of the tube remained frozen. What would happen if you heated the bottom of a test tube that has ice at the top? How would the heat be transferred to the ice?

Convection in Everyday Life

Since different parts of the earth's surface absorb the sun's heat better than others, the air near these parts of the earth will be warmed accordingly, and convection currents will result from the uneven heating. Small-scale local winds and the larger continental wind patterns are convection currents resulting from uneven heating of air near the surface of the earth.

Exercises

1. Water is a poor conductor, yet water is brought to a boil quickly in a pot or kettle. Explain.

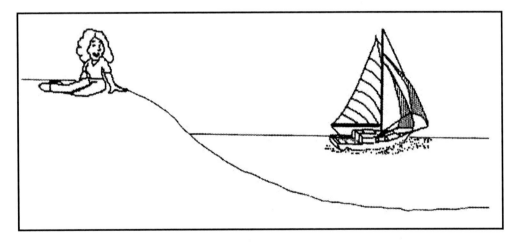

Figure 7.8

2. **Figure 7.8** illustrates a seashore scene. Water temperature stays quite constant day and night, but the land warms up during the day, so it has a higher temperature than the sea. At night, the land cools rapidly and is cooler than the sea.

   (a) Copy the diagram, and sketch the direction of the convection current near the seashore (i) in the daytime and (ii) at night.
   (b) When would you rather launch a sailboat to go out to sea — in the very early morning or in the evening? Why?

Challenge!

Cool air sinks near the North Pole and spreads 'down' toward the lower latitudes. The earth rotates on its axis in an anticlockwise direction as viewed from above the North Pole. Cut a paper disc the size of an old 33 rpm record, and place it on an old record player turntable (or on a 'Lazy Susan', which you can turn by hand). With the turntable rotating, run your pen from the 'pole' toward the 'equator'. Stop the turntable and examine the direction the 'wind' goes, as it flows from the poles down to our latitudes. Can you use the same model to check out how the prevailing westerlies originate?

(3) Radiation

Our primary source of thermal energy is the sun. Since the space between the sun and our planet is for all practical purposes 'empty', there is no way heat transfer by conduction or convection can occur. Heat transmission through a vacuum is possible, however, by the process of **radiation.** Any form of energy transmitted by radiation will be in the form of **electromagnetic waves**, and will travel at the speed of light. The various forms of **radiant energy** that originate in the sun include: radio waves, microwaves, infrared radiation (heat), visible light, ultraviolet light, X-radiation and gamma radiation. You cannot see infrared radiation, of course, but you can often feel it on your skin. When you sit in front of a fireplace, the warming effect you sense is due to infrared radiation. Infrared radiation can also be detected by photography or by electronic means.

Investigation 7-3 Absorbing Infrared Radiation

Purpose: **To find out whether a black surface or a shiny surface absorbs more infrared radiation in a given time.**

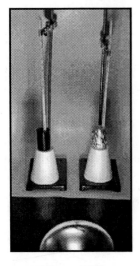

Figure 7.9

Procedure

1. Obtain two used, black plastic film containers. Leave one black, but cover the other container with aluminum foil. See **Figure 7.9**.

2. Fill each container with water, and measure the temperature of the water in each container. Prepare a chart like **Table 1**. Enter the starting temperature in the column under **0 min**.

3. Set the containers on insulating Styrofoam cups, the same distance (50 cm) from a source of infrared light, such as a 100-W lamp. After 1 min, measure the temperatures of the water in each of the containers. (Two students might read the temperatures simultaneously.) Record these temperatures in your table.

4. Repeat the measurements after 2, 3, 4 and 5 min. If necessary, continue taking readings until a definite pattern is established.

Table 1 Temperatures of Containers of Water Warmed by a Lamp

Time (minutes)	0	1	2	3	4	5
Temperature (°C) BLACK						
Temperature (°C) SHINY						

Concluding Questions

1. Which container, if either, warmed up more?
2. Try to explain what you observed.

A Crooke's radiometer, named after **Sir William Crookes (1832-1919)**, is illustrated in **Figure 7.10**. Four vanes are connected to a pivot in a glass bulb, which is partially, but not completely, evacuated. There are some air molecules inside the container. One side of each vane is black. The other side may be white or silvered.

Challenge! Design an experiment using an infrared light source, a mirror and a radiometer (**Figure 7.10**), and test whether infrared radiation reflects from a shiny surface the way visible light does.

Figure 7.10

Radiation in Everyday Life

Radiant energy falling on materials may be **absorbed** or **reflected**. The absorbed radiation increases the average translational kinetic energy of the molecules in the object, and therefore its temperature. A perfectly black object would absorb all the radiant energy falling on its surface. Light-coloured objects reflect more radiant energy. On a hot, sunny summer day, a good choice of outer-wear would be white, since it will reflect much of the infrared and visible radiation falling on your clothes.

In some parts of the world, radiant energy from the sun is reflected by well-placed mirrors to receivers in which water is heated and changed into steam. The steam is used to operate a turbine, which runs a generator to produce electricity.

Another way of collecting radiant energy from the sun is to use a convex lens to focus the radiation to a small area. The type of lens that is found in an overhead projector (called a **Fresnel** lens) can be used to make a solar furnace. On a sunny day, one of these Fresnel lenses can produce a temperature of over 1000°C at its focus.

Exercises

1. Carefully dismantle a thermos bottle and examine its construction. Assume it is filled with hot soup. How does the construction of the thermos bottle work to prevent heat loss by conduction, convection and radiation?
2. Good insulators usually have one thing in common: pockets of trapped air. Name at least six materials that provide excellent insulation, and which trap air within them. Materials could be housing insulators or clothing materials.
3. Which will melt faster on a bright, sunny day — fresh snow or dirty snow? Why?
4. A cold weather emergency survival suit is made of a reflecting plastic material with a thin coating of regular plastic. Why is the shiny, reflecting plastic on the *inside* of the suit facing your body? Why is it *not* wise to place this suit on someone who is already suffering from hypothermia?
5. Discuss the main forms of heat transfer involved in each of these situations:
   (a) A fireplace warms you as you sit in front of it.
   (b) Heat from the fireplace goes up the chimney.
   (c) Heat is transferred from an electric stove element into a frying pan.
   (d) Soup is heated to near boiling even though it does not conduct well.
   (e) Your house is warmed using a natural gas furnace system.

7.3 Measuring Thermal Energy

The amount of thermal energy in an object will depend on several factors. First, it depends on the **mass,** m, of the object. Second, it depends on the **temperature,** T, of the object. Third, it depends on the nature of the substance in the object. Different materials have different capacities for holding thermal energy. One material that has an exceptionally high capacity for holding thermal energy is water.

Specific Heat Capacity

It can be shown that to raise the temperature of a kilogram of water by one Celsius degree requires an input of 4 200 J. For comparison, it only requires an input of 450 J to raise the temperature of 1 kg of iron by 1 C°.

The amount of heat required to raise the temperature of one kilogram of a substance by 1 Celsius degree is called the **specific heat capacity** (c) of the substance.

For example, the specific heat capacity of water would be written, $c = 4200$ J/kg/C°. For iron, the specific heat capacity is $c = 450$ J/kg/C°.

The joule (J) is an appropriate unit for measuring heat, since the English scientist **James Joule (1818-1889)** did the first experiments to compare the specific heat capacities of different materials. **Table 7.1** lists some specific heat capacities.

Table 7.1 Specific Heat Capacities

Substance	J/kg/C°	Substance	J/kg/C°
water	4200	steam	2100
methyl alcohol	2400	aluminum	920
ethylene glycol*	2200	glass	840
ice	2100	iron	450
kerosene	2100	copper	430
(*antifreeze)		lead	130

Since the specific heat capacity, c, is the amount of **energy** that must be transferred to raise the temperature of one kilogram by one Celsius degree, then $c = \dfrac{\Delta E}{m \Delta T}$, where ΔE is the energy transferred, m is the mass of material, and ΔT is the change in temperature. Or,

$$\Delta E = m\, c\, \Delta T.$$

Examples

1. How much heat must be transferred into 5.0 kg of water to raise its temperature from 20°C up to 97°C?

   Solution: $\Delta E = m\, c\, \Delta T = (5.0\ \text{kg})(4\,200\ \text{J/kg/C°})(77\ \text{C°}) = 1.6 \times 10^6\ \text{J}.$

2. If 25 kJ of heat is transferred to 50.0 kg of water initially at 20.0°C, what will the final temperature of the water be?

   Solution: $\Delta E = m\, c\, \Delta T = mc\,(T_2 - T_1)$

   $2.5 \times 10^4\ \text{J} = (50.0\ \text{kg})(4.2 \times 10^3\ \text{J/kg/C°})(T_2 - 20.0\ °\text{C})$

   $\therefore T_2 - 20.0\ °\text{C} = \dfrac{2.5 \times 10^4\ \text{J}}{(5.0 \times 10^1\ \text{kg})(4.2 \times 10^3\ \text{J/kg/C°})} = 0.12\ \text{C°}.$

   $\therefore T_2 = 20.0°\text{C} + 0.12\ \text{C°} = 20.1°\text{C}$

Exercises

1. How much heat is needed to raise the temperature of 90.0 kg of water from 18°C to 80°C?
2. If 1.0 MJ (megajoule) of heat is transferred to 10.0 kg of water initially at 15°C, what will its final temperature be?
3. If 12 kg of water cools from 100°C down to room temperature (20°C), how much heat will it release to the environment?
4. Why is water such a desirable material to use as a coolant in a car engine?
5. If it takes 1200 J to raise the temperature of 0.500 kg of brass from 20.0°C to 26.2°C, what is the specific heat capacity of brass?
6. How much heat would be needed to warm 1.6 kg of ice from –15°C up to its melting point of 0°C?
7. A 5.0 kg block of lead at 250°C cools down to 20°C. How much heat does it give off in doing so?

Power of a Heat Source

Power is the rate at which energy is produced or consumed (or the rate at which work is done). In terms of our present needs, power is the rate at which heat is transferred.

$$P = \frac{\Delta E}{\Delta t},$$

where P is power, ΔE is the energy transferred, and Δt is the time interval during which the energy is transferred.

Investigation 7-4   Measuring the Power of a Hot Plate

Purpose: To measure the power of a hot plate indirectly, by measuring the heat transferred to a known mass of water in a given time.

Procedure

1. Measure out 300 mL of water into a 400 mL beaker using a graduated cylinder. Since water has a density of 1 g/mL, this will give you 300 g, or 0.300 kg of water.

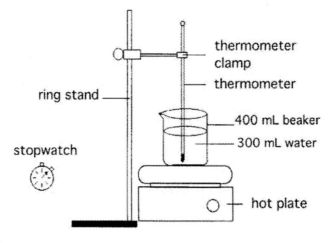

Figure 7.15

2. Arrange the thermometer as in **Figure 7.15**, so that it is not touching the bottom of the beaker.
3. Let the hot plate warm up for a minute or two, and then start your stopwatch and record the temperature of the water as precisely as you can. Record the temperature of the water every half-minute for 10 minutes. Stop the experiment if the water comes to a boil and use only your data for temperatures less than boiling temperature. Record your data in a table like **Table 7.2**.

4. Plot a graph with temperature on the Y-axis and time on the X-axis.
5. Find the slope of your graph, which is $\Delta T / \Delta t$. Units will be C°/s.

Table 7.2 Data for *Investigation 7-4*

Temperature (°C)										
Time (s)	0	30	60	90	120	150	180	210	240	→

6. Since the energy transferred to the water from the hot plate is $E = mc\ \Delta T$, then the power of the hot plate would be:

$$P = \frac{\Delta E}{\Delta t} = \frac{mc\ \Delta T}{\Delta t} = mc \text{ x [slope].}$$

Calculate the **power** of your hot plate using $m = 0.300$ kg, $c = 4200$ J/kg/C°, and the slope of your graph.
7. Find a cooled hot plate, and read the label on the hot plate to see what the manufacturer's power rating is for the hot plate.

Concluding Questions

1. What was your calculated power for the hot plate?
2. Calculate the percent difference between your calculated power and the manufacturer's rating, as follows:

$$\% \text{ Difference} = \frac{\text{manufacturer' s power rating - calculated power rating}}{\text{manufacturer' s power rating}} \text{ x } 100\%$$

3. Assuming your calculations were correct, and the manufacturer's rating was also correct, what is the **ratio** of the power you calculated (heat absorbed by the water per second) to the hot plate's rated power (heat given off by the hot plate per second). This ratio is the **efficiency** of the hot plate. You can convert your decimal fraction to a percent by multiplying by 100.

$$\text{Efficiency} = \frac{\text{Calculated Power Rating}}{\text{Manufacturer' s Power Rating}} \text{ x } 100\%$$

4. Why is the efficiency less than 100%?

Efficiency

For any energy-converting device, a convenient ratio to know is the ratio of the useful energy output of the device to the energy put into the device. This ratio is the **efficiency** of the device.

$$\text{Efficiency} = \frac{\text{Useful Energy out of Device}}{\text{Energy Put into Device}} \text{ x } 100\%$$

The efficiency rating gives us an idea of how much energy a device wastes as heat. One of the least efficient devices is an ordinary incandescent light bulb. Since it converts only 5% of its electrical energy into light and 95% into heat, a light bulb is only 5% efficient. An automobile might be only 10% efficient. (Where does all its wasted energy go?)

Electric motors may have efficiencies in the range between 60-90%, while transformers and generators may be 99% efficient.

Examples

1. To lift a 1200 N motorcycle a vertical height of 1.3 m onto a pickup truck, a motocross rider pushes the bike up a ramp 2.4 m, requiring an effort force up the ramp of 820 N. What is the efficiency of the ramp?

   Solution: Useful work done by the ramp = (1200 N)(1.3 m) = 1560 J
   Work put into using the ramp = (820 N)(2.4 m) = 1968 J

   $$\text{Efficiency} = \frac{1560 \text{ J}}{1968 \text{ J}} \times 100\% = 79\%.$$

   The ramp is 79% efficient. (Where did the other 21% of the input energy go?)

2. A 1500 W kettle warms 1.00 kg of water from 18°C to 88°C in a time of 3.6 min. How efficient is the kettle?

   Solution: Useful energy out of kettle in 3.6 minutes:

   $$\Delta E = mc\,\Delta T = (1.00 \text{ kg})(4200 \text{ J/kg/C}°)(70\text{C}°) = 294\,000 \text{ J}.$$

   Energy supplied by the kettle in 3.6 minutes:

   $$\Delta E = P\,\Delta t = (1500 \text{ J/s})(3.6 \text{ min})(60\text{s/min}) = 24\,000 \text{ J}.$$

   $$\text{Efficiency} = \frac{294,000 \text{ J}}{324,000 \text{ J}} \times 100\% = 91\%.$$

   The kettle is 91% efficient. (Where did the other 9% of the input energy go?)

Exercises

1. If you must do 500 J of work to operate a pulley system, and the pulley system lifts a 150 N load to a height of 3.0 m, how efficient is the pulley system?

2. A kettle that is 80% efficient is rated 1200 W. At what rate does the water in the kettle absorb energy (in watts)?

3. If a light bulb has an efficiency of 5.0%, at what rate does a 60 W bulb produce light energy?

4. For every megajoule of chemical potential energy in the fuel used to run a certain truck, only 120 kJ of useful work is done by the truck in making itself move. How efficient is the truck? Where are some of the places that the energy from the fuel is wasted?

Chapter Review Questions

1. (a) Change 250°C to kelvins.

   (b) Change 373 kelvins to °C.

2. A steel rod is at a temperature of 25°C. To what Celsius temperature must you raise it, in order to double its Kelvin temperature?

3. Why are metals such good conductors?

4. Why may a metal doorknob feel cold to the touch, while the wooden door feels relatively warm, when they are actually both at the same temperature?

5. Why is the water at the top of a hot water tank warmer than the water at the bottom of the tank?

6. In your home, what method(s) of heat transfer are involved when heat:

   (a) is distributed to your rooms from your furnace?

   (b) escapes through the walls of your house?

   (c) escapes from your roof to the atmosphere?

7. Is it strictly correct to say that insulation 'stops' heat transfer? Discuss.

8. Describe in what direction the vanes of a Crooke's radiometer turn when infrared light falls on them, and suggest a possible reason why they turn in that direction.

9. Why is an igloo warm?

10. Define **specific heat capacity.**

11. A certain metal has a specific heat capacity of 420 J/kg/C°, while water has a specific heat capacity of 4200 J/kg/C°. A kilogram of the metal and a kilogram of water are both at a temperature of 98°C. If both are allowed to cool to 18°C, which will give off more heat to the atmosphere, and how much more will it release?

12. If 10.0 kg of water at 25°C is heated by a 100% efficient 1500 W heater for 5.00 min, what will its final temperature be?

13. Why are coastal climates more moderate than inland climates?

14. How much heat is supplied by a 100% efficient 1200 W kettle in 10.0 min?

15. What is the efficiency of a 1500 W kettle if it supplies heat at the rate of 1400 W to the water in it?

16. A 1200 W kettle warms 800.0 g of water from 20°C to 99°C in 4.0 min. How efficient is the kettle?

17. A 60 W incandescent light bulb is 5% efficient. A 60 W fluorescent bulb is 15% efficient. How much more light will the fluorescent light bulb give off than the incandescent bulb, in the same period of time?

Well, *I* think he's a really **GOOD** conductor!

Ehren Stillman Cartoon

Test Yourself!

1. If water has a specific heat capacity of 4200 J/kg/C°, how much heat is needed to warm 50.0 kg of water from 15°C up to 85°C?

2. If 24 kJ of energy will warm 0.600 kg of a metal from 20° up to 220°C, what is the **specific heat capacity** of the metal?

3. A coffee percolator rated at 600 W supplies 500 W to the water in it. What is the **efficiency** of the kettle?

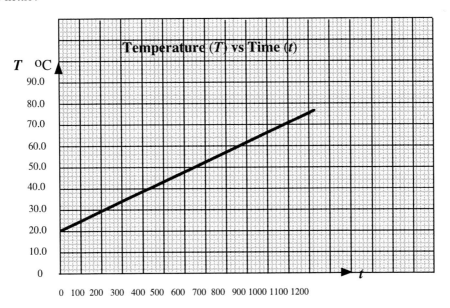

Time (s)

4. A light bulb is immersed in 0.500 kg of water, which has a specific heat capacity of 4200 J/kg/C°. The apparatus is well insulated, so that essentially all of the radiated heat is used to warm the water. Every 100 s, the temperature of the water is recorded. The graph above summarizes the data.

   (a) What is the slope of the above graph, expressed in proper units and in an appropriate number of significant figures?

   (b) Use the slope to calculate the useful heating **power** of the light bulb.

   (c) What is the most likely power rating of the bulb, as stamped on the bulb?

5. A 1500 W kettle warms 1.30 kg of water from 25.0°C to 99.0°C in 5.00 min. How efficient is the kettle?   (c = 4200 J/kg/C°)

6. If 5.00 kg of water at 10°C is heated for 2.00 min by a heater that supplies 1500 W to the water, what will the final temperature of the water be? (c = 4200 J/kg/C°)

Multiple Choice Questions

1. The temperature in kelvins of a sample of an ideal gas is directly proportional to
   A. the total energy of the molecules in the sample.
   B. the potential energy of the molecules in the sample.
   C. the number of molecules in the sample.
   D. the average translational kinetic energy of its molecules.

2. If the temperature of an object is 30°C, what is its temperature in kelvins?
   A. 303 K   B. 293 K   C. 283 K   D. 273 K

3. By what method can heat be transferred without the presence of matter?
   A. convection
   B. conduction
   C. radiation
   D. both conduction and convection

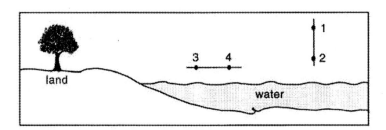

4. What is the direction of airflow at night in the above situation, assuming there are no major over-riding weather disturbances?
   A. from 1 to 2, and from 3 to 4
   B. from 2 to 1, and from 3 to 4
   C. from 1 to 2, and from 4 to 3
   D. from 2 to 1, and from 4 to 3

5. If you are sitting in front of an open fireplace, what is the main method by which heat is transferred to you?
   A. radiation
   B. conduction
   C. convection
   D. conduction and convection

6. When a pot of soup heats up, what is the main method by which heat is transferred within the soup?
   A. conduction
   B. convection
   C. radiation
   D. diffusion

7. In winter, why do the blades of your skates feel cooler to the touch than the boots?
   A. Metal is naturally cooler than leather or plastic.
   B. The metal blades conduct cold to your hand.
   C. The metal blades conduct heat from your hand.
   D. Metals attract the cold.

8. Heat transfer by radiation works best in a
   A. solid.
   B. liquid.
   C. gas.
   D. vacuum.

9. Because water has a very high specific heat,
   A. water conducts heat really well.
   B. water is slow to warm up and slow to cool.
   C. water is an excellent insulator.
   D. water has an unusually high boiling point.

10. How much heat does a 1500 W heater give off in one minute?
    A. 1500 J
    B. 90,000 J
    C. 5,400,000 J
    D. 25 J

11. A fluorescent lamp is about 15% efficient as a source of **light.** How much **heat** does a 40 W fluorescent lamp give off in one second?
    A. 40 J
    B. 6 J
    C. 34 J
    D. 1 J

12. A pulley system lifts a 500.0 N load up 10.0 m. The pulley operator exerts a force of 110 N over a distance of 50.0 m. How efficient is the pulley system?
    A. 110%
    B. 100 %
    C. 91%
    D. 9%

Chapter 8 Waves

Figure 8.1: If a wet finger is pushed around the edge of a wine glass filled with water, vibrations are set up, which cause a high-pitched, pleasant sound. Notice the waves that are generated in the water by the vibrations of the glass.

8.1 Good Vibrations

There are many kinds of waves in nature. You have heard of light waves, sound waves, radio waves, earthquake waves, water waves, shock waves, brain waves and, of course, the familiar wave created by a partisan crowd at a sports event.

Wave motion is an important phenomenon because it is so commonplace, and because it is one of the major ways in which energy can be transmitted from one place to another.

There are two basic kinds of waves. First, there is the **pulse,** which is a non-repeating wave. A single disturbance sends a pulse from the source outward, but there is no repetition of the event. For example, you may give a garden hose a quick 'yank' to one side, causing a pulse to travel the length of the hose.

Second, there is the **periodic wave.** Periodic waves are probably more familiar to you. You have watched water waves moving across a pond. The waves arrive at the shore of the pond at regularly repeated time intervals. Periodic means *recurring at regular intervals*. Water waves are caused by a disturbance of the water somewhere in the pond.

Whether the wave is a pulse or a periodic wave, a disturbance is **propagated** by the wave, usually through a material substance. The medium for electromagnetic waves (light, radio, X-rays, ultraviolet, infrared, gamma radiation, etc.) is not a material, but electric and magnetic fields created by charged particles.

To have a regularly repeating wave, there must be regularly repeating **vibrations.** For example, the regularly repeating sound waves from a tuning fork are caused by the disturbance of the air by the vibrations of the two tines of the fork. Vibrating electrons, which create disturbances in the electric field around the electrons, create the microwaves that cook your supper, or measure the speed of your car in a radar trap.

Investigation 8-1 An Introduction to Waves

Purpose: To make some observations on waves, using ordinary materials.

Procedure

1. Fill a large beaker or plastic ice cream bucket with water. Use a rubber hammer to make a tuning fork vibrate. Immerse the tines of the tuning fork in the water. Observe the waves on the surface of the water. Now wipe up all the water you spilled!
2. Fill a wine glass with water. Soak your finger in the water, and then run your finger around the edge of the glass until the glass starts to emit a high-pitched sound. See **Figure 8.1**. While you are doing this, watch the surface of the water near where your finger is making the glass vibrate. Try the same activity with varying depths of water. Will the glass vibrate when it is empty? What effect does adding water to the glass have on the **pitch** of the sound you hear?

Concluding Questions

1. What do your observations on the tuning fork in the water suggest might be the cause of the sound emanating from the fork?
2. What caused the pattern you saw on the surface of the water in the wine glass, when it was emitting sound?

8.2 Describing Waves

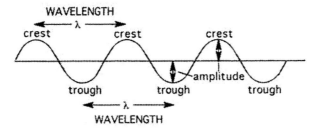

Figure 8.2

Wavelength (λ)

Figure 8.2 depicts waves emanating from a vibrating source. They could be water waves. The highest points on the waves are called **crests** and the lowest points are called **troughs**. The distance between successive crests (or between successive troughs) is called the **wavelength (λ)** of the wave. (The symbol λ is the Greek letter **lambda**.)

The height of the wave (its displacement from the horizontal line in the diagram) is the **amplitude** of the wave. The amplitude is shown on the diagram.

Wavelengths may be measured in metres, in the case of water waves, or in nanometers (1 nm $= 10^{-9}$), in the case of visible light. Microwaves may be measured in centimetres, while the waves produced by AC power lines may be kilometres long. Wavelengths of audible sounds range from millimetres up to metres.

Frequency (*f*)

Another important aspect of waves is the **frequency** of the waves. The frequency of the waves tells you 'how frequently' they and their source vibrate. If you are listening to a tuning fork, sound waves reach your ear with the same frequency as the vibrating fork. The fork's tines vibrate back and forth, for example, 256 times in one second if the frequency of the fork is 256 vibrations per second.

Frequency is measured in a unit called the **hertz (Hz)**. The unit is named after **Heinrich Hertz (1857-1894)**, who was the first scientist to detect radio waves. One hertz is one vibration per second.

$$1 \text{ Hz} = 1 \text{ s}^{-1}$$

A pendulum 24.8 cm long has a frequency of 1 Hz. Electrons vibrating to and fro in an alternating current circuit have a frequency of 60 Hz. Radio waves may be several **kilohertz (kHz)**, where 1kHz = 1 000 Hz, or they may be in the **megahertz (MHz)** range, where 1 MHz is equal to 1 000 000 Hz.

Period (*T*)

Related to the frequency of a vibration is the **period** of the vibration. The period is the time interval between vibrations. For example, if the period of a vibration is 1/2 s, then the frequency must be 2 s^{-1}, or 2 Hz.

Consider a pendulum. If its length is 24.8 cm, it will have a frequency of 1 Hz and a period of 1 s. If its length is 99.2 cm, it will have a frequency of 1/2 Hz and a period of 2 s. A pendulum 223 cm long will have a frequency of 1/3 Hz and a period of 3 s. As you can see, **frequency** and **period** are reciprocals of each other.

$$\text{frequency} = \frac{1}{\text{period}}$$

In symbolic form, $f = \dfrac{1}{T}$, or $T = \dfrac{1}{f}$.

Exercises

1. A dog's tail wags 50.0 times in 40.0 s.
   (a) What is the frequency of the tail? (b) What is the period of vibration of the tail?
2. A certain tuning fork makes 7 680 vibrations in 30 s. (a) What is the frequency of the tuning fork? (b)What is the period of vibration of the tuning fork?
3. Tarzan is swinging back and forth on a vine. If each complete swing takes 4.0 s, what is the frequency of the swings?
4. A helicopter pilot with nothing better to do counts 250 crests of water waves on a lake below him, in a distance of 100 m. What is the wavelength of the waves?
5. If the frequency of a sound is tripled, what will happen to the period of the sound waves?

8.3 Transverse and Longitudinal Waves

Figure 8.3 illustrates two ways to send a pulse through a long length of spring or a long slinky. In method (a), the spring is pulled sideways, so that the disturbance is at right angles to the direction that the pulse will travel. This produces a **transverse wave.** In method (b), several turns of the spring are compressed and let go. The disturbance is in the *same* direction as the direction the pulse will travel. This produces a **longitudinal wave. Transverse** means 'across' and **longitudinal** means 'lengthwise'.

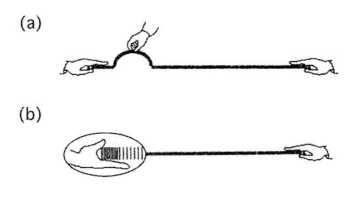

Figure 8.3

Investigation 8-2 Observing Transverse and Longitudinal Waves

Purpose: To observe pulses travelling in springs of different diameters.

Procedure

1. With your partner's help, stretch a long spring (approximately 2.5 cm diameter) to a length of 9 or 10 m. Hold on firmly, since the spring and you can be damaged if it is let go carelessly.
2. Create a **transverse pulse** by pulling a section of the spring to one side and letting it go abruptly. Observe the motion of the pulse and its reflection from your partner's hand.
3. Try increasing the **amplitude** of the pulse. Does this affect the speed of the wave through the spring?
4. Try tightening the spring. How does increasing the tension affect the speed of the pulse?
5. Observe the pulse as it reflects. Does a crest reflect as a crest or as a trough?
6. Have your partner create a pulse simultaneously with yours. Do the two pulses affect each other as they pass through each other?
7. Repeat **Procedures 1-6** using a long slinky, which is a spring with a much larger diameter.
8. Try sending a **longitudinal pulse** through each spring. To do this, bunch up a dozen or so turns of the spring, then let the compressed section go. Do longitudinal waves reflect at your partner's hand?

Concluding Questions

1. In which spring did the transverse waves travel faster — the small diameter spring or the slinky?
2. In which spring did the longitudinal waves travel faster?
3. Does the amplitude of the waves affect their speed through the spring?
4. Does spring tension affect wave speed? Explain.
5. When a wave travels through the medium (the spring), does the medium travel or just the disturbance in the medium?
6. When a wave reflects from a fixed end of the medium, does a crest reflect as a crest or is it reflected as a trough? (In other words, is the wave *inverted?*)

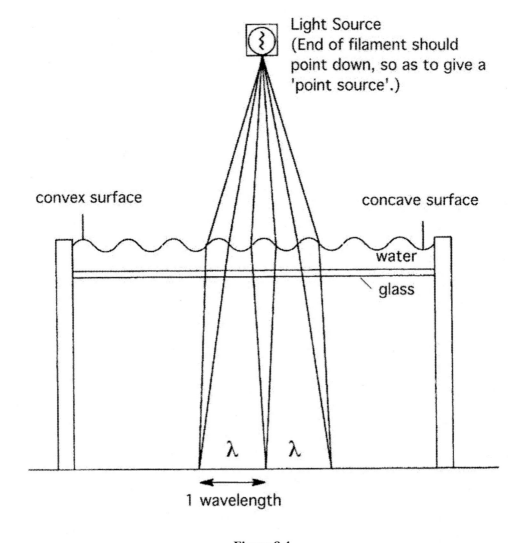

Figure 8.4

8.4 The Ripple Tank as a Wave Model

The ripple tank is an ingenious device that permits us to study the behaviour of waves, using a water wave model. If a series of waves is generated by moving a piece of wood dowelling back and forth in a regularly repeating motion, the waves will look like the ones in **Figure 8.4** if seen from the side. The actual water waves are **transverse** in nature.

If light from a point source (the end of the filament of a straight-filament, clear light bulb) is allowed to pass through the waves and fall on a large sheet of white paper, then (with some focusing) the light passing through the waves can be made to form bright lines on the paper underneath the crests of the waves. The crests act as convex lenses and make the light from the source converge (come together). The troughs, on the other hand, act as concave lenses and make the light from the source diverge (spread out). The image you see on the white screen consists of a series of bright lines with dark spaces between successive bright lines. The bright lines represent crests, and the dark areas troughs. The waves you see on the screen are longitudinal waves, whereas the actual water waves were transverse.

Investigation 8-3
Wavelength, Frequency, and Speed of Water Waves

Purpose: To investigate the relationship among wavelength, frequency and wave speed.

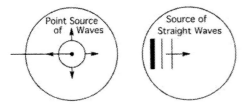

Figure 8.5

Procedure

1. Fill your ripple tank with water to a depth of approximately 2 cm. If your tank requires them, make sure the screen dampers are in place.

2. To generate a circular wave, touch the surface of the water at the centre of the tank with the tip of your finger. Is there any evidence that the wave speeds up or slows down as it travels from the centre of the tank to its perimeter?

3. Imagine a single point on one of the crests that you see moving out from the centre of the tank. What path would this *point* on the crest take?

4. Set up your wave generator so that it generates circular waves at regular intervals. Start with a low **frequency**. Note the **wavelength** of the circular waves (the distance between successive crests). Increase the frequency of the wave generator and observe how the wavelength changes.

5. Set up your wave generator so that it produces straight waves instead of circular waves. Try different frequencies to see the effect of frequency on wavelength.

Concluding Questions

1. Does a circular wave travel out at the same speed in all directions? How do you know this?
2. Describe what happens to the wavelength of a water wave when the frequency of the waves increases.

8.5 The Wave Equation

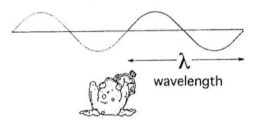

Freddie the frog (**Figure 8.6**) is sitting on the edge of a wave tank, watching the waves go by. See. He knows that the waves were produced by a wave generator, which vibrates up and down with a frequency f and a period,

$$T = 1 / f.$$

Figure 8.6

Being a dedicated physicist, Fred wants to know what the speed of the waves is. He watches a wave travel its own length (wavelength λ) and times exactly how long the wave takes to travel its own length. Since the waves are generated once every T seconds by the generator, then this T should be the period of the waves. To calculate the speed v of the waves, all he has to do is divide the wavelength by the period of the wave! In symbolic form, $v = \lambda / T$.

Now, since $T = 1/f$, or $f = 1/T$, then

$$v = \lambda f.$$

This relationship is a very important one, because it is true for *any kind of waves*. This includes sound waves, earthquake waves, waves in the strings of musical instruments, or any kind of electromagnetic wave (light, infrared, radio, X-radiation, ultraviolet, gamma radiation, etc.)! In words, the wave equation says

wave speed = wavelength x frequency.

Example:

What is the speed of a sound wave if its frequency is 256 Hz and its wavelength is 1.29 m?

Solution: $v = \lambda f = (1.29 \text{ m})(256 \text{ s}^{-1}) = 330 \text{ m/s}.$

Exercises

1. If waves maintain a constant speed, what will happen to their wavelength if the frequency of the waves is (a) doubled? (b) halved?
2. What is the frequency of a sound wave if its speed is 340 m/s and its wavelength is 1.70 m?
3. Waves of frequency 2.0 Hz are generated at the end of a long steel spring. What is their wavelength if the waves travel along the spring with a speed of 3.0 m/s?
4. A student measures the speed of water waves in her tank to be 25 cm/s. If the wavelength is 2.5 cm, what is the frequency of the waves?
5. The speed of light is 3.0×10^8 m/s. What is the frequency of light waves if their wavelength is 600 nm? (1 nm = 10^{-9} m) Consult a spectrum chart to see what colour of light this would be.
6. Some microwaves have a frequency of 3.0×10^{10} Hz. How long is a microwave of this frequency? (Microwave radiation travels at the speed of light.)

8.6 Properties of Waves

In the next *Investigation,* you will observe some of the properties of water waves. These properties apply to light and sound waves as well. The main purpose of the next investigation is to familiarize you with properties of waves that apply to **SOUND** and **LIGHT**, which are the topics of the chapters that follow.

Investigation 8-4   Properties of Waves

Purpose: **To observe important properties of waves, using water waves in a ripple tank as a model.**

Note! *This investigation will require several periods to complete. Most observations can be made in the form of neat sketches showing what happens when the procedures are followed.*

Part 1 Reflection of Circular Water Waves

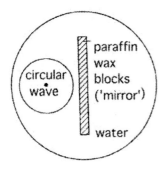

Figure 8.7

Procedure

1. Generate a circular wave by touching the surface of the water in the ripple tank at a distance of approximately 10 cm in front of a solid barrier, made of two paraffin wax blocks, standing on edge in the middle of the tank. (See **Figure 8.7**.) Observe the **curvature** of the wave as it arrives at the barrier and as it leaves. Is the wave less curved, more curved or does it have the same curvature after it reflects from the barriers? Sketch what you see.

2. From where does the **reflected** circular wave appear to come? Try generating a circular wave *behind* the barrier at the same time as you generate one in front of the barrier. Try different distances behind the barrier until you obtain a wave with the same curvature as the one that *reflects* from the other side of the barrier. (The wave from the point behind the barrier will look just as if it is passing through the barrier and joining the reflected wave on the other side!) If the waves were light waves and the waves were coming from an 'object', where would the 'image' of the object in the mirror (barrier) be located?

Concluding Question: How does the distance from the **object** to the **mirror** compare with the distance from the **mirror** to the **image**?

Part 2 Reflection of Straight Water Waves

Procedure

1. Set up the straight-wave generator so that it sends parallel straight waves toward a barrier made of paraffin wax blocks. The angle formed where the incident waves strike the barrier (labelled ∠i in **Figure 8.8**) is called the **angle of incidence.** Measure both the angle of incidence and the **angle of reflection** (∠r). Sketch what you see.

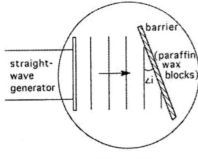

Figure 8.8

2. Adjust the barrier to change the angle of incidence. Measure the new angle of incidence and the new angle of reflection. Repeat for at least three other angles of incidence.

Concluding Questions

1. When straight waves strike a straight barrier, how does the angle of incidence compare with the angle of reflection?
2. When the waves reflect from the barrier, does their speed change? Does their frequency change? Does their wavelength change?

Part 3 Reflection of Waves from a Curved 'Mirror'

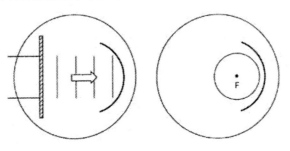

Figure 8.9(a)   **Figure 8.9(b)**

Procedure

1. This time, instead of a straight barrier, you will use a piece of rubber tubing, which curls into a shape that is approximately parabolic. Set up the rubber tubing 'mirror' so that it faces the straight-wave generator as in **Figure 8.9(a)**.
2. Observe what happens when the incident straight waves reflect from the **parabolic mirror**. What shape do the waves have after the reflection? Locate the point to which the waves appear to converge. This point is called the **focus** or **focal point** of the mirror. Sketch what you see.
3. Turn off the straight-wave generator. Use the tip of your finger to generate circular waves at the focus of the mirror. (See **Figure 8.9(b)**.) What shape do the *reflected* waves have this time? Sketch what you see.

Concluding Questions

1. Describe what happens to straight waves when they reflect from a parabolic reflector. Are parabolic reflectors ever used to reflect (a) light? (b) sound? Give examples.
2. Describe what happens when circular waves originating at the focus of a parabolic mirror reflect from the mirror. Name a device that does this with light waves.

Part 4 Diffraction of Water Waves

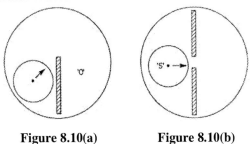

Figure 8.10(a)   Figure 8.10(b)

Procedure (Use sketches to describe what you observe.)

1. Set up a barrier (wall) near the middle of your ripple tank using a block of paraffin wax or similar object. See **Figure 8.10(a)**. Use the tip of your finger to generate waves on one side of the wall. Observe what happens to the waves as they spread past the edge of the barrier. If these were **sound waves,** and you were standing at O, would you hear the sound?
2. Set up the arrangement in **Figure 8.10(b)**, to simulate a doorway. Generate waves with the tip of your finger at **S**, and observe the waves as they pass through and beyond the door. If these were **sound waves,** could you hear the sound in the adjacent room?
3. Change the width of the 'doorway'. Does this affect the amount of spreading of the waves as they pass through?
4. Remove the barriers from the tank and place a small object near the centre of the tank. (Its shape is unimportant. A width of 2-3 cm would be appropriate.) Generate waves on one side of the obstacle using the tip of your finger. Let the waves pass by the object. Do they 'cast a shadow' as they pass it, or do they seem to carry on unaffected by the obstacle? What happens if you use an obstacle that is (a) bigger? (b) smaller?

The wave property you have been observing is common not only to water waves, but also to sound and light waves. In fact, any kind of waves exhibits the ability to spread out as they pass through narrow openings or around corners or small obstacles. The name of this property of waves is **diffraction**. You have probably seen examples of diffraction many times, perhaps without knowing what it was. If you look out at streetlights through a window screen or a fine mesh curtain, the *starburst* effect you see is due to diffraction of light waves as they pass by the screen. Diffraction is often used in television programs to obtain starburst effects in musical productions. Diffraction is commonplace with sound. You can hear someone talking around a corner mainly because of diffraction.

5. Set up your straight-wave generator and adjust the frequency so that the waves it produces are approximately 2 cm wavelength as seen on the screen on your table. By experimenting with different opening sizes and wavelengths, find out what the effect is of changing these two variables one at a time. Prepare a series of careful sketches showing how the waveforms look following diffraction.

6. Set up a small obstacle in the path of the straight waves. Experiment to see the effects of changing (a) wavelengths and (b) obstacle size. Sketch what you observe.

Concluding Questions

1. Is diffraction more noticeable with short wavelengths or long wavelengths?

2. Is diffraction more noticeable with small openings or large openings?

3. When straight waves pass through a small opening, what shape do the diffracted waves have? (Sketch a diagram.)

4. When straight waves pass by a small obstacle, what happens to the straight waves if the obstacle is (a) very small compared with the wavelength of the waves? (b) about the same size as the wavelength? (c) very large compared with the wavelength?

5. Describe at least three examples of situations you encounter on a daily basis that involve diffraction of waves of one sort or another. These might involve water waves, sound or light.

Diffraction of Light Waves: Figures 8.11 and **8.12** illustrate diffraction of red light of a single wavelength, from a helium-neon laser. In **Figure 8.11**, a laser beam was spread out using a concave lens, and the beam of light was allowed to cast a shadow of a small pinhead directly on photographic film. The photograph was taken in a dark room, with the lens removed from a camera so that light shone directly on the film when the shutter was opened. **Figure 8.12** was taken in a similar fashion, except that a simple sheet of film was used as a screen upon which to cast a shadow of a razor blade. No camera was involved. (A totally dark room must be used, of course.)

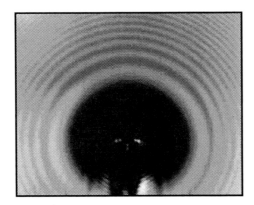

Figure 8.11 Light from a laser is diffracted as it passes by the head of a pin.

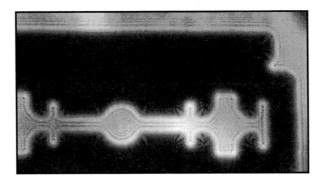

Figure 8.12 The shadow of a razor blade in red laser light shows evidence of diffraction of light.

Part 5 Refraction of Water Waves

(a) The Effect of Water Depth on Wave Speed

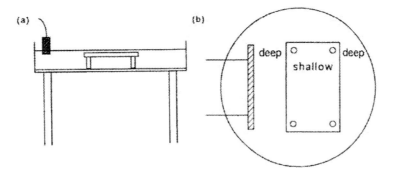

Figure 8.13

Procedure   (Sketch what you observe.)

1. To observe the effect of water depth on wave speed, you must arrange the ripple tank so that there is a region of deep water and also a region of shallow water over which water waves can pass. To do this, a rectangular sheet of transparent plastic is mounted in the tank using coins or washers to prop it up. Water is added to the tank until the level is approximately 1-2 mm above the top of the plastic sheet. **Figure 8.13** illustrates side and top views. The straight wave generator is used to provide the waves.
2. Generate continuous waves with the straight wave generator. Observe the wavelength of the waves in the deep water, and compare this with the wavelength in shallow water. What happens when the waves re-enter the deep water? Measure the wavelengths in deep and shallow water and record them.

You will recall that wave speed, wavelength and frequency are related by $v = \lambda f$. The frequency f is determined by the rate of vibration of the wave generator, and *will not change during transmission of the waves*. This means that the wave speed v is proportional to the wavelength λ. If you observe the wavelength changing, this means the wave speed is changing proportionally.

---

3. Calculate the ratio of the wavelength in shallow water to the wavelength in deep water, and thus calculate the ratio of the wave speed in shallow water to the wave speed in deep water.

(b) Refraction of Water Waves

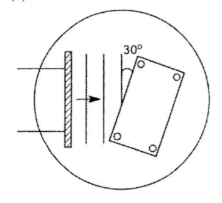

Procedure

1. Arrange the 'shallow' water region as in **Figure 8.14**, so that straight waves entering the shallow region meet its edge at an angle such as 30°. Adjust the generator frequency to obtain waves of long wavelength. Observe the waves as they pass into the shallow region.

Figure 8.14

2. Make the following measurements on the water waves, as seen on your 'screen'.
    (a) What is the wavelength in the deep water? in the shallow water?
    (b) What is the *ratio* of the wavelength in shallow water to the wavelength in deep water?
    (c) What is the *ratio* of the wave speed in shallow water to the wave speed in deep water? Where does the *change in speed* actually occur?
    (d) What angle does the incident wave make with the boundary between the deep water and the shallow water? (This is the **angle of incidence.**) What angle does the wave inside the shallow water make with the boundary? (This is the **angle of refraction.**)

3. Make a neat sketch illustrating what happens to water waves coming from deep water into shallow water. Show what happens to the waves when they again leave the shallow water.
4. Try different **angles of incidence**, such as 40° and 50°. Measure and record the angles at which the waves leave the boundary (**angles of refraction**).

When waves change direction on entering a different medium, the phenomenon is called **refraction**. Refraction is a very important property in nature, especially as it relates to visible light. In a later chapter you will learn how refraction is involved in the working of optical lenses. Refraction occurs with sound waves, when sound travels through different media, or when it travels through layers of air at different temperatures.

Concluding Questions

1. What happens to the speed of water waves when the waves pass from deeper water into shallower water?

2. You did not actually measure the wave speeds. How did you know the speeds had changed and by how much they had changed?

3. Why can you assume the wave frequency is constant as the waves proceed across the water in your wave tank?

4. When water waves enter shallow water in a direction such that the waves are parallel to the boundary, does the direction of the waves change?

5. When water waves enter shallow water from deep water in such a direction that the waves form an angle greater than 0° with the boundary, does their direction change? If so, in what way does it change? Is the **angle of refraction** greater than, equal to or less than the **angle of incidence**?

6. When water waves leave shallow water and return to deep water, how does their direction change? For the water waves leaving the shallow water, how does the **angle of refraction** compare with the **angle of incidence** for the water waves that were coming into the shallow water in the first place?

Part 6 Interference

You have observed several properties exhibited by water waves. You have seen reflection, diffraction and refraction of waves in a ripple tank. We shall now look at what happens when two waves interact with one another. For example, waves approaching a barrier may encounter waves reflecting from that barrier. What happens when the incoming waves meet the reflected waves? Also, waves from two entirely different sources may encounter each other. What happens when they do? When waves do interact with each other, the phenomenon is called **interference**.

(a) Interference in a Stretched Spring

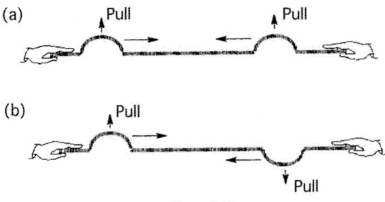

Figure 8.15

Procedure: (Sketch what you observe.)

1. To observe interference of waves in a slinky, hold one end of the slinky yourself and have your partner hold the other end of the stretched spring. Simultaneously, generate **transverse** disturbances in the same direction and with the same amplitude, as in **Figure 8.15(a)**. Observe what happens when the two pulses pass through each other near the centre of the slinky.

2. Repeat **Procedure 1**, but this time, generate simultaneous disturbances that have the same magnitude but opposite amplitudes, as in **Figure 8.15(b)**.

Concluding Questions

1. When the two pulses pass through each other such that a crest passes through a crest, as would happen in **Figure 8.15(a)**, what happens to the **amplitude** of the combined waves?

2. When a crest arrives at the same point as a trough, as would happen in **Figure 8.15(b)**, what happens to the amplitude of the combined waves?

(b) Interference in Water Waves

Procedure

1. Set up the arrangement in **Figure 8.16**. The generator generates straight waves, but as they pass through the twin slits, each slit causes **diffraction** and the two sets of circular waves are produced at the slits. Observe how the two sets of circular waves **interfere** with each other.

2. Each source of circular waves sends out successive crests and troughs, and the two sets of waves interfere with one another. Describe what you see on the screen where the **troughs** from one source of waves arrive simultaneously with the **crests** from the other source. What

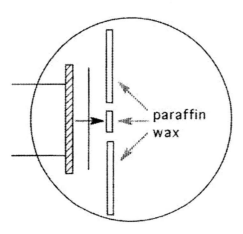

Figure 8.16

do you see in the areas where crests and troughs from one source arrive simultaneously with crests and troughs from the other source?

3. Replace the two-slit barrier with a twin point-source generator. Set up the twin point-source generator so that both vibrating point sources are **in phase**. This means that they both vibrate up and down in synchronization. (If one point source vibrated upward while the other vibrated downward, they would be **out of phase**.) This arrangement usually gives much better waves than the double slit arrangement.

Concluding Questions

1. When crests from one wave source arrive simultaneously with troughs from another wave source, what will you see on the screen at that point? Why?

2. When crests arrive with crests and troughs with troughs from two different wave sources, what will you see at that spot on the screen? Why?

3. Regions of zero disturbance on the screen appear as nearly straight lines called **nodal lines.** If a point on such a nodal line was a distance of $n\lambda$ from one point source of waves, where λ is the wavelength and n is an integer, how far would the same point be from the other point source? (Is there more than one answer to this question?)

4. Regions of maximum disturbance on the screen, sometimes called **maxima,** occur when the distance from one source is, say, $m\lambda$, where m is an integer and λ is the wavelength. What is the distance to the other source? Is there more than one possible answer? Explain.

Constructive and Destructive Interference

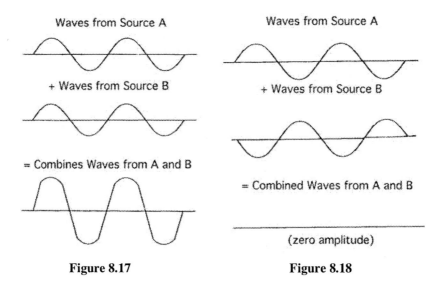

Figure 8.17   **Figure 8.18**

Figure 8.17 shows waves coming from two different sources — **A** and **B**. What happens if the two sets of waves arrive simultaneously at the same place? The result is shown in the third diagram. The amplitudes of the two sets of waves are additive. Since the waves from source **A** are *in phase* with the waves from source **B**, the resultant waves have *twice* the amplitude of the individual waves from **A** or **B**. This is an example of what is called **constructive interference.** Notice that crests are twice as high and troughs are twice as deep. In a ripple tank, you see **maxima** where there is constructive interference like this.

In **Figure 8.18,** the waves from source **A** are exactly *out of phase* with the waves from source **B**. A crest from source **A** arrives simultaneously with a trough from source **B**. The two sets of waves exactly cancel each other. This is an example of **destructive interference.** In a ripple tank, you see **nodal lines** where there is destructive interference like this.

Interference of waves occurs with all sorts of waves. You have seen interference of water waves in the ripple tank. You can hear interference of sound waves if you simply listen to a tuning fork as you rotate it slowly near your ear. Each tine of the fork produces a set of sound waves. Listen for constructive interference (extra loud sound) and destructive interference (minimum sound) as you slowly rotate the tuning fork.

8.7 Young's Experiment

The interference property of waves was first used to measure the wavelength of light by the English scientist **Thomas Young (1773-1829)**. Young's interference experiment, done in the year 1801, has great historical importance since it seemed to suggest very strongly that light is a **wave** phenomenon.

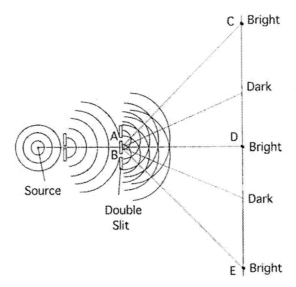

Figure 8.19

Figure 8.19 illustrates how Young's experiment was done. A single slit was illuminated by a source of light of one 'colour' (wavelength). Circular waves spread out from the single slit. When the wave front hits the double slit, each of these two slits acts as a new source of circular waves that travel toward a vertical screen. On the screen one sees a series of bright and dark bands of light. (A sheet of photographic film can be substituted for the screen.)

The Young's interference experiment can be illustrated very easily now using a classroom laser. The laser automatically produces one single wavelength, and the interference pattern is bright enough to see even in a well-lit room.

Interference Pattern in Young's Experiment

In **Figure 8.19**, the concentric circles represent successive **peaks** of light waves coming from the slits. **Troughs** are midway between the peaks, of course, and are not shown in the diagram because it becomes too cluttered with detail.

On the screen on the right, one would see a series of bright and dark bands, which is an interference pattern. At the bright bands (**C**, **D** and **E**), crests from the two slits arrive simultaneously, as do troughs. There is **constructive interference** of the two sets of waves. Notice that waves arriving at **D** have travelled the *same* distance from their respective slits.

Waves arriving at **C** or at **E** have travelled distances that differ by *exactly one wavelength* (λ). Again, the peaks arrive simultaneously and the troughs arrive simultaneously, and there is constructive interference causing the bright bands at **C** and **E**.

Figure 8.19 is simplified. There will be other **bright bands** further out on both sides of the central bright band. *These bright bands will occur wherever the difference in distance travelled from slits* **A** *and* **B** *is an integral number of wavelengths.*

At the dark bands (**nodal lines**) waves from the two sources arrive 'out of phase'. That is, when a crest from slit **A** is arriving, a trough from slit **B** is also arriving. The crest cancels the trough. This is destructive interference. The amplitudes of the two arriving waves cancel each other and you see no light.

Figure 8.20 shows the geometry of the situation, and how you can use the interference pattern to calculate the wavelength of the light. For simplicity, the first bright band adjacent to the central bright band is used.

CA is the distance from the screen to source (slit) **A**, and **CB** is the distance from the screen to the second slit **B.** The difference in these two distances is **BF**, which is one wavelength.

$$BF = CB - CA = \lambda$$

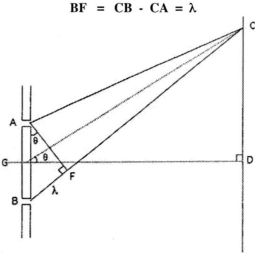

Figure 8.20

In the diagram, **GD** is the central maximum. (A bright band is seen on the screen at **D**.) A dashed line, **CG**, joins the mid-point of the two slits with the bright band at **C**. You will note that there are similar triangles on this diagram.

Since **ΔBFA ~ ΔCDG**, therefore $\dfrac{BF}{CD} = \dfrac{AB}{CG}$.

This means that the wavelength **BF** can be calculated as follows:

$$BF = (CD)\frac{(AB)}{(CG)},$$

or $\qquad \lambda = (CD)\dfrac{(AB)}{(CG)}.$

where **CD** is the distance on the screen between the central bright band and the first bright band to either side of it; **AB** is the distance between the two slits or sources; and **CG** is the distance from the mid-point of the two slits to the first bright band on the screen.

For the second bright band, $BF = 2\lambda$; for the third bright band, $BF = 3\lambda$; and for the 'nth' bright band, $BF = n\lambda$.

In general, for the nth bright band:

$$n\lambda = (CD)\frac{(AB)}{(CG)} \text{, and}$$

$$\lambda = \frac{(CD)(AB)}{n(CG)} \; .$$

This relationship can be used to calculate the wavelength of light from an interference pattern, or it can be used to calculate the wavelength of water waves in a ripple tank. In *Investigation 8-5,* you will do both measurements. As a challenge, you might also try measuring the wavelength of sound waves using interference of waves from two speakers producing sound of one known frequency.

Challenge

If you study **Figure 8.20**, you will notice if you are familiar with simple trigonometry, that the ratio of side CD to side CG of triangle CDE is equal to the sine of angle G (which is called θ on the diagram). You will see that the formula for the wavelength can, therefore, be written

$$\lambda = \frac{AB}{n} \sin\theta \; ,$$

where θ is the angle between the line GD (central bright band) and the line GC (nth bright band), and n is the number of the bright band. If the symbol d is used for the distance between slits (AB), the formula can be written

$$n\lambda = d \sin\theta.$$

Investigation 8-5
Measuring Wavelength Using Young's Method

Part A Wavelength of Water Waves

The wavelength of interfering water waves can be calculated using the formula and method described in **Section 8.7**. Since the waves are clearly visible on the screen, a direct check can be done on the formula by observation of the distance between successive crests seen on the ripple tank screen. Once you are satisfied that Young's method works for water waves, you can try it with light waves where the indirect method is the only method you can use!

Purpose: To measure the wavelength of (a) water waves in a ripple tank and (b) light waves from a classroom laser using the method of Young's Interference Experiment.

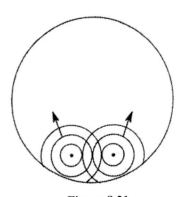

Figure 8.21

Procedure

1. Set up your ripple tank with two point sources vibrating 'in phase' as in **Figure 8.21**. On your 'screen', mark where the two sources are and label them **A** and **B**. Measure **AB**. Choose a location to represent where the screen in Young's experiment would be and draw a line like **CDE** in **Figure 8.19**.
2. Turn on your ripple tank motor and adjust the frequency until you obtain a clear, stable interference pattern. Locate a suitable site for point **C** and mark where **C** and **D** are on your diagram. Measure **AB, CD** and **CG** and count '**n**'. Calculate your wavelength using the formula,

$$\lambda = \frac{(CD)(AB)}{n(CG)} \ .$$

3. To check on this calculated value of the wavelength, leave the ripple tank motor running at the same frequency. Now use a hand stroboscope to make the waves appear 'stopped' on your ripple tank screen. Place a ruler directly on the screen next to the 'stopped' waves and measure their wavelength directly.
4. Calculate the percent difference between the wavelength you measured by Young's method and the wavelength you measured directly.
5. Repeat the experiment using waves that are (a) shorter and (b) longer.

Concluding Questions

1. What was the largest percent error you obtained using Young's method for measuring the wavelength of the water waves? According to your results, is the method a valid one to measure wavelength of interfering water waves?
2. What effect does increasing the wavelength have on the distance between successive bright bands? (Are the bands closer together for long wavelengths or for short wavelengths?)

Part B Wavelength of Light

Young's method can be used to measure the wavelength of the red light from a helium-neon laser. The only difficult problem is to obtain a two-slit barrier with a known distance between the slits. You may have available to you a photographic film, which has the slits incorporated into it and which provides you with distance AB. If so, use the commercially prepared film. Tape it directly in front of your laser so that the beam has to pass through the two slits. If you do not have a prepared film, you can prepare a double slit barrier using the following instructions.

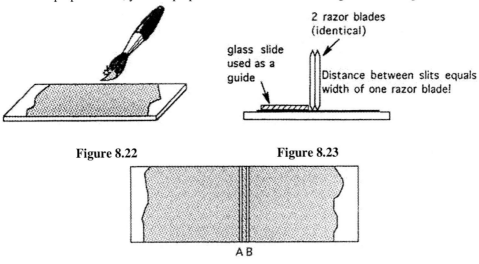

Figure 8.22   Figure 8.23

AB

Figure 8.24

Procedure

1. Paint one side of a microscope slide with graphite paint. (**Figure 8.22**) Allow to dry. Hold two identical twin-bladed razor blades side by side and draw the pair gently across the graphite painted slide, as shown in **Figures 8.23** and **8.24.** This should leave a pair of slits which are 'one razor blade width' apart. This is distance AB. Use a micrometer caliper to measure the width of one razor blade as precisely as you can and record this value of AB.
2. When you have a slide that works well, tape it in front of the laser beam and project the beam a measured distance across the room to a screen or wall. You should see several bright bands or spots on the wall. Choose a convenient number of 'n'. Measure CD and CG. (In this situation, GD will, for all practical purposes, be the same as GC. See **Figure 8.20.**)
3. Calculate the value of the wavelength of the red light from the laser. Then consult the manual that comes with the laser to see what the accepted value is.

Concluding Questions

1. According to Young's equation, what is the wavelength of the red light from your laser?

2. What is the percent difference between your calculated wavelength and the accepted value of the wavelength, according to the manual for your laser?

3. What are major sources of error in the technique you used to measure the wavelength?

Exercises

1. Yellow light from a sodium lamp passes through a pair of slits separated by a distance of 0.210 mm. On the screen 1.00 m away, an interference pattern is seen in which the distance between adjacent bright bands is 2.80 mm. What is the wavelength of the yellow light from sodium?

2. Two loudspeakers 0.500 m apart produce a pure tone of single frequency, and are in phase. At a distance of 5.00 m away from the speakers, if one walks slowly across in front of the speakers, one can hear successive maximum volume sounds at points 2.50 m apart. What is the wavelength of the sound? If the speed of sound is 330 m/s, what is the frequency of the sound?

3. Light from a hydrogen discharge tube passes through a double slit where the separation of the slits AB = 0.155 mm and falls on a film 1.50 m away. If the wavelengths of the colours of light coming from the hydrogen are (a) 656 nm, (b) 486 nm, (c) 434 nm and (d) 410 nm (where 1 nm = 10^{-9} m), how far from the central maximum (bright band for all four colours) will the first maximum (bright band) be for each of the four colours?*

* **Note:** If you have never seen the four colours emitted by hydrogen in a discharge tube, turn one on and look at it through a hand spectroscope. You see an interference pattern. The difference is that the spectroscope has a **diffraction grating** that has many, many slits instead of just two. There will be several thousand ruled lines (slits) per centimetre in the grating.

Chapter Review Questions

1. What is the difference between a pulse and periodic waves?

2. Explain, with the help of a sketch, what each of these terms means with respect to waves:
   (a) crest;
   (b) trough;
   (c) wavelength;
   (d) frequency;
   (e) amplitude.

3. What is a hertz?

4. How are frequency and period related?

5. A dog wags its tail 50 times in 20 s. What are (a) the frequency and (b) the period of vibration of the tail?

6. What is the difference between a transverse wave and a longitudinal wave?

7. For any kind of wave motion, how are wave speed, wavelength and frequency related to one another?

8. Alternating current in power lines produces electromagnetic waves of frequency 60 Hz that travel outward at the speed of light, which is 3.0×10^8 m/s. What is the wavelength of these waves?

9. If the speed of sound is 330 m/s, what wavelength does a sound of frequency 512 Hz have?

10. Name at least three properties of light that can be explained adequately with a wave theory.

11. Explain the difference between refraction and diffraction. Give an example of each phenomenon from everyday experience.

12. When waves slow down on entering a new medium, what happens to

    (a) their wavelength?

    (b) their frequency? and

    (c) their direction?

    Under what conditions will the direction *not* change?

13. What is

    (a) constructive interference?

    (b) destructive interference?

14. In a ripple tank, what causes a nodal line? a maximum?

15. Violet light of a single wavelength is made to pass through a pair of slits spaced 0.100 mm apart. On a film 6.0 m away, there are 10 uniformly spaced bright interference bands in a space of 24 cm. What is the wavelength of the violet light? Express your answer in nanometres.

Test Yourself!

(1-2) Please *complete* these diagrams, to show what happens to waves after they encounter the barrier or other obstacle. Also, *name the phenomenon* that occurs in each situation (refraction, diffraction, interference, or reflection).

1.

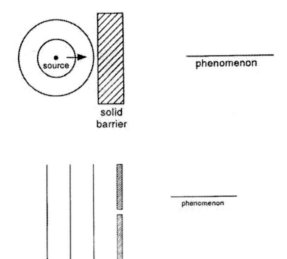

phenomenon _____

solid
barrier

2.

phenomenon _____

3. An observer counts 36 waves arriving at the shore of a beach, in a time of 3.00 min.
   (a) What is the **frequency** of the waves?
   (b) What is the **period** of the waves?

4. A small spider, which became lost while looking for its web site, is on the surface of an old phonograph record, which is spinning at 33 rpm (rotations per minute). It is trying to escape by jumping on the needle of the phonograph player. The spider misses the needle on the first try. How long will it have to wait for the next try?

5. The following diagram shows two parabolic reflectors. A small source of infrared heat is placed at the **focus** of one of the mirrors. Soon after, a match at the **focus** of the other reflector lights on fire. Draw a diagram showing how the wave model explains this.

Source of
Infrared
Radiation

Matchhead

6. At room temperature, sound has a speed of 3.4×10^2 m/s. What is the wavelength of sound from a tuning fork that vibrates at 256 Hz?

7. Light travels with a speed of 3.00×10^8 m/s. What is the frequency of red light, if its wavelength is 610 nm? (1 nm = 1 nanometre = 10^{-9} m)

Multiple Choice Questions

1. If you look at streetlights through a fine mesh curtain, you will see a 'starburst' effect. What phenomenon is involved in this situation?
   A. reflection
   B. refraction
   C. transmission
   D. diffraction

(2-4)

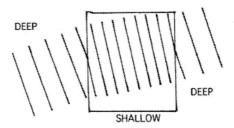

2. The above diagram shows water waves in a wave tank moving from deep water into shallow water, then back into deep water. What property of waves does this model illustrate?
   A. reflection
   B. refraction
   C. diffraction
   D. interference
   E. dispersion

3. What measurable property of the waves does not change as the waves move from one medium into another?
   A. wavelength
   B. frequency
   C. wave speed
   D. direction

4. According to the diagram, what can you conclude happens to the waves when they enter the shallow water?
   A. Wave frequency is reduced by about one half.
   B. Wave frequency is approximately doubled.
   C. Wave speed is approximately doubled.
   D. Wave speed is reduced by about one half.

5. You are leaning against a large, lonely tree in an empty field. You can hear a dog barking on *the other side* of the tree, a hundred metres away. What property of waves makes this possible?
   A. refraction
   B. diffraction
   C. interference
   D. dispersion

Chapter 9 Sound

9.1 Sound Waves

When a guitar string vibrates, it collides with air molecules around it. See **Figure 9.1**. Molecules near the string are alternately **compressed** together, and then **rarefied** (spread out). Regions of compression spread through the air, followed by regions of rarefied air. Compressions arrive at your ear with the same frequency as the frequency of vibration of the guitar string.

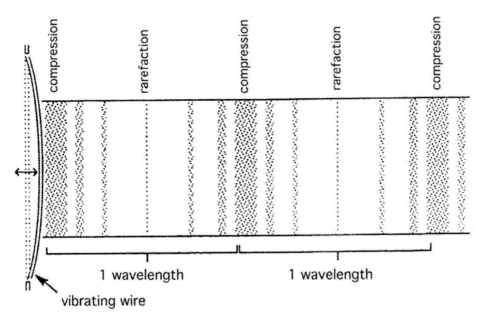

Figure 9.1

Figure 9.1 shows a simplified model of what might be seen if one could 'see' the air molecules in the region around a vibrating guitar string. Of course, this is a two-dimensional picture, and sound travels in *all* directions away from the vibrating source.

Vibrations cause sound. However, not all vibrations produce sounds! The human ear cannot hear all frequencies. The range of frequencies that a person can hear, called the **audible frequency range,** is (approximately) from 20 Hz up to 20 000 Hz (or 20 kHz). (One **hertz** is the same as *one vibration per second*.)

This is the range of hearing for a healthy young person with good hearing. Sounds with frequencies *below* 20 Hz are called as **infrasonic sounds**, and sounds with frequencies *above* 20 000 Hz are **ultrasonic sounds.**

There are many ways that sound vibrations can be produced. Your vocal chords vibrate to produce the sound of your voice. Vibrating wires (strings) produce the sounds of guitars, pianos, harps and violins. Vibrating reeds make the sound in a saxophone, while vibrating columns of air make the sounds of instruments such as the organ and the flute.

Investigation 9-1 What Frequencies Can You Hear?

Purpose: To determine your personal hearing range, using an audio frequency generator as a source of different frequencies.

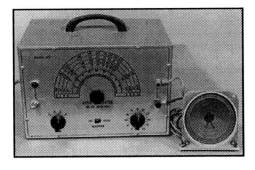

Figure 9.2

Most references claim that the hearing frequency range of a young person with excellent hearing is from 20 Hz to 20 000 Hz. Your teacher may use an **audio frequency generator** and a **loudspeaker** to produce frequencies ranging from 20 Hz up to 20 000 Hz, and you can find out what frequencies your ears can detect. **Figure 9.2** illustrates a simple arrangement for testing audible frequency hearing range. Results can be improved if an amplifier is used between the generator and the loudspeaker.

Procedure (Demonstration)

As the frequency of the generator is varied from the lowest it can produce (possibly 20 Hz) to the highest, try to match the sounds with those of familiar devices (motorboat, jet aircraft, siren, etc.) What is the highest frequency *you* could hear according to this experiment?

Concluding Question What is your personal audible frequency range?
(Note: For a more accurate measurement, see an ear specialist!)

9.2 Sound Media

Light can travel through a vacuum. It requires no material medium. You know that sound travels through air, since air is the usual medium for sound conduction. Can sound travel in a vacuum, as light does?

Investigation 9-2   Does Sound Travel in a Vacuum?

Demonstration

Turn on a small transistor radio full volume and place it on a foam pad inside a bell jar, which is sitting on a vacuum plate. Make sure the bell jar is properly sealed, and then evacuate the jar using a vacuum pump. Turn off the pump and listen for the sound of the radio. Let the air back in and listen for changes in volume of the sound.

Concluding Question: What do you conclude regarding air as a medium for sound?

The Speed of Sound

At a temperature of 20°C, which is normal room temperature, sound will travel about 340 m/s in air, which is the same as 1220 km/h. The speed limit for vehicles on a modern highway might be 100 km/h, so the speed of sound in air is 12 times this highway speed limit!

Although the usual medium for sound is the air around us, air is not a good conductor of sound. Many materials conduct sound much better than air. The best sound conductors are made of elastic materials such as steel, glass or aluminum. Inelastic materials do not transmit sound energy as effectively.

Extension

The speed of sound in air depends on the **temperature** of the air and on **atmospheric pressure**. For air at sea level air pressure, the speed of sound at 0°C is 332 m/s. The speed increases by about 0.6 m/s for every Celsius degree above 0°C.

$$v = 332 \text{ m/s} + [0.6 \text{ m/s·C}^{-1}]\, T$$

For example, the speed of sound at 40°C (a very hot day!) would be:

$$v = 332 \text{ m/s} + [(0.6 \text{ m/s·C}^{-1})(40°C)] = 332 \text{ m/s} + 24 \text{ m/s} = 356 \text{ m/s}.$$

Table 9.1 Speed of Sound in Various Materials

Medium	Speed (m/s)	Temperature (°C)
aluminum	5000	25
copper	3560	20
iron (steel)	5200	25
cork	500	
rubber	54	0
maple wood	4110	
granite rock	6000	
water	1500	25
air	332	0
air	344	20
hydrogen	1270	0
carbon dioxide	258	0

Exercises

Unless otherwise directed, assume that the speed of sound in air is 330 m/s. The speed of light is 300,000 km/s.

1. What is the speed of sound in a vacuum?

2. How might two astronauts communicate with each other on the moon where there is no atmosphere? Explain.

3. A dynamite explosion occurs at one end of a ridge of granite rock that is 3.0 km long. If you are at the other end of the ridge, how long will it take

   (a) before you *see* the explosion?

   (b) before you *hear* the sound travelling through the rock?

   (c) before you *hear* the sound coming through the air?

4. A lightning strike occurs 1.0 km away from you. How many seconds will it be before you hear the sound of the thunder?

5. In a space movie, an attacking space vehicle fires a weapon and hits an enemy craft. A loud explosion is heard. What is wrong with this scene?

6. Two rocks are banged together under water at the far side of a small lake 750 m away. If you are swimming in the water, how long will it take the sound to reach you? How much longer will it be before the sound reaches you through the air?

7. Imagine a parade where there is only one band at the head of the parade, followed by soldiers stretching a distance of over 300 m along the road. Would the last row of soldiers be in step with the front row? Discuss.

8. The speeds of high performance aircraft are often expressed as multiples of the speed of sound. If an aircraft travels at the speed of sound, its speed is said to have a **Mach number** of **1**.

   (a) How fast is a jet interceptor travelling, in km/h, if its speed is Mach 2.2?

   (b) What is the Mach number of a space shuttle travelling 7.5 km/s?

9.3 Properties of Sound

Pitch

The **pitch** of a sound is our subjective impression of the **frequency** of the sound. The very low pitch of the piano note from the far left of the keyboard has a frequency of 27.5 Hz, while the very high pitch from the far right of the keyboard has a frequency of over 4 000 Hz!

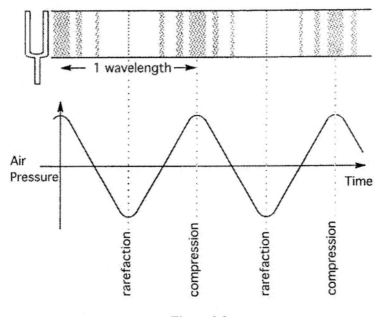

Figure 9.3

It is an interesting exercise to observe the waveforms of sounds of different pitches on the screen of an **oscilloscope**. Sound waves are **longitudinal** waves. (The air molecules vibrate to-and-fro in the direction of travel of the sound.) But the oscilloscope displays sound waves as if they were **transverse** waves. (In transverse waves, the vibration is in a direction *perpendicular* to the direction of travel of the wave. Water waves are a good example of transverse waves.)

What you see on the oscilloscope screen is actually a graph of air pressure vs time. A **compression** represents a region of unusually high air pressure, whereas a **rarefaction** is a region of low air pressure. **Figure 9.3** shows that a compression will register as a 'peak' in the pressure-time graph that you see on the oscilloscope screen. A rarefaction appears as a 'dip' in the graph.

Imagine you are listening to a high-pitched tone of frequency 3 000 Hz. This means that there are 3 000 compressions and 3 000 rarefactions arriving at your ear every second. If you were looking at this sound on the oscilloscope screen, you would see peaks for the compressions, and dips for the rarefactions. On the horizontal time scale, the peaks would be spaced 1/3 000 s apart, or 0.00033 s.

Investigation 9-3   'Seeing' Sound Waves

Purpose: To examine wave patterns due to sounds of different pitch, on an oscilloscope screen.

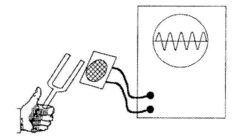

Figure 9.4

Procedure

1. Your instructor will have an oscilloscope set up to display sound waves. In the simplest set-up, a piezoelectric 'tweeter' speaker is used as a microphone, which is connected to the input jacks of the oscilloscope. (Improved results can be obtained using an amplifier in the set-up.)

2. Start by listening to sounds from sources of known frequency. Try tuning forks with frequencies such as 256 Hz, 512 Hz, and whatever other frequencies are available. Try speaking, whistling or singing at different frequencies. Sketch a typical waveform as seen on the screen for (a) low-pitched sound and (b) high-pitched sound.

3. Invite musicians to class to play notes of different pitch into the microphone, or play a recording of some complex music. Rarely will you see simple waveforms like those you obtained from a tuning fork, but the waveforms will be regularly repeated if the sounds are truly musical.

Concluding Question

How does the waveform of a low-pitched sound differ from that of a high-pitched sound?

Loudness

The frequency of sound vibrations is what determines the pitch of a sound. On the oscilloscope screen, the number of waves you see on the screen in a unit of time provides an indicator of the frequency, and therefore the pitch.

You may have noticed in *Investigation 9-3* that if the sound was *louder,* the height of the waves was greater. In fact, the **amplitude** is a measure of the loudness of a sound. The greater the wave amplitude is, the louder the sound will be.

The loudness of a sound depends on its intensity, a variable that can be measured. The **intensity** of a sound is *the amount of sound energy arriving per second on a square metre of area.*

$$\text{Intensity} = \frac{\text{Energy}}{\text{s} \cdot \text{m}^2} = \frac{\text{Power}}{\text{m}^2}.$$

Intensity is measured in **watts per square metre (W/m²)**.

A sound at the threshold of your hearing has an intensity of *one millionth of one millionth of a watt per square metre, or* 10^{-12} W/m²!

A quiet conversation between two people involves an intensity of sound of the order of 10^{-6} W/m². The *ratio* of these two intensities is $\dfrac{10^{-6}}{10^{-12}} = 10^{6}$.

In other words, the intensity of sound in a normal conversation is *one million times the intensity of sound at the threshold of your hearing!*

The **ratio** of a sound intensity to the intensity of sound at the threshold of hearing is often used to compare loudnesses. If a sound is 10^6 times as intense as sound at the threshold, we say its intensity is 6 **bels.**

The **bel** is named after **Alexander Graham Bell (1847-1922)**, Canadian inventor of the telephone. Since the bel is a large unit, the **decibel** is used instead, and the intensity of normal conversation is expressed as 60 decibels.

The intensity of sound at a rock concert might easily be 1 W/m². What is this intensity in decibels? The ratio of this intensity to the intensity at your threshold of hearing would be

$$\frac{1}{10^{-12}} = \frac{10^0}{10^{-12}} = 10^{12}.$$

Since the power of ten in the ratio is 12, the intensity of sound is 12 bels, which is the same as 120 decibels! This is a *very loud sound!*

Table 9.2 lists the intensities of various sounds both in W/m² and in decibels.

Table 9.2 Sound Intensities of Common Sources

Source	Intensity (W/m²)	Intensity (dB)
Jet taking off	10^2	140
Pain threshold	10^1	130
Loud rock band	10^0	120
Pneumatic chisel	10^{-1}	110
Metalwork shop	10^{-2}	100
Heavy traffic	10^{-3}	90
Vacuum cleaner	10^{-4}	80
Loud conversation	10^{-5}	70
Normal conversation	10^{-6}	60
Office noise	10^{-7}	50
Library	10^{-8}	40
Quiet country scene	10^{-9}	30
Whisper	10^{-10}	20
Rustling leaf	10^{-11}	10
Threshold of hearing	10^{-12}	0

Challenge

Use a **decibel meter** to measure sound intensities at various locations around the school. Here are some suggestions: normal classroom conversation; classroom when the teacher tells a joke; library; hallways during break; woodwork or metalwork shop; gymnasium during (a) gym class, (b) a sports event when spectators are cheering and (c) during a school dance when there is a live band playing music.

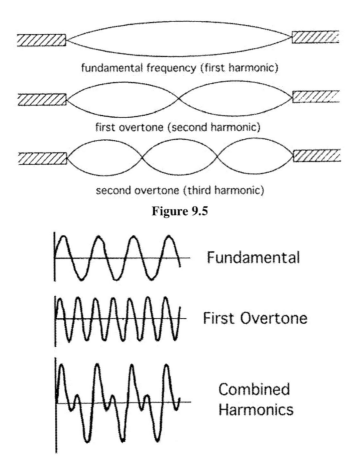

fundamental frequency (first harmonic)

first overtone (second harmonic)

second overtone (third harmonic)

Figure 9.5

Fundamental

First Overtone

Combined Harmonics

Figure 9.6

Sound Quality

Even if two different musical instruments play tones of equal pitch, you can tell one instrument from another. This is because each instrument has a characteristic **timbre** or **quality**. While both instruments produce the same **fundamental frequency**, the **overtones** they produce are different.

Overtones are frequencies that are twice, three times or even more times the fundamental frequency. *The quality of a sound an instrument produces depends on the number of overtones and their relative loudness.*

Figure 9.5 shows some of the vibration modes for a stringed musical instrument. The strings can be made to vibrate in several ways. A bow made of long strands of tightly stretched horsehair is used to make a violin or cello string vibrate. Fingers or picks make guitar or harp strings vibrate, while felt mallets initiate the vibrations in piano strings.

The fundamental frequency of a string depends on its thickness, its length and the tension on the string. A skilled musician can control which overtones (harmonics) the strings of his or her instrument produces.

Figure 9.6 shows the sound waves emitted by an instrument if the fundamental frequency and the first overtone (second harmonic) are produced (a) alone and (b) simultaneously. Notice that the combined frequency has a 'regularity' to it. The sound you hear when the two harmonics are produced simultaneously is richer and more interesting than either of the pure tones. Waveforms produced by different musical instruments playing the same note have different shapes because of the differing numbers and intensities of overtones, but the fundamental frequency will be the same for each one.

Investigation 9-4   Visualizing Sound Quality

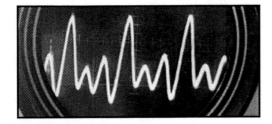

Purpose:

To compare waveforms of musical sounds from different instruments, using an oscilloscope.

Figure 9.7

Procedure

1. Set up the apparatus used In *Investigation 9-3*.

2. Have music students play a given note using different instruments (a clarinet, guitar, violin, or whatever is available).   Sketch the waveforms obtained from each instrument. (Waveforms on the screen can be photographed, as in **Figure 9.7**, using a 35 mm camera, with an exposure time of 1/30 s. Use a tripod.)

3. Make some 'noise', and examine its wave pattern on the screen. (You might try rubbing some sandpaper on wood, near the microphone.)

Concluding Question: How does the waveform of a musical sound differ from the waveform of a noisy sound?

9.4 Sound Wave Phenomena

Forced Vibrations

If you strike a tuning fork with a rubber hammer and just hold it in your hand, the sound from the fork will be quite faint and difficult to hear, even if you are a short distance away. Hold the base of the tuning fork on a tabletop and the sound will be much louder. The top of the table is now forced to vibrate in tune with the fork. The tabletop is acting as a **sounding board.**

Various musical instruments use sounding boards. Can you think of at least four stringed instruments that use sounding boards to amplify their sound? When a sounding board is used to amplify a sound (make it louder), the phenomenon is called **forced vibrations.**

Natural Frequency and Resonance

Any object, if it is reasonably elastic and can vibrate, has its own special **natural frequency** (or frequencies). Tuning forks, bells, stretched strings, and air columns in wind instruments all have natural frequencies. Even a child's swing has a natural frequency. A short tuning fork has a higher natural frequency than a long one. A tightly stretched violin string has a higher natural frequency than a loose one. A short pendulum has a higher natural frequency than a long pendulum.

Imagine you have a rather large friend sitting on a park swing. You can get even a massive person swinging with large amplitude if you time your pushes on the swing just right. If the frequency of your pushes, no matter how weak they are, is the same as the natural frequency of the swing (which is just a special pendulum), eventually the amplitude of the swing will become quite large. Whenever the frequency of the forced vibrations (in this case your pushing frequency) matches the natural frequency of an object, a large increase in amplitude will result. This phenomenon is called **resonance.** In *Investigation 9-5,* you will encounter some interesting examples of resonance.

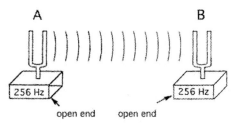

Figure 9.8

A pair of identical (matched frequency) tuning forks can be used to illustrate resonance. Fork A (**Figure 9.8**) is struck and made to vibrate at its own natural frequency (typically 256 Hz). This fork produces quite a loud sound due to: (a) its sounding board and (b) its air column, both of which resonate with the fork itself. Vibrations of the fork and air column send sound waves toward fork B. Fork B begins to vibrate at the same frequency as A, due to resonance. Each passing sound wave from A gives B a nudge, eventually making it vibrate with high amplitude, just like the child on a swing being made to vibrate by a series of successive nudges from a friend.

Investigation 9-5   Resonance

Purpose: To observe several examples of a phenomenon called resonance.

Procedure

1. See **Figure 9.8**. Strike fork A with a rubber hammer.
2. Stop fork A with your hand. Listen to fork B.
3. Over how great a distance can you make fork B resonate with fork A?

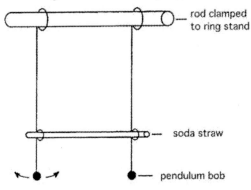

— rod clamped to ring stand

— soda straw

— pendulum bob

Figure 9.9

4. Set up a pair of identical pendulums, about 75 cm long, side by side and 25 cm apart. See **Figure 9.9**. Loop each string around a soda straw or thin wooden rod joining the two pendulums.
5. Set one of the pendulums vibrating gently, then watch carefully for an interesting example of resonance!

6. Try varying the position of the soda straw. Describe what you observe.

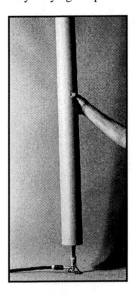

Figure 9.10

7. The violent motion of burning gases at the mouth of a Meker burner produces sounds of many frequencies. You can amplify some of these frequencies by holding a long carpet tube (or metal stove pipe) over the mouth of the burner. (**Figure 9.10**) The air column has a natural frequency depending on its length, and it will resonate with one of the frequencies from the flame. (Overtones will be produced as well.)

> *Caution!* If using a carpet tube, keep a pail of water handy in case the cardboard becomes overheated. If using a metal stovepipe, wear heat-resistant gloves.

8. If you have two carpet tubes or stovepipes, cut one so that it is 5-6 cm shorter than the other. 'Play' the pipes individually, then together on different burners. Describe the sound you hear!

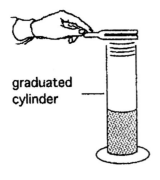

graduated cylinder

9. Use a rubber hammer to excite a tuning fork of known frequency. Hold the fork about 2 cm above a tall graduated cylinder (500 mL or larger) and direct the sound down into the graduate. Add water to the cylinder, thus changing the length of the air column, until the air column resonates at the frequency of the tuning fork. Record the tuning fork frequency and the length of the air column. Keep adding water to the graduate and find any other lengths of air column that produce resonance. Record these lengths. Is there any pattern to the lengths?

Figure 9.11

Concluding Questions

1. What conditions are needed for resonance to occur?
2. Could a musical note from one musical instrument cause resonance in a different musical instrument? (Ask your music teacher or a musician if you are in doubt.)
3. Tuning your radio is actually an example of resonance. What kind of vibrations is involved when your radio is resonating?
4. Why does a group of soldiers 'break step' when the soldiers walk across a rope suspension bridge?

Challenges

1. Find out how the speed of sound can be measured using the technique in **Procedure 9.**
2. Find out how resonance caused the new Tacoma Narrows Bridge in Washington to collapse in 1940.

Beats

If two sources of sound are made to produce sounds of slightly different frequencies simultaneously, you will hear **beats**. In *Investigation 9-5,* you heard beats when two carpet tubes were made to resonate. Having one tube a slightly different length than the other gave it a slightly different natural frequency.

You can produce beats using the two identical mounted tuning forks you used in *Investigation 9-5.* Attach a wad of Plasticine™ to one tine of one of the forks. Strike both tuning forks with a rubber hammer. The extra mass will change the natural frequency of one of the forks just slightly, and you should hear beats. Try varying the amount of Plasticine™ by taking a pinch off each time you strike the two forks. What happens to the **beat frequency**, as the forks become closer and closer to being the same frequency? How could a piano tuner use a tuning fork to tune a piano?

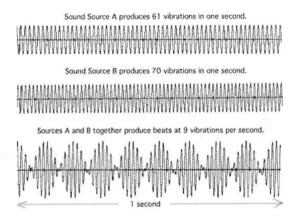

Sound Source A produces 61 vibrations in one second.

Sound Source B produces 70 vibrations in one second.

Sources A and B together produce beats at 9 vibrations per second.

1 second

Figure 9.12

Figure 9.12 shows how the amplitudes of two sets of sound waves, from sources of frequencies 61 Hz and 70 Hz, combine when they pass a point at the same time. To your ear, the combined sound would be a throbbing sensation due to the regular rise and fall of the combined intensities of the sources. Notice that the beat frequency is 9 Hz, which is the arithmetic difference between the two individual source frequencies. You can calculate the beat frequency f_B by finding the difference between the two frequencies being heard.

$$f_B = f_1 - f_2$$

Exercises

1. One tuning fork has a frequency of 440 Hz, while another has a frequency of 435 Hz. What will the frequency of the beats be?
2. One tuning fork is known to be accurate at 256 Hz. When it is struck at the same time as another fork, beats are heard every 0.20 s. What might the frequency of the second fork be?
3. If you hold a tuning fork near your ear while it is vibrating, and then rotate the fork slowly, what will its sound be like? Make a prediction, and then try it! What phenomenon is involved here?

Standing Waves

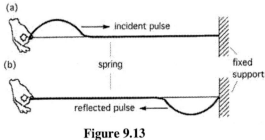

(a)

incident pulse

(b)   spring

fixed
support

reflected pulse

Figure 9.13

Tie one end of a long, stretched spring to a wall, or have a partner hold it tightly so that his/her end cannot move. (See **Figure 9.13**.) Shake your end of the spring so that a pulse travels down the length of the spring, and reflects back to you. Notice that upon reflection from the *fixed* end, the wave is *inverted*.

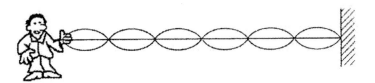

Figure 9.14

If you shake the spring with just the right frequency, the reflected waves will interfere with the incident waves, and you will observe a **standing wave. Figure 9.14** shows one possible standing wave pattern. Notice that parts of the spring are stationary. These parts are called **nodes.** At the nodes, the reflected waves are interfering *destructively* with the incident waves, thus producing a point of zero disturbance. The points on the standing wave where there is maximum amplitude result from *constructive* interference between the incident waves and reflected waves. These points of maximum disturbance are called **antinodes.** Notice that the distance between successive nodes, or between successive antinodes, is equal to *one-half the wavelength* of the waves in the spring.

You cannot obtain standing waves at all frequencies. If you can find out the lowest frequency at which you can obtain a standing wave (the **fundamental frequency** for the spring), you will be able to create other standing wave patterns using twice the fundamental frequency, three times the fundamental frequency, etc.

Standing waves occur in all musical instruments. In string musical instruments, the standing waves (**Figure 9.5**) are transverse waves. In wind instruments, the standing waves are longitudinal waves. When you hold a vibrating tuning fork over a glass cylinder full of air, you may create standing waves in the air column.

The Doppler Effect

When a fast car or motorbike approaches you, the pitch of its sound rises; as the vehicle goes by, the pitch lowers. The effect is quite noticeable if one watches a high-speed automobile race on television. What causes this change in pitch? Austrian physicist **C. J. Doppler (1803-1853)** was the first to explain the effect in terms of waves, and therefore the effect is called the **Doppler Effect**.

Figure 9.15 illustrates sound waves coming from a moving source. The vehicle is moving to the left. Sound waves coming from the vehicle are bunched in front of the vehicle, which is tending to catch up with its own sound. (The diagram exaggerates the effect.) The wave fronts (**compressions**) are closer together in front of the vehicle and further apart behind the vehicle.

The observer at **A** hears a *higher* pitch than normal, since more compressions and rarefactions pass his ear per second than pass the observer at **B**. Observer **B** hears the normal pitch of the vehicle's sound. Behind the vehicle, compressions are spaced out, since the vehicle is travelling away from the sound it sends in that direction. The observer at **C** hears a *lower* pitch than normal. Fewer compressions and rarefactions pass his ear per second than if he was at **A** or **B**. As the vehicle passes observer **A**, he will hear the pitch go from high to normal to low in a very short time interval. He will hear the **Doppler Effect.**

Ehren Stillman

Figure 9.15

The Sound Barrier

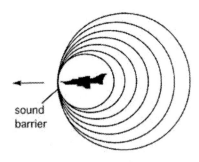

sound barrier

Figure 9.16

An extreme case of the Doppler Effect occurs when an aircraft (or bullet) travels at the same speed as the sound it is producing. At the leading edges of the aircraft, the compressions it creates (**Figure 9.16**) tend to bunch up and superimpose on each other. This creates a wall of compressed air — a barrier, called the **sound barrier**. Great thrust is needed from the plane's engines to allow the plane to penetrate the sound barrier, but once through the barrier, the plane experiences much less opposition to its movement through the air. The plane, once through the sound barrier, is then **supersonic.** Its speed is now greater than Mach 1!

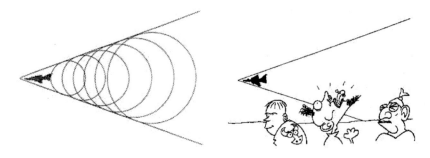

Figure 9.17   **Figure 9.18**

Shock Waves and the Sonic Boom

If a plane travels *faster* than sound, it gets ahead of the compressions and rarefactions it produces. In two dimensions (**Figure 9.17**), overlapping circular waves form a V-shaped **bow wave**, somewhat like what you see from the air looking down at a speedboat travelling through still water. In three dimensions, there is a cone of compressed air trailing the aircraft. This cone is called a **shock wave**.

When the shock wave passes you, you hear a loud, sharp crack called the **sonic boom**. See **Figure 9.18**.

Aircraft are not the only producers of sonic booms. Cracking whips and rifle bullets causes miniature sonic booms!

Chapter Review Questions

(Unless otherwise stated, assume the speed of sound in air is 330 m/s.)

1. Are sound waves **transverse** or **longitudinal**?
2. What range of frequencies is **audible** to a young person with good hearing?
3. What frequencies are (a) **infrasonic**? (b) **ultrasonic**?
4. In 5.0 s, how far would sound travel through
   (a) air? (b) a steel railway track? (c) water? (d) granite?
5. What is the speed of sound in air at (a) $0°C$? (b) $35°C$?
6. Why will sound 'carry' further when the air near the ground is cooler than the air higher up?
7. If the sound of thunder arrives at your ear 0.50 s after the flash of lightning arrives at your eyes, how far away from you did the lightning strike occur?
8. A top-secret aircraft travels at a speed of Mach 2.8. How fast is this in km/h?
9. What property of sound determines its pitch?
10. Sound waves can be displayed on an oscilloscope screen as transverse waves. What do the transverse waves on the screen really measure?
11. Sketch a sound wave, as seen on the oscilloscope screen, to represent a sound of frequency f. Now sketch what the sound wave will look like
    (a) if you make the same sound but *louder,* then
    (b) if you double the frequency of the sound.
12. Calculate the ratio of the intensity of sound from a loud rock band to the intensity of sound from a whisper. See **Table 9.2, Sound Intensities of Common Sources.**
13. What determines the **timbre** or **quality** of the sound from a musical instrument?
14. Why does a note played by a violin sound different than the same note played by a cello?
15. How does **noise** differ from musical sound?
16. Explain what these terms mean:
    (a) forced vibrations;
    (b) natural frequency; and
    (c) resonance.

17. A drum in the school music room starts to vibrate on its own when a certain note is played on another instrument nearby. What phenomenon is involved here?
18. What causes beats?
19. One organ pipe produces a sound of frequency 512 Hz. Another simultaneously produces sound of frequency 510 Hz. What beat frequency will be produced?
20. A piano tuner hears beats of frequency 0.50 Hz when he simultaneously strikes a tuning fork of frequency 264 Hz and a piano key. What is the frequency of the sound created by striking that key?
21. What is the Doppler Effect? What causes it?
22. What causes the **sound barrier**?
23. What is a **sonic boom**? What causes it?
24. On a calm, quiet day, you watch a golfer swing a golf club on a tee 520 m away. There is a delay of 1.55 s before you hear the sound of the club hitting the ball. What is the speed of sound according to this data?

Challenges

1. Find out how laser discs work.
2. Measure the speed of sound somehow.
3. Find out if you can make a 'prism' that will disperse sound frequencies the way a glass prism disperses different light frequencies.
4. Set up a ripple tank, and devise a way to show the Doppler Effect with water waves. Arrange the vibrator so that it can move at a steady speed through the water. (Special ripple tanks are available that produce the same effect by letting the water move at steady speed past a stationary source. If your school has one of these tanks, set it up and try it out.)
5. On a deserted road, tape record a car passing you as you stand by the road. Have the car driver sound the horn all the time he/she is passing you. Listen for the Doppler Effect when you play the tape back in class.

Research

1. What are some examples of infrasonic sounds?
2. What are some uses for ultrasonic sounds?
3. Is there such a thing as a 'light boom'?
4. Why are echoes fainter than the original sounds?
5. What shape are the reflectors used with microphones at games and when recording birdcalls? Why are they this shape?
6. With what topics does the science of **acoustics** deal? What qualities must a large auditorium have for its acoustics to be good?
7. How do police use the Doppler Effect to measure the speed of vehicles?
8. What do astronomers mean by the **red shift**? Why is measurement of the red shift important when studying distant stars?
9. How is high frequency sound used to treat kidney stones?

Test Yourself!

Multiple Choice Questions

1. Which one of these frequencies is in the **infrasonic** range?
   A. 10 Hz   B. 40 Hz   C. 3 000 Hz   D. 40 000 Hz

2. Through which material would sound travel fastest?
   A. granite rock   B. a vacuum   C. air   D. copper

3. The **pitch** of a sound depends primarily on its
   A. speed.   B. frequency.   C. volume.   D. quality.

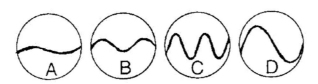

(4-5) The above drawings show what four different pure tones look like on an oscilloscope screen.

4. Which of the four pure tones had the **loudest** sound?   A   B   C   D

5. Which of the four pure tones had the **highest pitch**?   A   B   C   D

6. Compared with a 70 dB sound, an 80 dB sound has
   A. ten times the the intensity.
   B. ten times the frequency.
   C. 8/7 times the intensity.
   D. 8/7 times the frequency.
   E. 8/7 times the wavelength.

7. When two tuning forks are struck simultaneously, **beats** are heard, with a frequency of 0.1Hz. One of the tuning forks is known to have a frequency of precisely 512.0 Hz. What is the frequency of the other tuning fork?
   A. 511.9 Hz   B. 512.1 Hz   C. 51.2 Hz   D. 5120 Hz   E. either 511.9 Hz or 512.1 Hz

8. If a plane travels fast enough to penetrate the sound barrier, we say it is
   A. infrasonic.   B. ultrasonic.   C. supersonic.   D. Seattle Sonic.

Open-Ended Questions

1. (a) What causes the '**sound barrier**'? Use a sketch to illustrate your answer.
   (b) What is a '**sonic boom**'? Illustrate your answer with a sketch.

2. What is the **Doppler Effect** as it applies to sound? Illustrate your answer using a sketch.

3. On a certain warm day, the speed of sound is 350 m/s. If lightning strikes 2.1 km away from you, how long will it be before you hear the thunder caused by the strike?

Chapter 10 Light

Many useful devices have been developed because of growing knowledge of how light behaves. One can describe many of the properties of light without knowing exactly what light is, and one can invent many devices that use these properties. Cameras, eyeglasses, mirrors, microscopes, periscopes, magnifying glasses, spectroscopes and various kinds of projectors are some of the optical devices that use well-known properties of light. In this chapter, you will investigate some of the important properties of light.

10.1 The Speed of Light

The speed limit for the universe appears to be the speed of light in a vacuum, which is

2.99792458×10^8 m/s or 2.99792458×10^5 km/s.

In air, the speed of light is slightly less, but the difference does not appear until the fourth digit past the decimal point. For most   purposes, the speed of light in a vacuum or in air can be taken to be

3.00×10^8 m/s, or 3.00×10^5 km/s.

Just how fast is the speed of light? If a plane travels at the speed of sound, it is considered to be moving very fast. But the speed of sound is a mere 330 m/s. To get a rough idea of how this compares with the speed of light, round it off to 3×10^2 m/s. The ratio of speed of light to the speed of sound is approximately

$$\frac{3 \times 10^8 \text{ m/s}}{3 \times 10^2 \text{ m/s}} = 10^6!$$

The speed of light is about one million times the speed of sound! To travel the length of a typical classroom, light would take only about 10^{-7} s, or 0.000 000 1 s. Light from the moon takes 1.3 s to reach us, and light from the sun takes about 8.3 min to travel to earth!

Exercises

1. If light travels a million times as fast as sound, why does the sound from your television set appear to be 'synchronized' with the picture you see?
2. If a beam of light could be made to 'circle' the earth (using a series of mirrors), how long would it take the light to circle the globe if the earth's circumference is 4.0×10^7 m? Also, how many times could the beam of light circle the earth in one second?
3. The distance light travels in one year is called a **light year**. How many kilometres are there in one light year?
4. An imaginary star is four light years from earth. The star has a planet, upon which a large mirror has been installed. The mirror faces earth. A ten-year-old boy aims his telescope at the mirror. How old will the boy be when he sees his own image reflected back at him? How old will he look in the mirror?

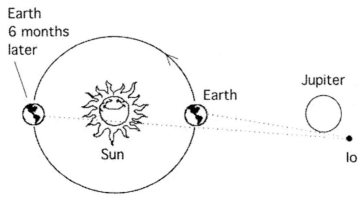

Figure 10.1

Measuring the Speed of Light

The usual method of measuring the speed of something is to measure the time it takes the object to travel a certain distance, then divide the distance by the time. Early attempts to measure the speed of light by simple means met with failure, because there was no method available to measure short time intervals with accuracy.

The first meaningful measurement of the speed of light was an indirect one made by the Danish astronomer, **Olaus Roemer (1644-1710)**. His real objective was to measure the periods of revolution of the moons of **Jupiter**. Jupiter's innermost moon is **Io**, and Io is bright enough that you can see it with a low-power telescope. Roemer measured Io's period of revolution by observing at what times Io disappeared into the shadow of planet Jupiter.

Roemer noticed that if he timed the period of revolution of Io while the earth was on the same side of the sun as Jupiter, he obtained a certain value. Six months later, when the earth was on the far side of the sun from Jupiter (**Figure 10.1**), Roemer waited to observe Io disappearing behind Jupiter, but found that there was an unexpected delay of approximately 1 000 s before the **eclipse** of Io occurred.

Roemer suspected, quite correctly, that the delay in the appearance of the eclipse of Io was due to the fact that light took 1 000 s to travel the added distance from Io to earth. Between the two sets of observations, light had to travel an extra distance equal to the diameter of the earth's orbit around the sun! Using Roemer's data, Dutch physicist **Christian Huygens (1629-1695)** calculated that since light from Io had to travel an extra 300 000 000 km to reach the observer's telescope. Since the delay in the arrival of the eclipse was 1000 s, then the light must be travelling the extra 300 000 000 km in 1 000 s, which would make the speed of light 300 000 km/s.

Huygens and Roemer actually had less accurate measurements than these to work with, and their result was quite a bit less (227 000 km/s), but nevertheless this was truly a major accomplishment, because they were the first to obtain even a 'ballpark' figure for the speed of light.

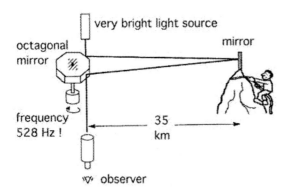

Albert Michelson (1852-1931) made the first truly accurate, direct measurement of the speed of light. He solved the problem of measuring short time intervals in a clever manner. **Figure 10.2** shows how Michelson measured the speed of light.

Figure 10.2

Light from a very intense light source was directed through a lens to an eight-sided mirror, from which it was reflected to a mirror on a mountain 35 km away. The light reflected back to the eight-sided mirror and was reflected through a telescope to an observer's eye. At first, the octagonal mirror was stationary, while adjustments were made so that the path of the light was such that it returned to the eye of the observer. Then the octagonal mirror was made to rotate at very high frequency. The spinning mirror creates a series of bursts of light. If it spins too slowly, light does not reflect to the observer. Likewise, if it spins too rapidly, light does not reach the observer. If the octagonal mirror is spun at just the right frequency, light reflecting from one side of the eight-sided mirror to the distant mountain and reflecting back will hit the proper spot *on the next section* of the eight-sided mirror and reflect to the observer. The observer will see a steady series of light bursts when the octagonal mirror makes 1/8 of a rotation while the light travels to the distant mountain and back.

The distance travelled by the light in Michelson's experiment was 2 x 35 km. The frequency of the rotating octagonal mirror was 528 Hz. This means that the mirror made one rotation in 1/528 s. The time for the mirror to make 1/8 of a rotation was:

$$\frac{1}{8} \times \frac{1}{528} \text{ s} = 2.37 \times 10^{-4} \text{ s.}$$

The *approximate* speed of light (Michelson was far more precise) was:

$$c = \frac{d}{t} = \frac{2 \times 35 \text{ km}}{2.37 \times 10^{-4} \text{ s}} = 3.0 \times 10^{5} \text{ km/s.}$$

Michelson's experiment was done early in the twentieth century. Improved techniques and laser light sources have made it possible to measure the speed of light with great precision. Michelson's measurement (299,920 km/s) was a great achievement, and he was awarded the Nobel Prize in physics.

Research: Find out how these scientists attempted to measure the speed of light before Michelson's precise measurements: **Galileo, Fizeau** and **Foucault**. Whose method did Michelson use, in a refined version?

10.2 Linear Propagation of Light

Shadow lengths can be predicted assuming that light travels in straight lines past the object.

Figure 10.3

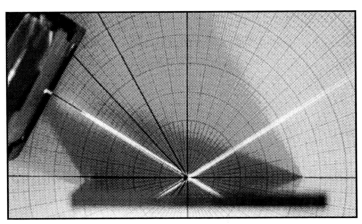

Figure 10.4

Light travels in straight lines — sometimes. See **Figures 10.3** and **10.4**. Over short distances, in a given medium such as air or water, light travels in a straight path. If light encounters a different medium or a reflecting surface, its path will change. Gravity can also deflect light from a straight path. Einstein predicted this long ago, and experiments verified his prediction. In most situations you will encounter, however, you may assume that the path of light in a given medium is straight. You can predict the size and shape of shadows by assuming linear propagation of light. You can also predict what will happen when pinhole cameras form images!

Investigation 10-1 Pinhole Photography

Purpose: To investigate images formed by pinholes.

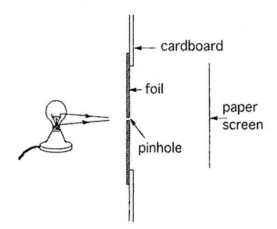

Figure 10.5

Procedure

1. Prepare a pinhole card like the one in **Figure 10.5**. Use a large sheet of stiff cardboard (say, 50 cm x 50 cm). Cut a window approximately 10 cm x 10 cm in the cardboard and tape a square of aluminum foil over the window. Make a pinhole in the foil using a hatpin or other pin. For a light source, use a clear light bulb so that you can see its filament.

1. Place the light bulb 30 cm in front of the pinhole. Hold a sheet of white paper on the other side of the pinhole card. Turn off the room lights and make the room as dark as possible. Describe the image you see on the white paper screen. Is it right side up or upside down? Is it larger, smaller or equal in size to the actual light bulb filament? Can the size of the image be changed? How do you make the image larger? smaller? brighter? How might you make the image appear 'right side up'? What happens if you make a second pinhole? a third pinhole?

Concluding Questions

1. The location and size of an image formed using a pinhole can be predicted by drawing rays of light from the object through the pinhole to the screen on which the image is to be projected. What is the smallest number of rays needed to locate the image and predict its size? Make a drawing that shows an object (lamp), a pinhole and a screen. Predict where and how large the image of the object will be.

2. Imagine that you projected an image of an object shaped like the letter **b** using a pinhole. What would the image look like? Would it look like a **b**, a **p**, a **q** or a **d**? Explain with a simple diagram.

10.3 Reflection of Light

Figure 10.6

You probably take mirrors for granted, since you use them all the time, probably without thinking about what they actually do to the light that strikes them. If you look into mirrors more seriously, they will probably give you a lot to reflect on!

If you look directly into a mirror and wiggle your left ear, which ear will your image wiggle? (If you have difficulty wiggling your ear, try winking your left eye instead.)

If you look at yourself in a wall mirror, note what fraction of your body you see in the mirror. Now walk back a few metres and look into the same mirror. Do you see more of your body, less or the same fraction of your body?

You are a basketball player, 2 m tall. What is the shortest mirror you need to see your whole self in it? (This is a 3-point question!)

At night, have you ever seen your image in your living room window? Why don't you see it during the daytime?

When you look into a mirror, where exactly *is* your image? Is it on the mirror surface, in front of it or behind it? If you move closer to the mirror, what happens to your image?

In *Investigation 10-2,* you will experiment with mirror images, and you should be able to answer some of these questions when you are finished.

Investigation 10-2 Looking into Mirrors

Part 1

Purpose: **To locate the image in a plane mirror.**

Procedure

1. Mount a sheet of clear glass or Plexiglas™ vertically, as in **Figure 10.6**. The Plexiglas will serve as a mirror. Place a candle approximately 20 cm in front of the mirror. Light the candle and turn off the room lights. You should see an image of the candle in the mirror. Measure the distance from the candle to the mirror. (This is called the **object distance**.) Obtain another unlit candle the same height as the burning candle. Place it behind the mirror, and move it around until it appears to be at the same location as the image of the candle. Measure the distance from the image location to the mirror. This is called the **image distance.**

2. Look very closely at the 'image' in the mirror. Can you see a faint second image?

Concluding Questions

1. Where is the image in the mirror? How does the image distance compare with the object distance?
2. According to your observations, where does the reflection of light occur in the 'mirror'?

Part 2

Purpose: To find out why the image in a plane mirror is 'behind' the mirror.

Procedure

1. Remove the light bulb section of your ray box. It will be your 'object' for this investigation. Set up your light source approximately 10 cm in front of a plane mirror. A clothespin can be used to mount the mirror vertically.
2. Use the five-slit opening of the plastic baffle for your ray box to create five beams of light from the bulb, as in **Figure 10.7(a)**. Use a sharp pencil to make a few marks to indicate the path of one of the beams (a) as it travels to the mirror and (b) as it leaves the mirror. See **Figure 10.7(b)**. *Don't move the mirror!* Do the same for another beam of light going and coming from the mirror. *Before you move the mirror,* draw a line along the silvered back edge of the mirror where the reflection occurs. Also, mark the position of the filament of the light bulb as accurately as you can.

Figure 10.7(a)

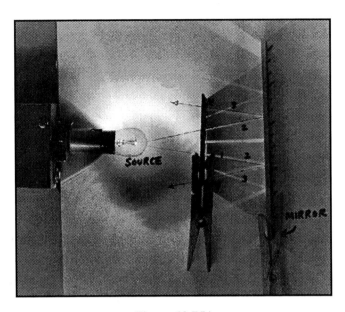

Figure 10.7(b)

3. Use your pencil marks as a guide to draw a line to show the path of the first beam of light (a) as it travelled to the mirror and (b) as it travelled away from the mirror after being reflected. Repeat for the second beam.

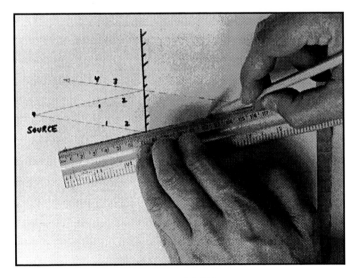

Figure 10.7(c)

When you draw a line to show the path that light takes, the line is properly called a **light ray**. See **Figure 10.7(c)**.

4. Look carefully at one of the reflected rays. If you were looking directly into the mirror when the light bulb was in front of the mirror, from what point would this ray *appear* to have come?
5. With your ruler, draw a dashed line 'behind' the mirror for about 12 cm beyond the end of the reflected ray as in **Figure 10.7(c)**. Repeat with the other reflected ray. Where do the two dashed lines meet? Mark this point with an 'X'. Is this the same location as the image you saw in the mirror? To find out, put the light bulb and the mirror back where they were before. Hold your pen where the 'X' is as you look into the mirror. Is the image where the dashed lines meet?
6. At the point where one of the beams reflects from the mirror, construct a line perpendicular to the mirror. This line is called a **normal** to the mirror. Measure the angle between the incoming or **incident ray** and the normal. This is called the **incident angle**. Also measure the angle between the normal and the **reflected ray**. This is the **angle of reflection**. Repeat this procedure for the other beam of light.

Concluding Questions

1. Compare the distance from the object to the mirror with the distance from the image to the mirror. Explain any difference you observe.
2. The image in a plane mirror appears to be behind the mirror. Explain why this is so. Where does the light you see coming from the image really originate?
3. For each beam, how did the angle of incidence compare with the angle of reflection? Is this consistent with what you observed with waves reflecting from a plane surface?

Challenge

Imagine that you wish to photograph your image in a plane wall mirror. You are standing 2 m in front of the mirror. At what distance should you set your camera lens? Try doing this if you can. Do not use a flash!

Investigation 10-3 Multiple Images

Purpose: To investigate multiple images in pairs of plane mirrors.

Figure 10.8 illustrates two pieces of Plexiglas™ arranged to give many images of a single candle. The Plexiglas acts as a mirror if the background is sufficiently dark.

Figure 10.8

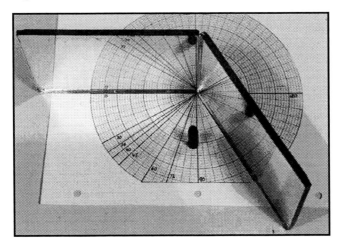

Figure 10.9

Procedure

1. Arrange two flat mirrors at an angle of 120°, as in **Figure 10.9**. Place a small object such as a golf tee or a rubber stopper approximately 10 cm in front of the mirrors. Look into the mirrors and count the number of **images** you can see. How many images do you see when the mirrors are at 180°? Gradually decrease the angle between the mirrors and watch what happens to the number of images.

Table 10.1

Angle between Mirrors	Number of Images
180°	
120°	
90°	
72°	
60°	
45°	
40°	
36°	

2. To investigate the relationship between the number of images and the angle between the mirrors quantitatively, try setting your mirror at each of the angles in **Table 10.1**. In each trial, keep your head still (to avoid counting the same image twice by mistake) and count the number of images carefully. Copy the table into your notebook and record your results. Be sure to compare notes with other students.

3. Look at the data. Can you figure out a simple rule that will allow you to predict how many images you will see if the mirrors are set at any one of these angles? *Hint!* There are 360° in a circle!

4. If you think you have the rule figured out, *predict* how many images you will see if you set the mirrors at these angles: (a) 30° (b) 24° (c) 20° (d) 0°! (To check out your prediction for 0°, you will have to set the mirrors at 0°, and then separate them, keeping them parallel with one another.)

Concluding Questions

1. What is the rule for predicting how many images you will see if you arrange two mirrors at an angle θ?

2. You wish to make a kaleidoscope toy with which you will see the same pattern repeated four times (including the object). At what angle should you arrange the two long plane mirrors inside the tube of the kaleidoscope?

Challenges

1. Make an 'infinity box'. Use one mirror tile as the floor of the box, and make walls out of four other mirror tiles. At the centre of the 'infinity box', place an interesting object such as a flickering light bulb or a small moving toy.
2. Create a 'movie theatre' in miniature, with a screen and a number of mirrors forming a box around the screen so that the image on the screen appears to be repeated in all directions 'off to infinity'.
3. Make a periscope on a large scale, using mirror tiles, so you can see down a hallway over the heads of students in the hall.
4. Use the technique of *Investigation 10-2* to locate multiple images with two Plexiglas 'mirrors' set at 90°. How many 'blank' candles will you need to locate where the images are? Is there any pattern to the locations of the images and object? Try 60°! Could you draw a circle through all the images and the object? Is this true at other angles?

Exercises

1. Why is the image you see in a plane mirror not considered a **real image**? (A real image is one formed by light arriving at a region in space, usually on a screen or film.) The image in a plane mirror is called a **virtual image**.

2. A child runs toward a mirror at 1.5 m/s. At what speed does she see her own image approach her?

3. How would you arrange three plane mirrors so that any beam of light striking them will reflect back on itself, no matter what angle it strikes the mirrors? (This technique was used when placing a reflector on the moon to reflect a laser beam from earth back to the earth. Of what use would such a combination of laser and mirrors be?)

4. How many images of yourself will you see if you look into a pair of hinged mirrors forming these angles? (a) 60° (b) 45° (c) 15° (d) 10° (e) 1° (Assume you can fit!)

5. Imagine you are 180 cm tall. What is the shortest mirror you can use if you want to see your whole beautiful self? Use a diagram to illustrate your answer. Will it matter how far from the mirror you stand?

6. Why is AMBULANCE written the 'wrong' way on the front of the vehicle? Write your own name in such a way that it looks 'right' when held up to a mirror. Draw a diagram to show why the letter 'b' looks like a 'd' in a mirror.

10.4 Refraction of Light

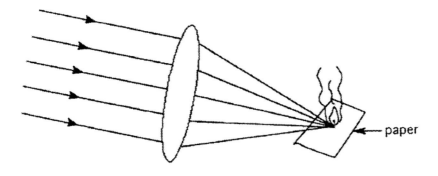

Figure 10.10

A hand magnifier lens can make the sun's rays converge to a small area on a piece of paper. It is possible to ignite the paper this way. Why does the light converge (come together)? The property of light involved here is called **refraction.** Refraction occurs when light travels from one medium (such as air) into another medium (such as glass). The change in direction of the light at the boundary of the two media is called refraction.

Investigation 10-4(A) Refraction of Light

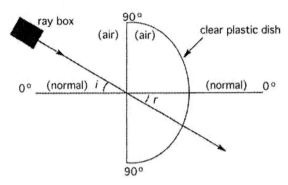

Figure 10.11

Purpose: To observe refraction of light travelling from air into
(a) water and (b) glass or Plexiglas™.

Procedure

1. Set up the clear plastic semi-cylindrical dish as in **Figure 10.11**. The centre of the flat side should be located on a **normal** drawn on a sheet of polar coordinate graph paper, as in the figure.
2. Turn off the room lights. Aim a narrow beam of light from a ray box along a line at an angle of 30° to the normal, so that it arrives at the centre of the flat side of the plastic dish. The beam should pass through the thin-walled dish without any noticeable deflection.
3. Pour approximately 100 mL of water into the dish. (If available, use water that has a grain or two of Fluorescein™ dye in it to improve the visibility of the beam in the water.) Observe the path of the beam of light now that there is water in the dish.   Record the angle formed by the refracted beam and the normal. This is called the **angle of refraction** (r). Also, record the **angle of incidence** (i), which is the angle formed between the incident beam and the normal.
4. Experiment by slowly changing the angle of incidence from 0° to 90° in small steps. Is the angle of incidence larger or smaller than the angle of refraction? What happens at 0°? at 90°? Does light entering water from air 'bend' toward the normal or away from the normal? Where does the 'bending' occur?
5. You are now ready to do some serious measuring of angles of incidence and angles of refraction. For each angle of incidence in **Table 10.2**, measure as precisely as you can the corresponding angle of refraction.

Table 10.2   Data for *Investigation 10-4(A)*

Angle of Incidence (i)	0°	10°	20°	30°	40°	50°	60°	70°
Angle of Refraction (r)								

6. Plot a graph with the angle of incidence (i) on the Y-axis and the angle of refraction (r) on the X-axis. *NOTE! This data will be used again later.*

7. Repeat **Procedures 1-6**, but this time replace the dish of water with a Plexiglas™ or glass semi-cylinder.

Concluding Questions

1. Describe what happens to a beam of light when it enters water or Plexiglas™ from air.
2. Find the slope of the *straight* part of each graph. What units would this slope have? What relationship exists between the angles of incidence and the angles of refraction for the angles where the graph is straight? Which refracts light more, water or Plexiglas™ (glass)?
3. Is the refraction of light similar in any way(s) to the refraction of water waves? Discuss.

Snell's Law of Refraction

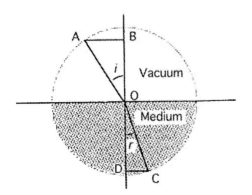

Figure 10.12 shows a ray of light travelling from a vacuum into a medium such as glass. The ray refracts toward the normal. The incident ray is labelled AO and the refracted ray OC. In the diagram, AO and OC are radii of the same circle, therefore they are equal in length. AB is the distance of the incident ray from the normal and CD is the distance of the refracted ray from the normal. The angle of incidence is i; the angle of refraction is r.

Figure 10.12

The two triangles ABO and CDO are right-angled triangles. In these two triangles, trigonometry tells us that

$$\sin i = \frac{AB}{OA}, \text{ and } \sin r = \frac{CD}{OC} = \frac{CD}{OA}.$$

Dutch mathematician **Willebrord Snell (1591-1626)** discovered that there was an *exact* relation between the angle of incidence and the angle of refraction for light travelling from one medium into another. You will recall that in *Investigation 10-4(A)*, for *small* angles, the angle of incidence was proportional to the angle of refraction (or vice versa). Snell was able to show that there was a relation that was true for *all angles greater than 0°*.

In **Figure 10.12**, $\dfrac{\dfrac{AB}{OA}}{\dfrac{CD}{OC}} = \dfrac{\sin i}{\sin r} = n$, where n is a constant for a given medium, and is called the **index of refraction** of the medium into which the light is moving from a vacuum.

Snell's Law looks like this for light going from a vacuum into any medium:

$$\frac{\sin i}{\sin r} = n,$$

where n is the **index of refraction** of the medium into which the light is moving.

For water, the index of refraction is 1.33, or approximately 4/3. For glass, the index of refraction is approximately 3/2. (Different kinds of glass have slightly different indices of refraction.) **Table 10.3** lists some indices of refraction.

Table 10.3 Indices Of Refraction

Water at 20°C	1.333
Diamond	2.42
Glass	1.5-1.9 (depends on composition)
Air	1.00029
Quartz Crystal	1.54

Note! The **index of refraction** depends on the *colour* (wavelength) of light used and on the *purity, temperature* and *composition* of the material into which the light is travelling.

Notice that the index of refraction of air is very, very close to 1. In other words, there is very little refraction when light travels from a vacuum (as in space) into air. Also, this means that the indices of refraction for light travelling from air into other media will be essentially the same as for light travelling from a vacuum into the same media.

Investigation 10-4(B) Refraction of Light

Use your data from *Investigation 10-4(A)* to plot a graph of the sine of the angle of incidence against the sine of the angle of refraction for (a) water and (b) Plexiglas™ (glass). Determine the indices of refraction (n) of both materials from the slopes of the graphs.

Exercises (Where possible, use a diagram to illustrate your answer.)

1. Light entering a block of glass at an angle of incidence of 18.5° leaves the boundary between the air and the glass at an angle of 12.0°. What is the index of refraction of this type of glass?
2. Light is incident on diamond at an angle of 10.0°. At what angle will it refract?
3. A beam of light is incident on a sheet of glass in a window at an angle of 30°.   Describe exactly what path the light beam will take (a) as it enters the glass and
   (b) as it leaves the other side of the glass. Assume n = 1.500.
4. What optical device is designed specifically to separate the colours in 'white light' using the fact that different wavelengths (colours) have different indices of refraction in glass? Which colour refracts most?

Investigation 10-5
Internal Reflection and the Critical Angle

Purpose: To observe what happens to light coming from a medium of higher index of refraction into a medium of lower index of refraction, and to find out the necessary condition for *total internal reflection* of light.

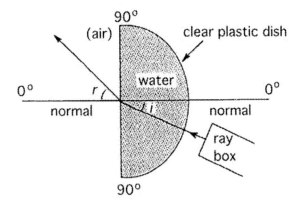

Figure 10.13

Procedure

1. You will use the plastic dish full of water that you used in *Investigation 10-4(A)*, but this time you will observe what happens when the light travels from water out into the air. Set up the equipment as in **Figure 10.13**.

2. Examine your data table from *Investigation 10-4(A)*. Shine light through the *round* side of the dish so that it passes through the water, hitting the centre of the flat side of the dish at angles of incidence that are the same as the angles of refraction in *Investigation 10-4(A)*. Is the path of light reversible for some of the angles? Is it reversible for *all* the angles?

3. Gradually increase the angle of incidence of the light going from water into air until you can no longer observe refraction. What is the *smallest* angle at which you can observe *no* refraction and *only* reflection? This angle is called the **critical angle** (i_c) for water. Record this angle. At incident angles less than the critical angle, refraction and *weak* reflection can both be observed.

At any angle equal to or greater than the critical angle, all light coming from the water will reflect back into the water. This is called **total internal reflection.** At angles equal to or greater than the critical angle, the water-air boundary acts as a perfect mirror.

4. Repeat **Procedures 1** to **3** using the Plexiglas™ (glass) semi-cylinder. What is the critical angle for Plexiglas™ (glass)?

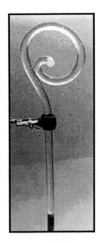

Figure 10.14

Concluding Questions

1. What is the critical angle for
   (a) water?
   (b) Plexiglas™ (glass)?

2. Sketch how light can be made to travel by total internal reflection through the curved plastic 'optical pipe' in **Figure 10.14**.

Using Snell's Law to Calculate the Critical Angle

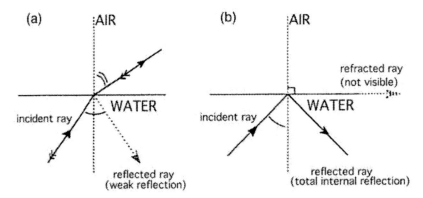

Figure 10.15

In **Figure 10.15**, if a ray of light is coming from air into water, Snell's Law might be applied, and

$$\frac{\sin i}{\sin r} = n_w,$$ where n_w is the index of refraction of water.

For angles *less than the critical angle,* the path of light is *reversible.* For a ray of light coming from water out into air, what *was* the incident angle now becomes the angle of refraction and vice versa. For light going *from water out into air,*

$$\frac{\sin i}{\sin r} = \frac{1}{n_w}.$$

Consider what happens as the incident angle *approaches the* **critical angle,** i_c. (See **Figure 10.15**.) The angle of refraction *approaches 90°*. Just as the critical angle is approached, we can write:

$$\frac{\sin i_c}{\sin 90^0} = \frac{1}{n_w} \; ,$$

where n_w is the **index of refraction** for light coming from air into water.

Solving for the critical angle, since $\sin 90^0 = 1.0000,$

$$\sin i_c = \frac{(1)(1.0000)}{n_w} = \frac{1.0000}{1.33} = 0.750,$$

$$\text{and} \;\; i_c = 48.6^0 .$$

The critical angle for water is therefore 48.6º. How does this value compare with your measured value for the critical angle for water, from *Investigation 10-5?*

Exercises

1. Calculate the critical angle for diamond, which has an index of refraction of 2.42.
2. What is the critical angle for a glass that has an index of refraction of 1.500?
3. A certain material has a critical angle of 52.0º. What is its index of refraction?

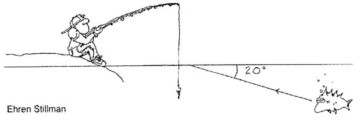

Ehren Stillman

Figure 10.16

4. Why can't the fisherman in **Figure 10.16** see the specific ray shown coming from the fish? Can the fisherman see the fish at all?

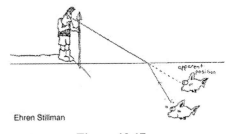

Ehren Stillman

Figure 10.17

5. (a) The fisherman wants to spear the fish in **Figure 10.17**. Should he aim
   (i) at the apparent position of the fish?
   (ii) 'above' the fish? or
   (iii) 'below' the fish? Use a diagram to explain your answer.

(b) A 'high tech' fisherman wants to 'zap' the fish with a laser. Should he aim the laser at the fish, 'below' the fish or 'above' the fish? Explain.

6. Draw a diagram showing how you might use two prisms (45°-45°-90°) as 'mirrors' in a periscope. Show how the prisms must be arranged to act as mirrors.

7. Why can you see more than one image in a mirror made with very thick glass? Use a simple sketch to illustrate the effects of internal reflection within the glass of the mirror.

Brain Buster

8. Show that, in general, for light travelling from a medium with index of refraction n_1 into a medium with index of refraction n_2, $n_1 \sin \theta_1 = n_2 \sin \theta_2$.

Research Ideas

1. Why do diamonds sparkle?
2. How is the science of fibre optics employed to transmit telephone signals?
3. How does the refraction of light lengthen your day by several minutes?
4. What causes a mirage?
5. Why does a swimming pool never look as deep as it really is?
6. How can an expert quickly tell the difference between a real diamond and a fake diamond made of glass?

10.5 Polarization of Light

You may wear Polaroid sunglasses, which reduce the glare when you are driving along on a bright, sunny day. Photographers use polarizing filters to produce special effects in their photographs. A polarizing filter, for example, makes the sky appear bluer and clouds whiter. The property of **polarization** is usually taken as evidence for the wave nature of light. It can be explained quite nicely if we assume that light behaves as waves do. *Investigation 10-6* will introduce you to the phenomenon of polarization of waves.

Investigation 10-6 Polarization

Purpose: To observe examples of polarized waves.

Figure 10.18

Procedure

1. You can produce your own polarized waves quite easily. Have your lab partner hold one end of a long spring while you set it vibrating by moving it up and down until you get a wave pattern set up in the spring. The waves you are producing are **vertically polarized.** Notice that the waves are transverse waves. You can just as easily produce **horizontally polarized** waves by making the spring vibrate horizontally.

Light waves can be polarized. Light waves are **electromagnetic waves**, which means that electric and magnetic fields are involved. Details of the nature of polarized light must be left to later physics courses, but it is still possible to observe some of the *effects* of polarized light, using readily available materials.

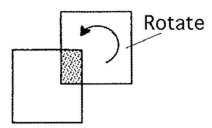

Polarizing filters on overhead projector

Figure 10.19

2. (a) Place a small sheet of polarizing filter material on the overhead projector stage. The light that passes through this filter will be polarized one way or another. (**Figure 10.19**)

    (b) Place a second sheet on the overhead projector stage, and let part of it overlap the first sheet. Rotate either one of the sheets slowly through a full circle. Sketch what you observe happening.

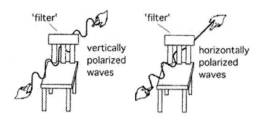

Figure 10.20 illustrates one model of how a polarizing filter works. In this case, the 'filter' consists of the vertical posts on the back of a kitchen chair. These permit vertically polarized 'waves' to go through, but not horizontally polarized waves.

3. Look out the window at the sky through a polarizing filter. **Caution!** *Do not stare at the sun!* Rotate the filter through a full circle. Can you find an alignment that makes the blue sky darker and the clouds whiter than usual? Can you find an alignment that makes a roadway seem to have less glare?

Glass windows, water surfaces and roadways produce a glare, due to the reflection of light from these surfaces. The light reflecting from roads, windows and water surfaces is generally polarized *horizontally*. Polaroid™ sunglasses have filtering material inserted so that it lets vertically polarized light through but *not* horizontally polarized light. This is why these sunglasses reduce glare from these surfaces.

4. Write the letter 'e' on a sheet of plain white paper. Place a calcite crystal over the letter 'e'. The light passing through the calcite crystal is **refracted** in two different planes. (This is called **double refraction**.) Find out if the calcite crystal polarizes the light coming through the calcite. Hold a sheet of polarizing filter between the crystal and your eye. Rotate the filter slowly through a full circle. Observe what happens and record what you see.
5. Place a drop of copper (II) sulfate (bluestone) solution on a microscope slide. Allow the water to evaporate so that small crystals of copper (II) sulfate form. Place the slide on the stage of a microscope. Hold one sheet of polarizing filter below the objective lens and one piece of polarizing filter between the eyepiece lens and your eye. Slowly rotate one or the other of the filters. You should see some interesting colour effects. These are caused by a combination of polarization and interference of light waves.
6. Place a sheet of polarizing filter on the stage of an overhead projector. On top of it, place a tall jar or beaker of clear corn syrup. Look down at the corn syrup through a second sheet of polarizing filter. Rotate the second filter slowly through 90°!

Concluding Questions

1. Why is polarization considered good evidence that light consists of waves rather than particles?
2. Why are the polarizing filters in sunglasses arranged to transmit only vertically polarized light?
3. When photographing a water surface, a photographer may use a polarizing filter. Why would this improve the picture?
4. Does a calcite crystal act as a polarizing filter? Explain.

10.6 Dispersion of White Light

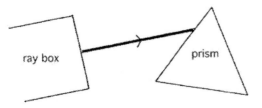

Figure 10.21

In *Investigation 10-5* (**Internal Reflection and the Critical Angle**), you may have noticed that when you shone light from water or Plexiglas out into air, just as you approached the critical angle the white beam of light from the ray box became highly coloured. The white light was **dispersed** into all the colours of the rainbow. To better observe dispersion, you can use a triangular glass prism. This is what Isaac Newton used back in 1672. His source of light was a narrow beam of sunlight coming through a hole in a blind. The band of colours into which the beam of white light was dispersed by the prism he called a **spectrum.**

Investigation 10-7 Dispersion and Other Colour Phenomena

Purpose: To observe examples of dispersion and other coloured light phenomena.

Procedure

1. Use a narrow beam of light from a ray box as a source of 'white' light. Place an equilateral triangular prism in the path of the narrow beam. (**Figure 10.21**) Experiment to see what alignment of the prism gives the best dispersion of the light. A white sheet of paper under the prism will show the spectrum well.
2. When you have a well-dispersed beam, note which colour is refracted least, and which colour is refracted most. List all the colours you can see, starting with the colour that is refracted least.
   Optional: If you have a prism-type spectroscope in your school, aim it at a white light source (such as a clear showcase bulb). The spectroscope will permit a much better distinction of the various colours in the spectrum.
3. Use a convex lens to re-unite the colours dispersed by the prism into a single spot of white light.
4. Remove the convex lens. You should now have the dispersed beam visible on the white paper screen in front of you. Try placing pieces of coloured cellophane paper (red, blue and green) in the path of the dispersed beam. What affect does each coloured filter have on the beam? What colours does each filter (a) subtract from the beam? (b) allow to pass through?
5. Three groups can team up for this experiment. Use coloured filters to produce beams that are (a) red, (b) green and (c) blue. (**Optional:** Use red, green and blue floodlights, if available.) Experiment to see what colours you see when these coloured beams are allowed to fall on the same surface: (a) red and blue; (b) red and green; (c) blue and green; and (d) red, blue and green. Record your observations.

Concluding Questions

1. Why is it that, for precise work, the colour of light (frequency) should be specified when stating an index of refraction for a material?

2. For a material such as glass, would the index of refraction be greater for red or for violet?

3. (a) What are the distinguishable colours in the continuous spectrum obtained from an incandescent source such as your ray box light bulb?
   (b) Are *all* these colours needed to give the effect of white light?

4. Red, blue and green are sometimes called the **primary light colours**. How can you produce yellow from these colours? How can you obtain cyan (blue-green)? magenta? How can you produce white?

Challenges!

1. How do stage crews use spotlights of different colours to produce different colours on stage?
2. How is the addition of primary coloured lights used in a colour television set?
3. What is a Newton Colour Wheel? Why does it give the impression of white when it is spun rapidly and examined under bright light?
4. A Newton Colour Wheel, if examined under a strobe light at different frequencies, will produce beautiful shades of colour, none of which is on the colour wheel. The colours are the same as you would get if you mixed pigments, as an artist mixes paint. Explain this. You may have to read up on **persistence of vision.**

10.7 The Rainbow - Dispersion by Raindrops

If you have ever looked at a rainbow really carefully, you probably have noticed these conditions prevailed:

   (a) The sun was behind you.
   (b) There were rainclouds in the sky in front of you.
   (c) The rainbow forms an arc of a circle.
   (d) In the primary bow (the brightest one), red is at the top and violet at the bottom.
   (e) In the secondary bow, if it is visible, the colours are in reverse order.

Figure 10.22 (a) illustrates what happens inside the raindrops. White light from the sun refracts as it enters a drop. The white light is dispersed into component colours during the refraction. All colours of light experience internal reflection at the back of the drop, then are refracted again and further dispersed as they leave the drop at the 'front'.

When you see a rainbow, you see the dispersive effects of millions of drops of water, not just one or two! You see red at the top of the primary bow with all the other rainbow colours below, ending in violet.

Sometimes a secondary, fainter, rainbow may be seen above the primary rainbow. A secondary rainbow has the colours in reverse order. **Figure 10.22 (b)** shows the double internal reflection that happens inside droplets producing a secondary rainbow.

Primary Rainbow

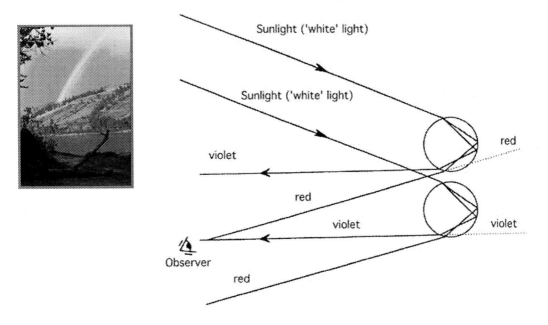

Figure 10.22(a)
The red part of the rainbow is 42° from the 'axis' of the bow; violet is 40° from the 'axis'.

Secondary Rainbow

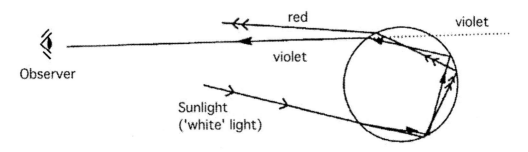

Figure 10.22(b)

Reversed colours of the secondary rainbow (higher) are due to double reflection of the sun's light within the droplets.

10.8 Colour and Wavelength

The wavelengths of the various 'colours' of light in air can be measured using Young's method or a more sophisticated spectroscope. Wavelengths of visible light range from 3.8×10^{-7} m for violet light to 7.6×10^{-7} m for red light. Wavelengths are often expressed in nanometres (nm), where **1 nm = 10^{-9} m**. **Table 10.4** lists some typical wavelengths in the visible range.

It is interesting to note that if your eye detects light in the range of wavelengths between 560 nm and 590 nm, it perceives the light as 'yellow'. If, however, it sees a mix of colours, one in the range between 630 nm and 760 nm (red) and the other between 490 nm and 560 nm (green), it again perceives the light as being 'yellow'!

Table 10.4 Wavelengths of Visible Light

Colour	Range of Wavelengths
red	630-760 nm
orange	590-630 nm
yellow	560-590 nm
green	490-560 nm
blue	450-490 nm
violet	380-450 nm

Wavelengths and the Speed of Light

For light travelling in space or in any vacuum, all wavelengths travel with the same speed. Red light and violet light travel with equal speed in a vacuum. Even in air, the speeds of various colours of light are just about the same. In a material with an index of refraction greater than one, there is a measurable difference in the speeds of different colours (wavelengths). The more a wave of visible light is slowed down, the more it refracts. Blue light is refracted more than red light because it is slowed down more as it enters a medium.

Wave Speed and Index of Refraction (Enrichment):
Proof That the Index of Refraction $= n = \dfrac{v_1}{v_2}$.

Consider a wavefront (labelled **Aa** in **Figure 10.23**) arriving at the boundary between two media. Medium 2 is one in which light slows down from speed v_1 to speed v_2. In the time t it takes for the wavefront at end **A** to reach the boundary **B**, the wavefront in medium 1 travels a distance **AB**, which equals $v_1 t$.

In the same time t, end **a** of the wavefront travels a distance **ab** inside medium 2, and distance **ab** equals $v_2 t$.

In **Figure 10.23**, you will notice that sin i = **AB/aB** and sin r = **ab/aB**. Therefore the index of refraction, n, is equal to

$$n = \frac{\sin i}{\sin r} = \frac{AB/aB}{ab/aB} = \frac{AB}{ab} = \frac{v_1 t}{v_2 t} = \frac{v_1}{v_2}.$$

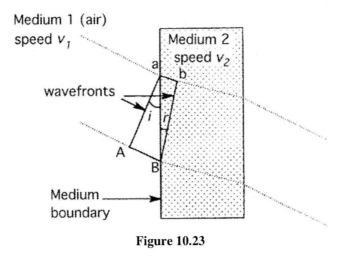

Figure 10.23

Therefore, the ratio of the speeds of light in the two media is equal to the index of refraction. That is,

$$\frac{v_1}{v_2} = n.$$

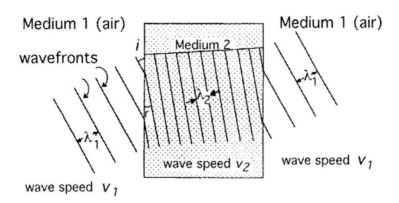

Figure 10.24

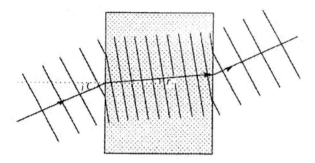

Figure 10.25

When a beam of light of wavelength λ_1 enters a medium in which its speed is reduced from v_1 to v_2, its wavelength is reduced to λ_2 and the beam is refracted as in **Figure 10.24.** When the waves leave the 'slow' medium, the speed is returned to the original v_1 and the wavelength is again λ_1. Refraction of a beam entering the second medium at an angle greater than 0^0 is caused by the change in speed of the waves.

To understand what causes refraction, imagine that a wavefront consisted of a row of soldiers marching side by side down an asphalt road. The row of soldiers suddenly encounters a muddy field (the second medium). As soon as the well-disciplined soldiers (wavefront) reach the muddy field, each soldier in turn is slowed down, but tries to remain in step with adjacent soldiers. The wavefront is therefore refracted as it enters the slower medium. When the wavefront leaves the muddy field, the process is reversed, and the wavefront returns to its original direction.

You will recall that for water, the index of refraction is 1.33. Snell's Law applied to light entering water from a vacuum (or air) says that $\dfrac{\sin i}{\sin r} = 1.33$.

The speed of light in air is 3.00×10^8 m/s.

The speed of light in water is 2.25×10^8 m/s.

The *ratio* of the speed of light in air to the speed of light in water is

$$\frac{3.00 \times 10^8 \text{ m/s}}{2.25 \times 10^8 \text{ m/s}} = 1.33.$$

Note that the ratio of the speeds is equal to the index of refraction for water. This relation holds for other media as well. In general,

$$\frac{\sin i}{\sin r} = n = \frac{v_1}{v_2}.$$

You will notice that the angle of incidence in **Figure 10.24** is shown as the angle between the incident wavefront and the boundary between the two media. Also, the angle of refraction is shown as the angle between the refracted wavefront and the boundary between the media. When you did *Investigation 10-4,* the angle of incidence was taken as the angle between the incident ray and the normal. The angle of refraction was defined as the angle between the refracted ray and the normal. *In* **Figure 10.25**, *lines have been drawn showing the paths taken by a single point on a wavefront as it moves into and out of the second medium.* These lines, in effect, are identical with the incident ray and the refracted ray used in *Investigation 10-4.* A little geometry will convince you that the incident angle i in **Figure 10.25** is equal to the incident angle i in **Figure 10.24**. Likewise, the angle of refraction r is the same in both diagrams!

Exercises

1. Are waves on a lake polarized? Explain.
2. Are sound waves polarized? Discuss.
3. When a photographer uses a polarizing filter in front of his camera lens, he or she must adjust either the time of exposure or the aperture (opening) of his lens. Explain why.
4. What is the difference between refraction and dispersion? How are the two phenomena related?
5. What are two devices that can be used to disperse white light into a spectrum?
6. If you were to shine a beam of laser light of one wavelength through a glass prism, would the laser light (a) refract? (b) disperse? Explain your answer.
7. When we say that the index of refraction of water is 1.33, what 'qualifiers' should we add to this statement?
8. Three outdoor spotlights coloured red, blue and green are aimed at the same spot on a snow-covered front yard. What colour will you see at that spot? How might you produce a yellow spot with the spotlights available to you?
9. What three phenomena are involved in the production of a rainbow? Under what conditions will you see a rainbow? What are the colours in the primary rainbow, listed from the top of the bow and going down?
10. In a vacuum, which colour of light travels fastest — red, blue or green? Explain. Which colour travels fastest in a block of glass?
11. The index of refraction of a certain type of glass is 1.50. What is the speed of light in glass? (The speed of light is 3.0×10^8 m/s in air.)
12. At what speed does light travel in diamond, which has an index of refraction of 2.42?
13. Light travels with a speed of 1.95×10^8 m/s in a quartz crystal. What is the index of refraction of the quartz crystal?

Brain Buster

14. A laser sends red light of wavelength 650 nm from air into water in a swimming pool. What wavelength will the light have in the water? What colour would light of this wavelength appear if it were in air? Why does a swimmer under the water see the light as red? The index of refraction of the water is 1.33.

10.9 Wavelengths We Use But Cannot See

If a beam of white light is dispersed with a prism, and the spectrum viewed on screen, you will see all the colours from violet to red on the screen. In the early nineteenth century the English astronomer **William Herschel (1738-1822)** was experimenting to see which colours of light gave the greatest heating effect when allowed to shine on a blackened bulb of a thermometer. He moved the thermometer bulb through the various parts of the visible spectrum and observed increases in temperature caused by the different colours of light. He discovered to his surprise that the greatest heating effect was observed if the bulb was placed *beyond* the red end of the visible spectrum! This is how **infrared radiation** was discovered.

Infrared radiation is extremely important to us. Infrared radiation from the sun provides most of the thermal energy requirements of the planet. Scientists have developed infrared photographic techniques that permit satellite pictures of features on the earth's surface, which can be taken through clouds or fog or smoke. Objects can be photographed in the dark using infrared photography. Some auto focus cameras use infrared for focusing, which means they work in the dark. Infrared has many uses, including heat lamps, physiotherapy and medical diagnostic photography. Astronomers are now making good use of infrared images of the stars and other objects in the universe.

Infrared wavelengths cover a wide range, the shortest wavelength beginning at the red end of the visible spectrum (760 nm) and the longest wavelength being approximately 300 000 nm. Beyond the infrared lies the radio part of the spectrum.

In 1801, the German physicist, **Johann Wilhelm Ritter (1776-1810)**, was studying the effect of visible light on the chemical compound silver chloride, $AgCl$. When light falls on silver chloride, the white compound decomposes and forms silver (which appears black) and chlorine, which escapes into the atmosphere. This is similar to the chemical reaction employed in photography where silver bromide is used.

Ritter knew that the effect was most noticeable at the violet end of the spectrum. He was surprised to find that if silver chloride was placed in a region beyond the violet end of the visible spectrum, the decomposition of the silver chloride was even more pronounced! Thus, **ultraviolet radiation** was discovered.

You cannot see ultraviolet, but it is wise to know about it anyway. It is ultraviolet light that gives you a suntan or sunburn. Too much exposure to the sun or to ultraviolet-rich sunlamps can be dangerous. Ultraviolet can also damage parts of your retina, thus impairing your vision.

'Black lights', sold for the purpose of making posters fluoresce, are actually sources of ultraviolet light. They also give off light in the violet part of the spectrum. Some black lights are essentially mercury vapour lamps, like fluorescent lamps used to light your classroom. Instead of having an inner coating of fluorescent chemicals, they have a violet-coloured glass tube that allows violet and ultraviolet light to pass through it.

Challenges!

1. Examine a variety of materials to see which ones fluoresce in ultraviolet light. (In **fluorescence**, a material absorbs one wavelength of light and emits light of a different wavelength. Fluorescent paints and felt marker inks absorb ultraviolet light, which is invisible to the eye, and emit brightly coloured light.) Try shining ultraviolet light from a 'black light' on teeth, white shirts, various items of clothing, minerals known to be fluorescent, etc. Make your own fluorescent posters using fluorescent felt pens. Obtain some Fluorescein dye and add a small amount to water in various vessels with interesting shapes. Examine the vessels in ultraviolet light.

2. Find out the difference between **fluorescence** and **phosphorescence**.

10.10 Diffraction of Light (Demonstration)

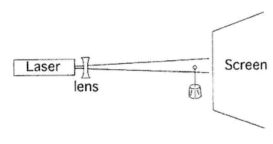

Figure 10.26

A simple demonstration of **diffraction** is illustrated in **Figure 10.26.** A lens is placed in front of a classroom laser (or a laser pointer) to spread the beam. (A concave lens might be used. A convex lens will work providing the distance to the screen is greater than the focal length of the lens, since the light diverges after the focal point.)

A small object such as a pinhead (No, not your lab partner!) is placed in the path of the laser beam so that its shadow is cast on a screen. In an earlier chapter you observed diffraction of water waves. If light consists of waves, then it should exhibit diffraction*. Examine the shadow of the pinhead on the screen. Is there any evidence that light has been diffracted?

Using the same equipment, examine the shadow of a razor blade, the wire stem of the hatpin and some mosquito netting! Let the laser beam pass through a small opening between two razor blades. Is it diffracted as it passes through the slit?

It is not necessary to own a laser to observe diffraction. If you examine a distant streetlight through a narrow gap formed with two adjacent fingers, you will see diffracted light. Streetlights seen through a mesh curtain appear 'star like'. This, too, is diffraction. TV camera operators often use special diffraction filters to give stage lights a 'starburst' look. These filters are made of glass with lines etched on the glass. Diffraction filters can be purchased for any camera.

---

*Scientists now know that particles, too, can produce diffraction effects.

10.11 Scattering of Light: Blue Skies, Red Sunsets

Why is the sky blue? The sun sends us visible light of all colours from violet to red. The brightest part of the sun's light is in the yellow-green part of the spectrum. On the moon, the 'sky' appears black. So why is our sky blue (during daytime, that is!)?

The phenomenon involved here is called **scattering**. When light encounters particles in the atmosphere, these particles temporarily absorb the light. Then, electrons in the particles (atoms, molecules and small dust particles or water droplets) vibrate and re-emit the light in all directions. The light is thus scattered.

You have probably noticed that with sound, small vibrating objects have high natural frequencies (short wavelengths) and large vibrating objects have low natural frequencies (long wavelengths). Small tuning forks give off high-pitched sounds, while large tuning forks give off low-pitched sounds. Tuning forks can pick up sounds from the air if the sounds have the correct 'pitch' (wavelength) and re-emit the same pitch as they absorb. This is called **resonance**.

If you have ever put your ear to a seashell, you have observed resonance. The cavity of the seashell absorbs the pitch corresponding to its own natural frequency, and then re-emits that pitch. (You didn't *really* believe you were 'listening to the ocean', did you?)

Atoms in the air absorb light if it is the correct frequency, then re-emit light of that frequency in all directions. Short wavelengths such as in the ultraviolet and violet are scattered the most easily. You cannot see ultraviolet, and your eyes are not very sensitive to violet. Your eyes are quite sensitive to blue, so the sky appears blue. (Your eyes are even more sensitive to green and yellow, but the molecules of nitrogen and oxygen in the air do not scatter these colours nearly as well.)

If the atmosphere contains a lot of dust, the small particles of dust will scatter the longer wavelengths of the spectrum. Under these circumstances, the sky will be less blue and whiter, since your eyes are seeing all the wavelengths (colours) at once. A truly 'clear' sky tends to be a darker blue. A good heavy rain shower will clear the air of much of its dust, and the sky may appear bluer after a rainstorm.

Dusty air will appear 'hazy'. Clouds appear white due to scattering of a full range of frequencies by water droplets of different sizes and 'natural frequencies'.

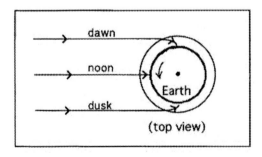

At sunrise and sunset, light from the sun must travel through more air to reach you. (**Figure 10.27.**) In the process, much of the violet, blue and green light is scattered. Long wavelength red light is scattered the least. This is why the sky looks orange-red at sunrise and sunset.

Figure 10.27

Challenges!

1. Why does only a small fraction of the ultraviolet light reaching our planet reach us?
2. Why are scientists seriously concerned about the possible depletion of ozone (O_3) in our upper atmosphere?
3. Imagine a planet with an atmosphere made of molecules that scatter red light better than violet and blue. What would the sky look like? What would a sunrise look like?
4. Find out why water is blue-green in colour. What effect does water have on infrared and red wavelengths? Why does everything look blue-green at a depth in seawater? Why do red sea animals look black in deep water?

Chapter Review Questions

1. How long does it take light from the sun to reach Pluto, which is (on average) a distance of 5.9×10^{12} m from the sun?

2. Why is it not practical to use a pinhole instead of a lens to make a 'slide projector'?

3. What is one advantage a pinhole camera has over a lens camera?

4. You are 1.6 m tall. What is the shortest wall mirror you need to see your whole body, while standing, in the mirror?

5. You are standing 1.5 m in front of a mirror. How far away from your image are you?

6. In a clothing store, a pair of large mirrors is hinged so that the angle between them can be changed. How many images will you see of yourself if you adjust the mirrors so that the angle between them is (a) 90°? (b) 45°?

7. A beam of light makes an angle of 35° with the normal as it approaches a flat glass block. If the index of refraction of the glass is 1.60, at what angle will the refracted beam enter the glass, relative to the normal? At what angle will the beam leave the other side of the block of glass if the walls are parallel?

8. What is a quick way of estimating the index of refraction of water or glass, for small angles of incidence, without using Snell's Law?

9. What is the critical angle for a glass that has an index of refraction of 1.52?

10. The critical angle of a liquid is 45°. What is the index of refraction of the liquid?

11. Use a diagram to show why refraction causes a coin in the bottom of a swimming pool to look larger and closer than it really is.

12. What does it mean to say that a wave is vertically polarized? Why is polarization of light a strong indicator that light behaves like waves?

13. What does the phenomenon of dispersion tell you about the refraction of different colours (wavelengths) of light?

14. What causes a rainbow? Illustrate your answer with a diagram.

15. Why does red light refract less than violet light?

16. How can the speed of light in a medium other than air be calculated from its index of refraction?

17. At what speed would light travel in a glass with an index of refraction of 2.0?

18. How was infrared light discovered?

19. What are at least five uses for infrared light?

20. How was ultraviolet light discovered?

21. What is fluorescence?

22. Why are fluorescent lights given that name?

23. Give an example of diffraction of light that you would experience in everyday life.

24. Why is the sky blue? Why is the sky bluer in a region away from heavily populated areas?

25. What makes a sunset orange or red?

26. What phenomenon is involved in fibre optics? What are two applications of fibre optics? Describe each application in some detail.

27. Why are fire trucks frequently painted greenish-yellow?

28. Why may an asphalt driveway appear 'wet' in the distance, even though it is dry?

Test Yourself!

Multiple Choice Questions

1. What phenomena are primarily involved in the making of a rainbow?
    A. reflection and refraction
    B. reflection and interference
    C. reflection, refraction and dispersion
    D. refraction, interference and diffraction

2. What phenomena are mainly responsible for the blueness of the sky?
    A. reflection and refraction
    B. polarization and interference
    C. diffraction and interference
    D. scattering and resonance

3. Why do sunsets appear red?
    A. Blue light is scattered less than red.
    B. Red light is scattered less than other wavelengths.
    C. Red light is reflected by the ozone layer.
    D. Red light is scattered more than other wavelengths.

4. What property of light is used in lenses?
    A. refraction
    B. reflection
    C. diffraction
    D. interference

5. When a prism spreads light into its component colours, what is the phenomenon called?
    A. reflection
    B. diffraction
    C. interference
    D. dispersion

6. Which two colours of spotlight will produce a yellow colour if they are projected on the same spot on a white screen?
    A. red and blue
    B. red and green
    C. green and blue
    D. red, green and blue

7. In a primary rainbow, what is the colour at the top of the bow?
    A. red
    B. blue
    C. violet
    D. green

8. What are the three primary light colours?
    A. green, red and blue
    B. red, violet and yellow
    C. cyan, magenta and yellow
    D. red, white and blue

9. When white light enters glass from air, what colour is refracted most?
    A. violet
    B. blue
    C. red
    D. yellow
    E. All colours are refracted equally.

10. Sun tan and sun burn are caused by
    A. infrared light.
    B. ultraviolet light.
    C. red light.
    D. all visible wavelengths.

11. Which colour of light travels faster in a *vacuum?*
    A. red
    B. violet
    C. Both have the same speed.
    D. Light cannot travel in a vacuum.

12. A spotlight photographed through a glass filter with thin grooves in it will appear to have a 'starburst' effect around it. What phenomenon is primarily involved here?
    A. reflection
    B. refraction
    C. diffraction
    D. dispersion

13. Two plane mirrors are 'hinged' and arranged to form an angle of 36° with each other. If you look into the mirrors, how many images will you see of a coin placed between them?
    A. 9   B. 10   C. 11   D. 35   E. 36

14. You are standing 2.0 m in front of a mirror, and you wish to take a picture of yourself. At what distance should you focus your camera?
    A. 1.0 m   B. 2.0 m   C. 3.0 m   D. 4.0 m   E. infinity

15. If you run toward a mirror at 5.0 m/s, how fast does your image approach *you?*
    A. 2.5 m/s   B. 5.0 m/s   C. 10.0 m/s   D. 0 m/s

16. A basketball player is 2.2 m tall. How high a mirror does she need to see the entire length of her body?
    A. 1.1 m   B. 2.2 m   C. 0.55 m   D. 4.4 m

17. When light of a certain pure colour enters a new medium at, say, 30°, what property of the light does *not* change?
    A. speed
    B. direction
    C. frequency
    D. wavelength

18. Diamonds are noted for their brilliance and colour when viewed in a well-lit environment. What property or properties account for this?
    A. internal reflection
    B. refraction
    C. dispersion
    D. All of these
    E. None of these

19. A blue spotlight and a yellow spotlight are shone on the same area of a white screen. What colour will you see on the screen?
    A. black   B. yellow   C. cyan   D. magenta   E. white

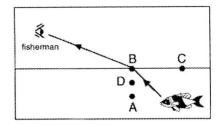

20. Where should the fisherman aim his spear if the fish, which is not moving, is to be eaten tonight?
    A. At A
    B. At B
    C. At C
    D. At D

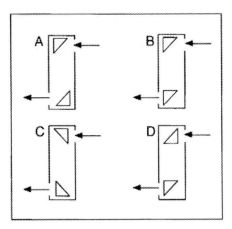

21. Two prisms are to be used to make a periscope. Which of the diagrams above shows the correct way to align the prisms inside the periscope?

    A   B   C   D

22. When white light enters a body of water from air,
    A. all colours of light travel at the same speed in the water.
    B. red light travels at the fastest speed in the water.
    C. violet light travels at the fastest speed in the water.
    D. all colours speed up in the water.

23. A beam of light enters a liquid at an incident angle of 35°. It refracts at 25° to the normal. What is the **index of refraction** of the liquid?
    A. 0.71   B. 1.4   C. 0.74   D. 10°

24. Diamond has an index of refraction of 2.42. If light enters the diamond at an angle of incidence of 63.0°, at what angle will the light refract?
    A. 0.3682°   B. 2.42°   C. 21.6°   D. 26.0°

25. Light speed is 3.00×10^8 m/s in air. What is its speed in a plastic, whose index of refraction is 1.453?
    A. 2.06×10^8 m/s
    B. 3.00×10^8 m/s
    C. 4.36×10^8 m/s
    D. 0.484×10^8 m/s

Open-Ended Questions

1. What is the **critical angle** of a glass, if its index of refraction is 1.58?
2. Light of frequency 5.00×10^{14} Hz is emitted by a laser. If light speed is 3.00×10^8 m/s, what is the wavelength of the light, in nanometres?
3. Light speed in a vacuum is 3.00×10^8 m/s. How fast does light travel in diamond, if the index of refraction of diamond is 2.42?

Graphical Analysis

4. A student wishes to find the **index of refraction** of a block of glass. She shines light into the block at various **angles of incidence** ($\angle i$) and measures the **angles of refraction** ($\angle r$) for each incident beam of light. Here is her data:

angle of incidence	$\angle i$	0^0	5.00^0	10.00^0	15.00^0	20.00^0	25.00^0
sin i							
angle of refraction	$\angle r$	0^0	3.33^0	6.65^0	9.94^0	13.20^0	16.40^0
sin r							

(a) Use a suitable graph to determine the **index of refraction** of the glass. Use the most precise method, which involves **Snell's Law**.
(b) According to your graph, what is the index of refraction of the glass?
(c) What would the critical angle be for this type of glass?

Chapter 11 Optics

You use many optical devices in your daily life, including eyeglasses, binoculars, cameras, microscopes, telescopes and your own eyes. In this chapter you will learn how some of these devices work. Much use will be made of **ray diagrams** when explaining how light behaves when it passes through or into optical components such as lenses and curved mirrors. You will recall that a **ray** is simply a line that one draws to show the path that light takes. A ray is a mathematical convenience, and *not* a physical reality!

11.1 Curved Mirrors

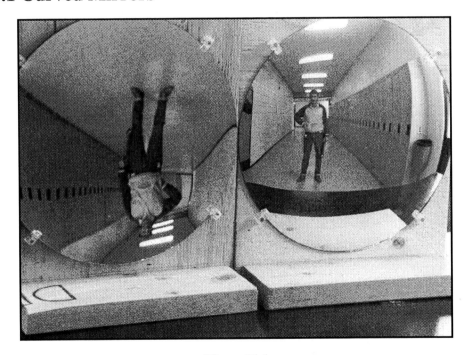

Figure 11.1

The images you see in *curved mirrors* can be quite different from what you are accustomed to seeing in a plane mirror. If you stand close to a large **concave** mirror and look into it, you will see yourself 'right side up' and 'larger than life'. Some make-up or shaving mirrors are slightly concave. If you walk back from a concave mirror, you will find that at a certain distance your image is suddenly inverted and looks small. See **Figure 11.1(left)**. **Convex** mirrors always make you look smaller than real life, no matter what distance you are from them. See **Figure 11.1(right)**. You see convex mirrors in shops, where they are strategically placed so that the shop owner can obtain a wide-angle view of the store and the customers in it. Some rear view mirrors may have a small convex section on them so that the driver gets a wider angle of view of what is behind him. (What precautions must be taken when using a convex mirror to see what is following your vehicle?)

Investigation 11-1 An Introduction to Curved Mirrors

Purpose: To observe how light reflects from concave and convex mirrors.

Part 1 Convex Mirrors

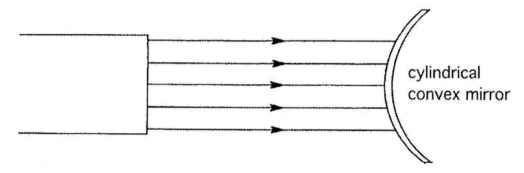

Figure 11.2

Procedure

1. Set up a ray box with a five-slit baffle, and adjust the position of the lens of the ray box so that all five beams are parallel. Aim the parallel beams at a **cylindrical convex mirror**, as in **Figure 11.2**.

2. Carefully mark the position of one of the incident beams and the reflected beam corresponding to it. Trace the outline of the reflecting surface of the mirror. Remove the mirror. Draw a normal to the mirror at the point of reflection. Measure the angle of incidence and the angle of reflection. Does the reflection resemble what happened at a point on a **plane mirror**?

3. Obtain a **spherical convex mirror** from your instructor. (Its shape is like a section of a sphere.) Look into the mirror and describe the image you see. Is it right side up or inverted? Is it larger than your face, smaller or the same size?

Concluding Questions

1. Why is a convex mirror called a **diverging mirror?**

2. Why does a convex mirror give a *wide-angle view* when you look at it?

3. Describe the nature of the image you see in a diverging mirror. Is it **real** or **virtual**? **enlarged** or **diminished**? **erect** or **inverted**?

4. What would *you* look like in a tall, vertical mirror shaped like a cylinder?

Part 2 Concave Mirrors

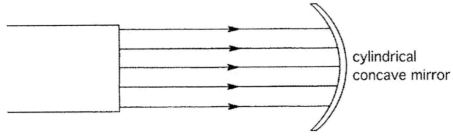

cylindrical
concave mirror

Figure 11.3

Procedure

1. Aim the five parallel beams from your ray box at a cylindrical concave mirror, as in **Figure 11.3**. Sketch the incident and reflected beams.

2. Block the light from the outermost beams coming from the ray box, so that only the middle part of the cylindrical mirror is being used. Do you notice an improvement in the focussing? (Is the focussed light concentrated in a smaller area than before?) Sketch the incident and reflected beams again.

3. Measure the distance from the **vertex** (geometric centre) of the concave mirror to the point where the light comes together on the axis of the mirror. This distance is called the **focal length** (*f*) of the mirror.

Concluding Questions

1. Why is a concave mirror called a **converging mirror?**

2. Why are concave mirrors used in some telescopes?

3. Does a cylindrical mirror focus *all* the incoming parallel beams of light to a single point? Discuss.

Part 3 Finding the Focal Length of a Spherical Concave Mirror

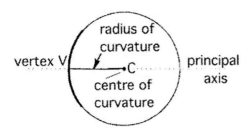

For future investigations, you will need to know the **focal length** of a spherical concave mirror. It is important to measure the focal length of your mirror carefully, and to label the mirror so that you use the same one later. (Use a small piece of masking tape.)

Figure 11.4

The point where parallel rays of light converge in front of a concave mirror is called the **principal focus (F)**, if the focussing occurs on the **principal axis** of the mirror. The principal axis is an imaginary line passing through the **vertex** and the **centre of curvature** of the mirror. See **Figure 11.4**. If you were drawing the mirror in two dimensions, you would place your compass at the centre of curvature and draw the mirror with a certain radius. This radius would be the mirror's **radius of curvature.**

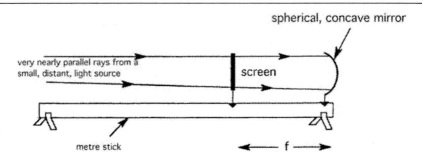

Figure 11.5

Procedure

1. Set up your spherical concave mirror on an optical bench so that it faces a small light source, such as the bulb from an opened ray box or a candle flame, which is *at least 5 m away.* See **Figure 11.5**. The rays of light coming from a small, distant source will be very close to being parallel. Wherever they converge in front of the mirror will be very, very close to being the focal point. If the focal point is on the principal axis of the mirror, it will be the **principal focus**. The distance from the vertex of the mirror to the principal focus is the **focal length** of your mirror.

2. To see where the light from the distant source focusses, you will need a screen. Since you do not want to block the light coming into the mirror completely, cut a strip of file card about 1 cm wide and mount it in a screen holder in front of the concave mirror. Move the screen back and forth in front of the mirror until you see a sharply focussed, very small image of the distant light source. If the light source is sufficiently far away and small, the image you see will be, for practical purposes, a point. The distance from the vertex of the mirror to this point is the **focal length** of your mirror.

3. Identify the mirror in some way so that you are sure to get the same mirror for the next investigation. *Record its focal length for future use.*

Concluding Questions

1. If you placed the light source closer to the mirror (say 1.5 m), would the light from the source come to a focus? Would it converge at the **principal focus**? Discuss.

2. Why is it important to use a *distant* light source when you are trying to measure the focal length of a concave mirror?

Images in Concave Mirrors

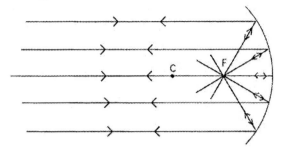

A good quality concave mirror is designed (shaped) so that rays of light incident on the mirror's surface will reflect *predictably.* Rays parallel to the principal axis will reflect through a single point, which is the principal focus. See **Figure 11.6.**

Figure 11.6

Reflection is reversible, of course, so that light coming from the principal focus will reflect parallel to the principal axis. Of course, any ray incident on the mirror will reflect in such a way that the angle of incidence equals the angle of reflection.

Diagrams used to illustrate concave mirrors are circular and two-dimensional. An inexpensive concave mirror is spherical in three dimensions. A top quality concave mirror is not quite spherical, but the ideal mirror will be discussed later!

Predicting Where an Image Will Form

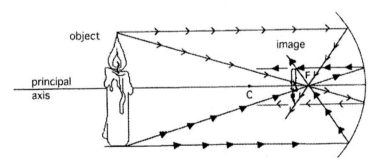

Figure 11.7

You can predict where a concave mirror will form an image if you simply keep in mind what the mirror was *shaped* to do. In **Figure 11.7**, two rays have been drawn coming from the top of the object (a candle). The ray that is parallel to the principal axis will reflect from the mirror and pass through the principal focus **F**. A second ray passes through the principal focus, reflects off the mirror and goes out parallel to the principal axis. Where these two rays *converge* is where there will be an **image** of the top of the candle flame. A similar pair of rays has been drawn coming from a point at the bottom of the candle, and these rays reflect and *converge* at a point in front of the mirror. The image of the bottom of the candle forms on a line just above the image of the top of the flame. Any number of pairs of rays might be drawn from points elsewhere on the candle. All of these pairs of rays will converge on a line the same distance from the mirror as the other image points.

In **Figure 11.7**, the object is located quite far from the mirror. It is at a distance greater than the focal length and also greater than the radius of curvature of the mirror. Notice that the image is: (a) **real** (It can be seen on a screen); (b) **smaller than the object**; and (c) **inverted** (upside down).

In the following **Exercises,** you will be asked to draw similar ray diagrams for objects at different distances from the concave mirror.

Exercises

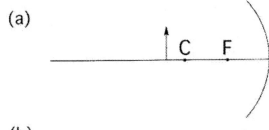

1. Copy and complete these ray diagrams to show where the image of the object will form, and what its relative size will be. Use **Figure 11.7** as a guide.

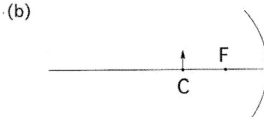

2. Describe the nature of the image in each of the situations in **Exercise 1**.

   Is it real or virtual?

   Is it enlarged or diminished in size?

   Is it erect or inverted?

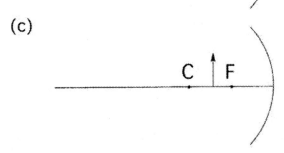

Figure 11.8

The Concave Mirror as a Magnifier

If you place your face very close to a concave mirror, so that you are closer than the principal focus, as in **Figure 11.9**, you see an **enlarged virtual image** in the mirror. Unlike a real image, a virtual image is right side up. The location of the image can be predicted using a ray diagram.

A ray coming from the top of the object in a direction parallel to the principal axis will reflect through the principal focus, as usual. To locate the image, a second ray is drawn in a

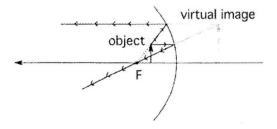

Figure 11.9

direction such that it appears to have come *from* the principal focus. This ray will reflect out parallel to the principal axis. The reflected rays *do not converge anywhere.* In fact, they diverge and cannot possibly form part of a real image.

Now, imagine you are looking into the mirror. From what point would the two reflected rays *appear* to come? If you extrapolate the two rays back behind the mirror, they appear to be coming from a point at the top of the virtual image in **Figure 11.9**. Similar pairs of rays might be drawn from other points on the object, and coinciding image points would be found on the line representing the virtual image in the figure.

It is interesting to draw ray diagrams and attempt to predict where images will form in front of concave mirrors. Prediction should be followed by experiment, however, to confirm or disprove the theory upon which a prediction is based.

In *Investigation 11-2,* you will test the predictions made about images formed by concave mirrors.

Investigation 11-2 Locating Images in Concave Mirrors

Purpose: **To locate images formed by a concave mirror.**

Procedure

1. Mount your concave mirror at the far end of your optical bench or metre stick. Measure off a distance equal to the **focal length** of your mirror and mark the position of the **principal focus** on your metre stick with an **F** written on masking tape. At a distance equal to two focal lengths (**2f**), write a letter **C** on the tape.

2. Place a suitable object (a small candle or a miniature light bulb) at the other end of the metre stick or optical bench. The object distance D_o will be greater than 2f. Locate the image by moving a thin white card back and forth in front of the mirror until you see the image of the object in sharp focus. Measure the distance from the vertex of the mirror to (a) the object (D_o) and (b) the image (D_i). Record these distances. Is the image in the approximate spot predicted in the exercises preceding this investigation?

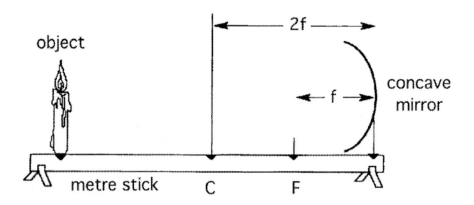

Figure 11.10

3. Try a second object position at a distance greater than 2*f*. Locate the image and object and measure D_o and D_i.

4. Place the object at a distance of 2*f* from the mirror. Locate the image and measure D_o and D_i.

5. Place the object at a distance of approximately 1.5*f* from the mirror. Locate the image and measure D_o and D_i.

6. Place the object at the focal point **F**. Can you use this set-up to make a spotlight?

7. Place the object at a distance less than *f* from the mirror. Can you form a real image? Look directly into the mirror. Can you see a virtual image? Describe the image.

Concluding Questions

1. Draw ray diagrams showing where and why the real images formed when the object was at these distances: (a) >2*f*,   (b) 2*f*,   (c) 1.5*f*   and (d) *f*.

2. If the concave mirror is being used as an astronomical telescope, where will the image form?

3. If the mirror is being used in an automobile headlight or in a spotlight, where will you place the object?

4. Why is it difficult to obtain a good image of the object when it is at **F**?

5. In general, what object distance range will give a real image?

6. In general, what object distance range will give a virtual image?

The Mirror Equation

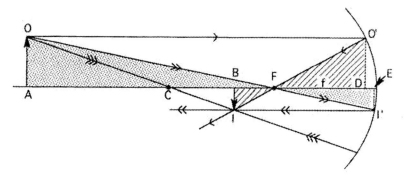

Figure 11.11

Can the location of an image formed by a concave mirror be predicted by calculation? There is an equation for concave mirrors that permits you to do this quite easily. To show where the equation comes from, some simple geometry will be used. In **Figure 11.11,** a third ray has been drawn from the object to the mirror. This ray passes along a radius of the mirror, and therefore strikes the mirror perpendicularly, and reflects right back on itself.

Several triangles are created in **Figure 11.11**. Notice that ΔIBF and ΔO'DF are *similar*. The height of the object is OA, which equals O'D. Distance FD is approximately equal to the focal length *f* of the mirror. The diagram exaggerates the difference between FE (*f*) and FD. You may assume that FD is very, very close to being equal to the focal length, *f*.

SinceΔIBF is similar to ΔO'DF, ∴ $\dfrac{IB}{O'D} = \dfrac{BF}{FD}$.

Now O'D is the same as OA (the height of the object) and FD is almost equal to *f*, so

$$\frac{IB}{OA} = \frac{BF}{f} \quad . \quad (1)$$

Notice that Δ OAF is similar to Δ I'EF, so that

$$\frac{I'E}{OA} = \frac{EF}{AF} \quad .$$

Now I'E is the same as IB (height of the image) and EF is almost equal to *f*, so

$$\frac{IB}{OA} = \frac{f}{AF} \quad . \quad (2)$$

Combining equations (1) and (2),

$$\frac{BF}{f} = \frac{f}{AF} \quad . \quad (3)$$

Now image distance $D_i = BF + f$, and object distance $D_o = AF + f$, so we can re-write equation (3) like this:

$$\frac{D_i - f}{f} = \frac{f}{D_o - f} \, .$$

Therefore,

$$(D_i - f)(D_o - f) = f^2, \text{ or}$$

$$D_i D_o - f D_o - f D_i + f^2 = f^2, \text{ or}$$

$$D_i D_o - f D_o - f D_i = 0 \, .$$

Dividing through by $f D_i D_o$ gives $\quad \frac{1}{f} - \frac{1}{D_i} - \frac{1}{D_o} = 0 \, ,$

which can be re-arranged to read

$$\frac{1}{D_o} + \frac{1}{D_i} = \frac{1}{f} \, .$$

This equation will be referred to as the **Mirror Equation.**

Example: A concave mirror has a focal length of 20.0 cm. If an object is 1.00 m in front of the mirror, where will the image form?

Solution:

$$\frac{1}{D_o} + \frac{1}{D_i} = \frac{1}{f} \, , \text{ so}$$

$$\frac{1}{D_i} = \frac{1}{f} - \frac{1}{D_o} \, .$$

Therefore, $\quad \dfrac{1}{D_i} = \dfrac{1}{20.0 \text{ cm}} - \dfrac{1}{100.0 \text{ cm}} = \dfrac{4}{100.0 \text{ cm}}$

$$D_i = 25.0 \text{ cm.}$$

The image forms 25.0 cm in front of the mirror.

Exercises   Use the **Mirror Equation** to solve **Exercises 1-6**.

1. A real image forms 25.0 cm in front of a concave mirror, which has a focal length of 20.0 cm. How far is the object from the mirror?

2. An image forms in front of a concave mirror at the same distance from the mirror as the object. Solve for the object or the image distance in terms of the focal length, f.

3. What is the focal length of a concave mirror that forms an image on a screen 40.0 cm away, of an object that is 20.0 cm in front of the mirror?

4. An object is placed 10.0 cm in front of a concave mirror of focal length 15.0 cm. Solve for D_i. Why is the answer negative?

5. What shape of 'trick' mirror would make a thin person look larger? A large person look thinner? A tall person look shorter? A short person look taller?

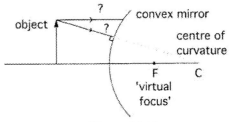

Figure 11.12

6. Draw a diagram similar to **Figure 11.12**. Use two rays to show where the image of the arrow will be. Can a convex mirror form
   (a) a real image?
   (b) an enlarged image?

Challenges

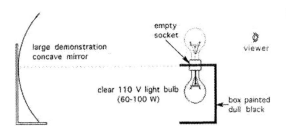

Figure 11.13

1. If you have a demonstration concave mirror available, make the apparatus in **Figure 11.13**. The object is a clear light bulb, mounted upside down at a height such that the base of the socket is level with the principal axis of the mirror. The empty socket is immediately above. At what distance from the vertex of the mirror must the object be placed so that its real image will appear in the empty socket? This must be done in a dark room, and the viewer must be looking into the mirror as in the figure.

Figure 11.14

2. A commercially available double concave mirror (called a **Mirage**™) creates a very realistic image at the opening of the top mirror. See **Figure 11.14**. Is this image **real** or is it **virtual**? Can you draw a ray diagram to explain why the image forms where it does?

The Ideal Shape for a Concave Mirror

Figure 11.15

The concave mirrors you have used so far have been either cylindrical (with the ray box) or spherical. These mirrors are relatively inexpensive to manufacture and are adequate for many uses. You probably noticed that they do not focus light precisely.

Parallel rays entering the mirror are converged to a narrow region, but not precisely to a point. There is some **aberration.** For precision work, as in quality telescopes, aberration must be avoided. The mirror must be shaped perfectly. What is the perfect shape for a concave mirror? In two dimensions, the name of the perfect curve for a concave mirror is a **parabola.** The three-dimensional equivalent of a parabola is called a **paraboloid.** To visualize what a parabola looks like, imagine a baseball being tossed into the air by a fielder to a catcher. The path the ball takes is parabolic. **Figure 11.15** shows what a parabola looks like.

Reflecting telescopes use parabolic mirrors. Radio telescopes are also parabolic in shape, but they are much larger than optical telescopes.

Challenge

Obtain a dozen or so small plane mirrors (as used with ray boxes). Aim a laser beam at one of these mirrors, and adjust its alignment so that it reflects the beam through a point, which you have chosen to be the principal focus. (See **Figure 11.16**.) Repeat this with another plane mirror immediately adjacent to the first. Adjacent mirrors must be touching each other, and all must reflect the incident beam, which is kept parallel to the principal axis, through the same principal focus. By repeating this process, determine the shape of mirror that reflects *all* incoming beams to the same focus. Mark the reflecting points on a large sheet of graph paper. Try plotting your Y measurements vs the *squares* of your X measurements. What is the **equation** for your second graph? Is this the equation of a parabola?

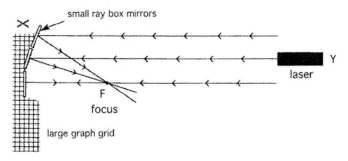

Figure 11.16

11.2 Lenses

The word **lens** comes from a Latin word meaning *lentil,* perhaps because of the resemblance of the shape of a lens to the shape of a bean.

Lenses are among the most common applications of physics you will encounter in everyday life. In addition to the lenses in your own eyes, you may wear glasses as well. Lenses are found in all kinds of projectors, in binoculars, telescopes, microscopes, photocopiers, and hand magnifiers.

Investigation 11-3 is a descriptive introduction to lenses.

Investigation 11-3   Focussing on Lenses

Purpose: To observe how the property of refraction is used in lenses.

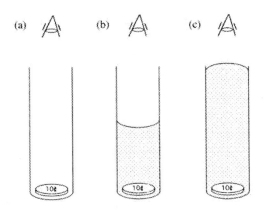

Figure 11.17

Procedure

1. Place a dime in an empty test tube, as in **Figure 11.17(a)**. Sketch a circle the size of the dime as you see it when you look straight down the test tube. Now add water to the test tube until it is partially full, as in **Figure 11.17(b)**. Draw a circle showing the apparent size of the dime as you see it now. Add more water to the test tube until it is just about overflowing. The top surface will be **convex** as in **Figure 11.17(c)**. Draw a circle to show the apparent size of the dime now.

2. Set up your ray box so that parallel beams of light pass through a **concave cylindrical lens** [**Figure 11.18(a)**]. Sketch how the light refracts travelling through the concave lens. Do the same with a **convex** lens [**Figure 11.18(b)**]. Repeat with both lenses together [**Figure 11.18(c)**]. Try separating the two lenses by a centimetre or two.

3. (a) Fill a small Florence flask with water. Use the flask as a *magnifying glass* to read the writing on this page. See **Figure 11.19**.
   (b) Light a candle. Darken the room and use the Florence flask as a **slide projector** to project an image of the flame on the wall of your classroom.

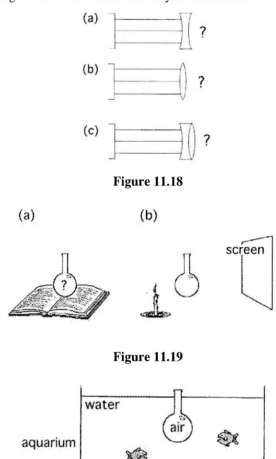

Figure 11.18

Figure 11.19

Figure 11.20

4. Place a water-filled aquarium near a window. Push an *empty* Florence flask down into the aquarium. See **Figure 11.20**. Look out the window through the empty flask. Describe the image you see. Now remove the empty flask, fill it with water and look at the same scene through the water-filled flask. Record what you saw in both situations.

Types of Lenses

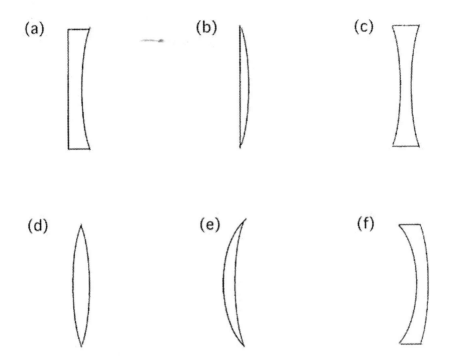

Figure 11.21

Lenses come in various shapes and sizes. There are two basic types of lens, one concave and the other convex. A concave lens made of glass will cause incoming parallel rays of light to diverge (spread out). A convex lens made of glass will cause incoming parallel rays to converge. Each of the lenses in **Figure 11.21** can be given a descriptive name. See if you can figure out the reason behind each name.

(a) plano-concave   (**Plano** means flat.)   (b) plano-convex

(c) double concave   (d) double convex

(e) concavo-convex   (f) convexo-concave

Eyeglasses may be either concavo-convex or convexo-concave.

The Terminology of Lenses

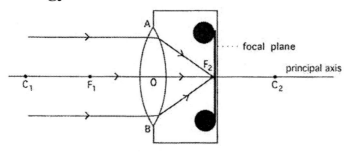

Figure 11.22

A **biconvex lens**, like the one in the simple camera in **Figure 11.22**, has two spherical surfaces. For each surface, there is a **centre of curvature** (C_1 and C_2). For a symmetrical lens, the **radius of curvature** (OC_1 or OC_2) would be the same on both sides of the lens. The line passing through C_1, O and C_2 is the **principal axis** of the lens. The lens is shaped so that parallel rays from a very distant source will refract and converge to a **focal point**. If the focal point is on the principal axis, it is called the **principal focus**. The lens has two principal foci, labelled F_1 and F_2.

In **Figure 11.22**, a film is located at the **focal plane** of the lens. A photograph of an object that is very far away will be in focus on the focal plane. For every point on the **object**, light will focus at a corresponding point on the **image**, which is on the focal plane.

The diameter of the lens is called the **aperture**. In adjustable cameras, the aperture can be changed to suit different lighting conditions, or for special effects desired by the photographer. The size of the aperture is expressed as a fraction of the **focal length**, f, of the lens. The focal length is the distance from the middle of the lens (**O**) to the principal focus (**F**).

Typical apertures on an adjustable camera are: *f/22, f/16, f/11, f/8, f/5.6, f/3.5* and so on. The smallest opening of this group is *f/22*. The aperture is only 1/22 times the focal length. On a dull day, or in a low-light situation, one might wish to use an aperture of *f/2.8*, where the aperture is 1/2.8 times the focal length. In addition to varying the aperture of the lens, how else may a photographer control how much light reaches the film during an exposure?

Predicting Where Images Will Form

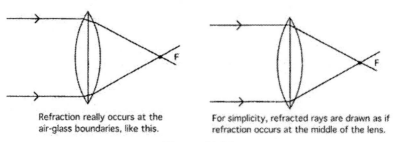

Refraction really occurs at the air-glass boundaries, like this.

For simplicity, refracted rays are drawn as if refraction occurs at the middle of the lens.

Figure 11.23

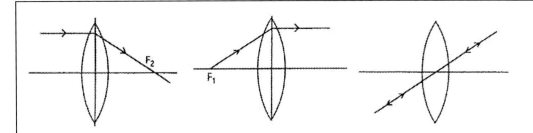

Figure 11.24

You can predict where a lens will form an image if you know the **focal length** of the lens. The following three facts, illustrated in the above diagrams, are helpful in predicting where the image will form:

1. **Rays arriving at the lens parallel to the principal axis will converge to the principal focus of the lens.**
2. **Light coming from the principal focus will leave the lens parallel to the principal axis.**
3. **A ray passing through the centre of a thin lens will go through approximately straight.**

Note that the rays in **Figure 11.24** are drawn as if they refracted at the centre of the lens. This is just a useful simplification. The refraction actually occurs at both the air-glass boundaries of the lens.

Investigation 11-4 Locating Images Formed by Convex Lenses

Problems: (1)   **To predict where images will be formed by a thin convex lens when the object is at different positions on the principal axis.**

            (2)   **To test each prediction by experimenting with a thin convex lens and an optical bench.**

Procedure

Part 1

1. Copy **Figures 11.26 (a)** to **(e)** into your record book. By drawing at least two rays, *predict* where the image will form for each object location. Use **Figure 11.25** as a guide.

2. Describe what each **image** will look like. For example, will it be larger than, smaller than or the same size as the object? Will it be right side up or upside down? Will it be **real** or **virtual**?

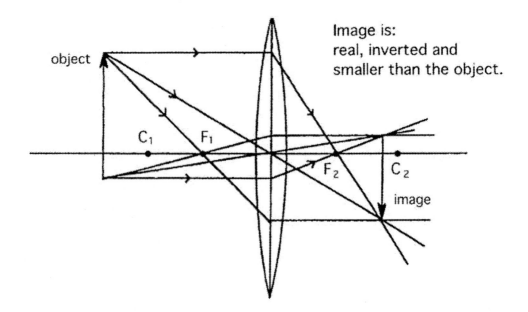

Figure 11.25

Concluding Questions

1. The arrangements in **Figures 11.26 (a), (b) and (c)** are often used in photography. Which arrangement of object and lens would be used in:

   (a) a camera photographing a distant landscape?

   (b) an enlarger?

   (c) a slide or movie projector?

   (d) an overhead projector?

   (e) a camera that is capable of photographing a ladybug full size?

2. (a) Will you get a real image if you place an object at **F**, as in **Figure 11.26(d)**?

   (b) What would happen if you placed a small bright light source right at **F**?

3. (a) Will you get a real image if you place an object between **F** and the lens, as in **Figure 11.26(e)**?

   (b) Give an example of a situation where you would use this arrangement.

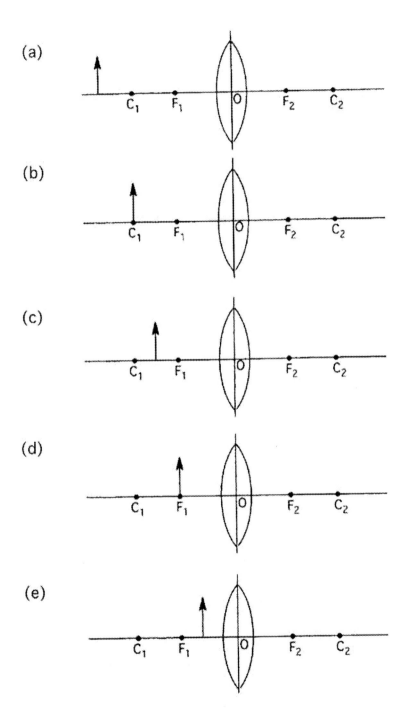

Figure 11.26

Part 2

You are given a convex lens, a small light source (bulb or candle) and an optical bench. Your job is to set up the apparatus the way it would be in each of the five diagrams in **Figure 11.26**, and to test the predictions you made with your ray diagrams.

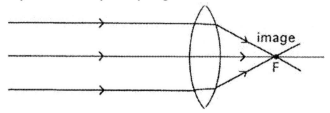

(a) Parallel rays from a distant source converge at principal focus **F**.

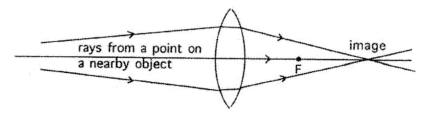

(b) Diverging rays from a close source converge on an image point, but *not* to the principal focus **F**!

Figure 11.27

Procedure

1. First, measure the **focal length** of your lens so that you know where to mount the lens in relation to the object. To do this, you need a *distant light source* so that the rays coming from it are essentially parallel as they arrive at the lens. Note that rays from a source too close will be diverging significantly, and will not converge in the focal plane. (See **Figure 11.27**.) Use a light source at least 5 m away. When you have measured the focal length, f, record it. The principal focus **F** of your lens will always be this distance from your lens. The centre of curvature **C** is twice as far from the lens as the principal focus **F** is. For example, if your focal length is 25 cm, then the radius of curvature will be 50 cm.
2. In **Figure 11.26(a)** of your predictions, the object is at a distance, D_o, greater than the radius of curvature **CO**. Where did you predict the image would form? Move your lens to a position where it is a distance greater than $2f$ from the object. Locate the image by moving your screen around until you see a sharply focussed image on it. Was your prediction correct?
3. Test your prediction in **Figure 11.26(b)**.
4. Test your predictions in **Figures 11.26 (c), (d)** and **(e)**. In **Figure 11.26(e)**, try looking through the lens toward the object. Is this a **real** image or a **virtual** image?
5. Replace the **convex** lens with a **concave** lens. Can you produce a real image with it? Describe the image you can obtain with a concave lens!

Concluding Questions

1. You wish to project a slide on a screen. One of the letters on the slide is a **p**. When you place the slide in the projector, how must the letter look when you insert the slide (as seen from behind the projector)? (a) **p**   (b) **d**   (c) **b**   (d) **q**   Explain.
2. When you use an overhead projector, why do you not have to write upside down to get an image right side up on the screen?
3. You wish to make a solar furnace using a very large convex lens. Where would the object that is to be heated be placed in relation to the lens?
4. You wish to photograph a spider 'life size'. Where must (a) the spider and (b) the film be located in relation to the lens of the camera? (Assume the lens is a simple convex lens.)

Challenges

1. If you have never done it before, learn how to make a photographic print from a negative, using the school's enlarger.
2. Photograph something that moves very, very fast and make it appear 'frozen'. Develop and print the photograph yourself.
3. Experiment by photographing an outdoor subject using a variety of different f-stops (apertures). What effect does the aperture used have on the depth of field of the photograph?

The Lens Equation (for *Thin* Lenses)

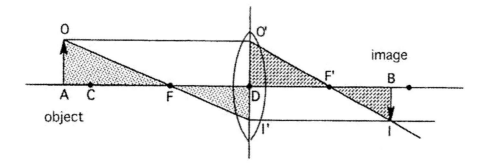

Figure 11.28

Recall that the location of an image formed by a concave mirror can be predicted using the mirror equation, $\dfrac{1}{D_o} + \dfrac{1}{D_i} = \dfrac{1}{f}$.

As you will see in the following proof, the same equation applies to lenses. In **Figure 11.28**, $\triangle IBF'$ is similar to $\triangle O'DF'$, therefore

$$\frac{IB}{O'D} = \frac{BF'}{FD} \, ,$$

but O'D = OA and F'D = f,

so
$$\frac{IB}{OA} = \frac{BF'}{f} . \qquad (1)$$

ΔI'DF is similar to ΔOAF,

$$\therefore \quad \frac{I'D}{OA} = \frac{DF}{AF} ,$$

but I'D = IB and DF = f,

so
$$\frac{IB}{OA} = \frac{f}{AF} . \qquad (2)$$

Combining equations (1) and (2),

$$\frac{BF'}{f} = \frac{f}{AF} .$$

Therefore
$$\frac{D_i - f}{f} = \frac{f}{D_o - f} .$$

$$(D_i - f)(D_o - f) = f^2,$$
$$\therefore \ D_i D_o - D_o f - D_i f + f^2 = f^2, \quad \text{or}$$

$$D_i D_o - D_o f - D_i f = 0.$$

Dividing by $D_o D_i f$,

$$\frac{1}{f} - \frac{1}{D_i} - \frac{1}{D_o} = 0.$$

Rearranging terms, the lens equation becomes

$$\frac{1}{D_o} + \frac{1}{D_i} = \frac{1}{f} .$$

Exercises

1. A convex lens has a focal length of 50.0 mm. How far from the lens will the image form of an object that is 5.00 m away?
2. An object is 100.0 mm away from a lens of focal length 50.0 mm. How far from the lens will the image form?
3. A real image forms 60 mm away from a lens when the object is 30 mm from the lens. What is the focal length of the lens?
4. An object is 25 cm away from a lens of focal length 50 cm. Where will the image form? Will it be a **real** image or a **virtual** image?
5. The distance from the lens of someone's eye to the retina is 20.0 mm. If the image of a book held 40.0 cm in front of the eye is in sharp focus, what is the effective focal length of the lens?

6. Show that the magnification caused by a convex lens (H_i/H_o, where H_i is the height of the image and H_o is the height of the object), is equal to D_i/D_o (the ratio of the image distance to the object distance).

7. A candle 5.0 cm high is located 80.0 cm in front of a convex lens of focal length 20.0 cm. How high will the image of the candle appear to be on the screen?

8. A candle is placed 30.0 cm from a convex lens of focal length 20.0 cm. What will the magnification be? Will the image be real or virtual?

9. By convention, a concave (diverging) lens has a negative focal length. Draw an object, 5.0 cm high, at a distance of 10.0 cm in front of a concave lens of focal length -6.0 cm. How far from the lens will the image form? Will it be real or virtual? Enlarged or diminished in size? Right side up or inverted? How high will it be? On which side of the lens will it be?

11.3 Optical Instruments

There are many kinds of devices that use lenses and mirrors to assist us to see things better. In this chapter, we shall emphasize two optical instruments that most people will frequently use: the human eye and the camera.

The Eye

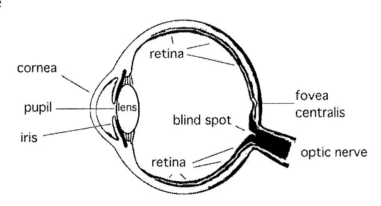

Figure 11.29: Note that the image on the **retina** is *inverted.* The brain somehow turns the image 'right side up'.

The human eyeball is approximately spherical in shape, and is kept firm by a jelly-like fluid called the **vitreous humour**. Light enters the eye through a transparent layer called the **cornea**. The cornea has no blood vessels in it, and is transparent to light. Notice that the cornea has considerable curvature to it. The cornea is actually responsible for most of the refraction that produces the image in your eye! The eye **lens** does the 'fine focussing'.

When you look into someone's eyes, the coloured portion you see is called the **iris**. The iris may be brown, green, hazel, blue or other colours depending on the pigments in it. The colour of your eyes is inherited.

The iris serves a very important function. It contains one set of muscles, which can open the iris, and another set, which can close it. Inner muscles are circular, so when they contract, they make the opening smaller; outer muscles are radial, so when they contract, they make the opening larger. The iris is very similar to the diaphragm of a variable aperture camera. Many quality cameras mimic the action of the eye, as they vary their aperture according to the amount of light arriving at the lens.

The opening in the iris, called the **pupil,** looks black but is actually transparent. Most of the light entering the eye is absorbed and does not reflect back out, so the pupil appears to be black. The size of the pupil varies according to how much light the iris detects. Look into your partner's eyes. Ask him or her to cover one eye with a hand. Watch how the pupil of the other eye becomes larger (dilates).

Light passing through the pupil then goes through the lens. The eye lens is not rigid like a camera lens. It is quite elastic and can change its shape! Under normal viewing conditions, the shape of the lens is disc-like and fairly flat, and the lens can easily focus images of distant objects on the **retina**. When you look at something close to you, the muscles surrounding the lens (**ciliary muscles**) relax, and the lens becomes more convex (bulged). This shortens its effective **focal length** and permits focussing of the image of a near object on the retina.

The **retina** of the eye is the innermost layer of the eyeball. It lines the inside of the eyeball, and is made up of millions of light-sensitive nerve cells. One type of nerve cell, the **rod**, is sensitive to dim light and is particularly sensitive to variations in intensity (brightness) of light. Rods contain a chemical called rhodopsin, which requires vitamin A for its production. If someone suffers from night blindness, he or she will have difficulty adjusting to darkness after encountering the bright headlights of an approaching vehicle. Night blindness indicates a shortness of vitamin A.

Another type of nerve cell in the retina is the **cone**, which is capable of detecting colour. Three kinds of cones detect the three primary light colours (red, blue and green). Collectively they somehow recognize all the various hues of objects around us. People who suffer from colour-blindness have defective cones and cannot recognize all colours. The cones work best in brightly lit conditions. At night, it is very difficult to recognize colours accurately as most objects look grey in faint light.

Two locations on the retina are of special interest. These are shown in **Figure 11.29**. The **fovea centralis** has cones but no rods. This small, yellowish spot on the retina is especially sensitive to detail. When you read a map or a meter scale, for example, your eye tries to keep the critical detail focussed on the fovea centralis. At the other extreme is the **blind spot**. This is where the nerve fibres from all the nerve cells in the retina gather and leave the eye as the optic nerve, which transmits impulses to your brain. At this gathering point, there are no rods or cones, and therefore it is a **blind spot**.

Challenges

1. What is an 'after-image'? What is the difference between a positive after-image and a negative after-image?

2. What is the advantage of having binocular vision?

3. What causes 'red eye' in photographs? How can a photographer avoid 'red eye' in his or her photographs?

Defects in the Eye

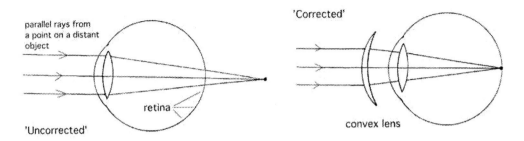

Figure 11.30

Farsightedness (Hypermetropia or Hyperopia)

To see properly, light rays entering your eye must focus on the retina. If for some reason your eyeball becomes misshapen and too short, rays will tend to focus *behind* the retina instead of on it. This causes **farsightedness**. Farsightedness can be corrected with eyeglasses having convex lenses. (**Figure 11.30**)

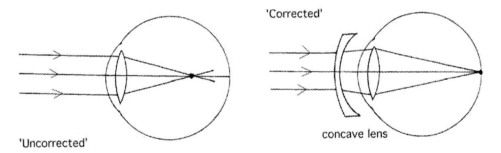

Figure 11.31

Nearsightedness (Myopia)

If the eyeball is misshapen such that it is too long, then light rays from a distant object tend to focus *in front of* the retina, and the image you get will be blurred. A concave lens (**Figure 11.31**) can be used to correct this vision defect. (Note! The front side of the lens is convex, but the backside is concave to a degree that the overall effect is the same as a concave lens.)

Astigmatism

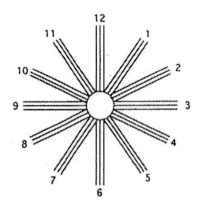

Figure 11.32

If the cornea or the lens of your eye is unevenly curved, light passing through either of these parts of the eye will be distorted. Part of the object you are looking at will be in focus, while other parts are not. Eyeglasses can have lenses that correct for this defect. The lenses must be especially shaped to compensate for flaws in the curvature of your cornea or lens. A chart like the one in **Figure 11.32** is used to determine whether you have **astigmatism**. If you do, some lines will appear to be sharply in focus, while others are blurred.

The Camera

The 'lens' of a quality camera is actually a **compound lens**. In the example in **Figure 11.33**, the compound lens has six elements. Compound lenses overcome various aberrations that occur with simple lenses.

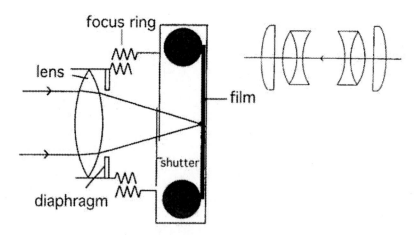

Figure 11.33

A simple camera with a fixed lens forms an image of a distant object at a certain distance from the lens, which is equal to the focal length of the lens. If the focal length is 50 mm, then the film must be 50 mm from the lens if you are to obtain a sharply focussed image of a distant object. If you try to photograph an object that is relatively close to the camera, the image will be fuzzy because it is *out of focus*. Manufacturers of simple cameras recommend that you photograph objects only if they are at least a certain minimum distance away from the camera.

Imagine you wish to photograph an object that is relatively close to your camera lens. The image will form at an image distance greater than the focal length (say, 50 mm). On an optical bench, you would move the screen (film) back away from the lens. With a camera, the lens is moved away from the film if the camera is an adjustable one, as most 35 mm cameras are. (A 35 mm camera is one that uses film that has frames 35 mm wide.)

Figure 11.33 shows the essential parts of an adjustable camera. The lens in a quality camera is not one lens but several **elements**, which make up what is called a **compound lens**. The shapes and chemical combinations of the glass in the lenses are chosen to minimize distortions in the image caused by various aberrations.

A 35 mm camera will have a focussing ring which moves the lens further from the film or closer to the film, so that objects at different distances can be photographed and have their images *in focus* on the film.

The amount of light striking the film in the camera can be controlled in two ways:

(1) The **shutter** controls the **time** during which the film is exposed to light. Typical shutter speeds are 1/30 s, 1/60 s, 1/125 s, 1/500 s and 1/1000 s. Notice that each time interval is approximately one-half of the previous time interval (called the **shutter speed**).

(2) The **aperture control** is a diaphragm, which can control the size of the opening (aperture) of the lens, thus allowing more or less light to reach the film during the time of exposure. The aperture ring on the camera is labelled with a series of numbers called *f* - **stops**. Typical *f*-stops are *f*/2.8, *f*/3.5, *f*/5.6, *f*/8, *f*/11 and *f*/16. These numbers indicate relative apertures. If the *f*-stop is *f*/8, this means that the diameter of the lens opening (**aperture**) is equal to one eighth of the focal length. ($d = f/8$) If the *f*-stop is *f*/11, this means that the aperture is one eleventh of the focal length. ($d = f/11$) The odd looking numbers of the *f*-stops are carefully chosen so that each time you change your aperture setting by one *f*-stop, you either double or half the amount of light that enters the lens during the exposure.

Example: How does changing the f-stop from *f*/8 to *f*/11 change the amount of light entering the lens of a camera?

Solution: Consider a 50 mm focal length lens, with an aperture (opening) of *f*/8. The amount of light passing through the lens depends on the *area* of the opening. The opening is approximately circular, so its area is:

$$A = \pi r^2 = \pi \frac{d^2}{4} = \pi \frac{(f/8)^2}{4} = \pi \frac{\left[\frac{50 \text{ mm}}{8}\right]^2}{4} = 31 \text{ mm}^2.$$

Now consider the same lens, with an aperture of *f*/11. The area of the lens opening is now:

$$A = \pi r^2 = \pi \frac{d^2}{4} = \pi \frac{(f/11)^2}{4} = \pi \frac{\left[\frac{50 \text{ mm}}{11}\right]^2}{4} = 16 \text{ mm}^2.$$

Increasing the f-stop number from *f*/8 to *f*/11 reduces the amount of light passing through the lens by one-half. Likewise, if you change your f-stop from *f*/11 to *f*/16, you reduce the amount of light passing through the lens by one-half again.

Exercises

1. Your camera light meter indicates that if your shutter speed is 1/125 s, the proper aperture (*f*-stop) to use is *f*/8. If you prefer to use a shorter time of 1/500 s, how should you adjust your *f*-stop so that the picture will still be properly exposed?
2. Your light meter indicates that with a shutter speed of 1/250 s, an *f*-stop of *f*/16 will give the proper exposure. To photograph a motorbike in motion, you prefer to use 1/1000 s. What *f*-stop must you choose?

Aberrations in Camera Lenses

Spherical Aberration

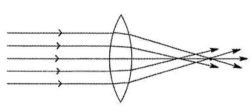

Figure 11.34

For a spherical lens, rays close to the principal axis focus further out from the lens than do rays that are further from the axis. The effect is shown exaggerated in **Figure 11.34**. There is actually not a single precise focal point, but a small focal region. The distortion produced by this effect is called **spherical aberration.** The effects of spherical aberration may be reduced by using small apertures such as *f* /16. High quality lenses are shaped to minimize spherical aberration.

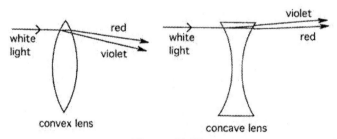

Figure 11.35

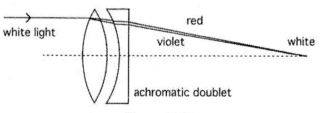

Figure 11.36

Chromatic Aberration

Since the index of refraction of the glass in a lens depends on the colour (wavelength) of light passing through it, white light passing through a lens experiences some **dispersion**. When light passes through a convex lens, the violet light is refracted more than the red (**Figure 11.35**). Likewise, light passing through a concave lens is also dispersed, with the violet being refracted more, but in this case diverging away from the principal axis.

To reduce **chromatic** (colour) **aberration**, lens makers make compound lenses, which are designed to cancel the effects due to chromatic aberration of a pair of lenses that are cemented together. The curvatures of the two lenses must be such that chromatic aberration is eliminated while still having an overall converging of the rays entering the lens. **Figure 11.36** shows how an **achromatic doublet**, a compound lens, corrects for red and violet aberration.

Turning the Image Right Side Up in Your Viewfinder

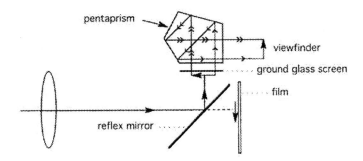

Figure 11.37

The real image formed by a camera lens is, of course, inverted on the film. When you look through the viewfinder of a typical 35 mm camera, you see the image right side up. What you see in the viewfinder is 'what you will get' in your photograph. Why is the image right side up in the viewfinder?

Figure 11.37 shows how a combination of a mirror and a five-sided prism is used to achieve the erect image. The plane mirror flips up when you release the shutter, so that light can get to the film. You may have noticed that when you take a photograph with a 35 mm camera, there is an instant when you can see nothing through the viewfinder.

A **single lens reflex camera** (SLR) is one that has one lens for both taking the picture and viewing. When you are composing the photograph, the **inverted image** formed by the lens is focussed on a **ground glass screen (Figure 11.37)**. A **pentaprism** re-inverts the image so you see it 'right side up' through the viewfinder. When you push the shutter button, the hinged **reflex mirror** flips up and the light from the lens falls on the film instead of on the ground glass screen. Many 35 mm film cameras are single lens reflex cameras. Less expensive cameras have a viewfinder that is separate from the lens. What you see through the viewfinder is not quite what the camera lens 'sees', and one has to be careful not to cut off people's heads in pictures taken with these cameras!

Other Optical Instruments

The Hand Magnifier

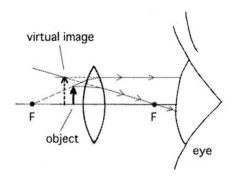

Figure 11.38

The simplest kind of microscope is a magnifying glass, which is a single convex lens. **Figure 11.38** indicates how it is used. The object is placed inside the principal focus. Rays from a point on the object diverge as they pass through the lens, so they cannot form a real image. A person looking into the lens, however, sees an **enlarged**, **erect**, **virtual image** of the object.

A crude magnifier can be made from either a drop of water or a rounded blob of glass made by melting some thin glass tubing and letting it solidify into a spherical shape.

Compound Microscope

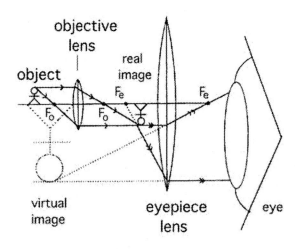

Figure 11.39

In a compound microscope, there are two lenses. As **Figure 11.39** shows, the **objective lens** forms an **enlarged real image** just inside the principal focus of a second lens, called the **eyepiece lens.** The real image serves as an **object** for the eyepiece lens, which acts as a magnifier for the first image. The final image is a virtual image (formed by the eyepiece lens) of the real image (formed by the objective lens). The final image is an inverted image of the object, because the real image was inverted by the objective lens.

Telescopes and Binoculars

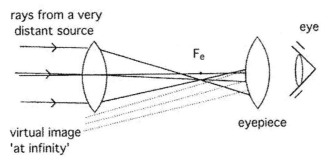

Figure 11.40

In the **astronomical telescope (Figure 11.40)**, the objective lens produces an inverted image that is magnified further by the eyepiece lens. The final image is virtual and inverted, but in astronomical work this is unimportant. In a **terrestrial telescope**, as used by a birdwatcher or a sea captain, it is important to have an upright image. This can be accomplished by adding a third lens in between the objective and the eyepiece. The objective lens forms an inverted real image. The third lens forms another real image, which is an inverted image of an inverted image! The eyepiece lens then magnifies the second real image. The final image is a virtual, upright image. A pair of **binoculars** is really two terrestrial telescopes side by side, except that the image is made right side up by using a pair of prisms inside each 'telescope' to invert the image laterally and vertically so that the final image is right side up.

Challenges

1. Find out how prisms are used to produce a 'right side up', 'right way around' image through binoculars.
2. Find out what a **Fresnel lens** is. (There is one in your classroom's overhead projector, and there may be one in the spotlights in your theatre.) What is the advantage of a Fresnel lens over a regular glass lens?
3. Figure out how your classroom overhead projector works.
4. Why are there so many lenses in a slide or movie projector? What are the **condenser lenses** used for? Why does the slide projector bulb sometimes have a concave mirror inside it?
5. Why does the manufacturer strongly recommend you not touch an overhead projector bulb with your bare hands? (What effect does oil have on infrared light?)
6. Find out how a zoom lens works.
7. What does a photographer mean by **depth of field**? Why does an f-stop like $f/22$ give far more depth of field than an f-stop of $f/2.8$?
8. Why are moon charts printed upside down?
9. If you wished to take a photograph through a microscope or a telescope, how would you change the arrangement of the eyepiece lens so that the final image was real and on the film of the camera? (The camera's own lens is removed.)
10. You are looking through a microscope at a tiny bug crawling from the bottom left corner of your slide to the top right corner. What will you see through your eyepiece lens?

Chapter Review Questions

1. Why do shopkeepers often place large convex mirrors at strategic locations in their stores?

2. Some light bulbs for slide projectors have a concave mirror built into them. Why is the filament of the light bulb placed at the centre of curvature of the mirror?

3. You wish to form an enlarged real image of a light bulb filament using a concave mirror. Where should the light bulb filament be placed, in relation to the mirror's vertex?

4. If you use a concave mirror in a spotlight, where should you place the filament of the light bulb?

5. If you use a concave mirror as a dressing or make-up mirror, where do you place your face in relation to the mirror?

6. An object is 2.5 m away from a concave mirror with a focal length of 1.0 m. Where will the image form? Will it be real or virtual?

7. A concave mirror has a focal length of 12.0 cm. Where is the object located if the image forms 15.0 cm from the mirror?

8. What is the focal length of a concave mirror if a real image, of an object 6.0 m away, forms 3.0 m from the mirror?

9. What is the ideal shape for a concave mirror, as used in a good quality telescope?

10. Why is a convex lens sometime called a 'burning glass'?

11. In a movie, a nearsighted young boy is shown using the lenses from his eyeglasses to light a fire, by focussing the sun's rays on some dried grass. What is wrong with this scene?

12. What are two things a photographer can do to change the amount of light getting to the film in a camera, during an exposure?

13. You wish to use a convex lens to achieve each of the following types of image. Where, in relation to the lens and the principal focus and/or centre of curvature, should you place the object?
    (a) a small, real, inverted image
    (b) a large, real inverted image
    (c) a real image the same size as the object
    (d) a large, erect virtual image

14. A camera lens focussed at infinity forms a real image 50 mm from the lens. How far out from the film must the lens be moved to focus on a person standing 3.0 m in front of the lens?

15. A telephoto lens forms an image on the film, which is 138 mm away, of an object 6.25 m in front of the lens. What is the focal length of the lens, in mm?

16. Why might the cornea of the eye be considered a 'lens'?

17. What is the function of these parts of the eye?
    (a) cornea (b) iris (c) pupil (d) retina (e) rod (f) cone (g) fovea centralis (h) optic nerve

18. What is the **blind spot**, and why is it 'blind'?

19. What is **hypermetropia**, and how is it corrected?

20. What is **myopia**, and how is it corrected?

21. What is **astigmatism**, and how is it corrected?

22. Discuss similarities between the camera and the human eye.

23. Why are compound lenses used in quality cameras?

24. Your camera light meter indicates that an f-stop of $f/8$ will give a properly exposed picture if the shutter speed is 1/60 s. You prefer to use an f-stop of $f/3.5$ because this will make a rose you are photographing appear in sharp focus, while the more distant background will be intentionally blurred. What shutter speed must you use?

25. How do lens makers correct for (a) spherical aberration and (b) chromatic aberration? Why does a curved mirror not have chromatic aberration?

26. What is the advantage of a single lens reflex camera over a camera with a separate lens for viewing the image?

27. In a slide or movie projector, where, in relation to the lens and its principal focus, must the slide be inserted? How must the slide or film be inserted? Why?

Test Yourself!

1. Copy and complete the following ray diagram, to show where the **image** of the candle will form, and what its relative size will be.

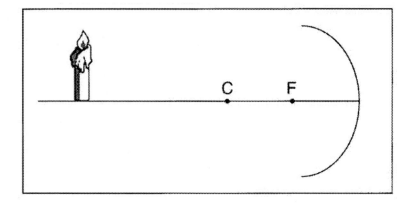

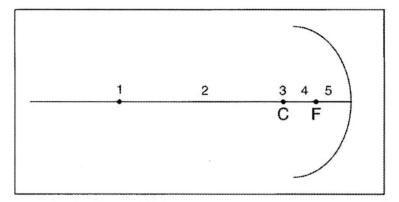

2. You wish to use a concave mirror (above) as a 'makeup' mirror, so that your image appears 'right side up' and magnified larger than life. In relation to the mirror, where should your face be located if you are using the mirror for this purpose?

   A. at 1
   B. at 2
   C. at 3
   D. at 4
   E. at 5

3. What is the distance from a concave mirror to a real image, if the focal length of the mirror is 15.0 cm, and the object is 45.0 cm in front of the mirror?

4. Copy and complete the following ray diagram to show where the image of the candle will form, and what its relative size will be.

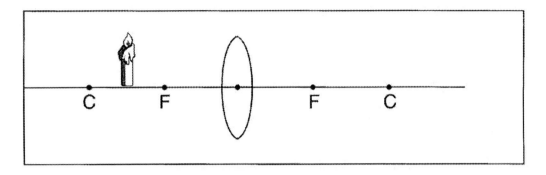

5. What is the focal length of a lens, if it forms a real image 20 mm away from one side of it, when a small lamp is placed on the other side, 30 mm from the lens?

6. The light meter of your camera suggests a properly exposed picture could be taken using a 1/125 s time exposure, with an aperture of f/11. You prefer to use 1/500 s, because you are trying to 'stop' action in a football game.

If you use 1/500 s, what f-stop should you use? Explain your choice.

Chapter 12   Static Electricity

12.1 Early History of Static Electricity

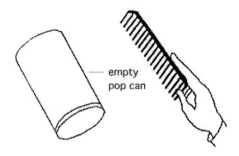

If you rub a balloon against your hair, you will probably be able to pick up bits of hair, dust, paper or thread with the balloon. **Figure 12.1** shows a light aluminum pop can being pulled along a table by the attraction of a comb that has just been run through someone's dry hair.

Figure 12.1

Certain materials, when rubbed with cloth, fur or wool, have an attractive effect on small, unattached objects. This effect was observed more than 2500 years ago in ancient Greece. **Amber**, a fossilized resin from trees, was used in those days for decoration and for barter. The Greeks noticed that amber, when rubbed against cloth, would pick up bits of dust, hair, straw and similar materials. The 'attractive power' of amber was not really understood, and it remained a mystery for many centuries.

The phenomenon of attraction by rubbed objects was not investigated with any seriousness until an Englishman, **Dr. William Gilbert (1544-1603),** studied it in some depth. Dr. Gilbert was the personal physician of Queen Elizabeth I. He was also a scientist of some note! Dr. Gilbert observed that many materials, amber included, if rubbed with appropriate fabrics, could be *electrified* so that they attracted small objects. Words like electricity, electrified, and later electron, originate with the Greek word for amber, which is **elektron.**

Charles Du Fay (1698-1739), a French scientist, went a step further than Gilbert when he showed that there were apparently *two kinds of electricity*. In *Investigation 12-1,* you will do an experiment similar in principle to the Du Fay experiments, but using modern materials.

Investigation 12-1   Two Kinds of Electric Charge

Purpose: To observe evidence that there are two kinds of electric charge.

Note: This activity is best done on a "dry" day!

Procedure

1. Rub a vinyl plastic strip with wool or fur. Dip the strip into a jar of fine sawdust to check whether the vinyl is 'electrified'. (The strip should pick up some sawdust.) If it is, tape the strip to a supporting insulating rod (glass or plastic) as in **Figure 12.2**, so that it hangs vertically.

2. Rub a second vinyl strip with wool, and when you have checked that it is electrified, bring it close and parallel to the hanging vinyl strip. Observe what effect the two strips have on each other. Do they attract each other or repel?

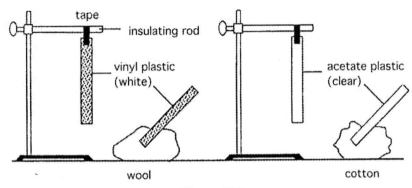

Figure 12.2

3. Rub an acetate strip with cotton. Check whether it is electrified using the sawdust, and then hang it from an insulating support rod. Rub a second acetate strip with cotton, check that it is electrified, and then bring it close to the first acetate strip. Do the two electrified acetate strips attract each other or repel?
4. Bring a freshly electrified acetate strip near a freshly electrified vinyl strip suspended vertically from a rod. What effect do the two electrified strips have on each other?

Concluding Question

Do your observations suggest that there is one kind of electricity or two? Explain.

12.2 Positive and Negative Charge

Charles Du Fay observed that two amber rods rubbed with fur would *repel* each other. Two glass rods rubbed with silk would also repel each other. If, however, an electrified glass rod were brought near an electrified amber rod, the two rods would attract each other. Du Fay came to the conclusion that there must be two kinds of electricity.

Du Fay called the two kinds of electricity **vitreous** (meaning glassy) and **resinous** (referring to amber, which is formed from tree resin). Eventually these terms were replaced by **positive electricity** and **negative electricity**. The modern terms were introduced by **Benjamin Franklin (1706-1790).** Franklin actually thought there was only one kind of electricity. In his view, an object that had an *excess* of electricity was positive; one with a deficiency of electricity was negative. His view was incorrect, but the terms he introduced are still used.

By convention, a glass rod rubbed with silk is said to have a **positive charge.** An amber rod rubbed with wool or fur is said to have a **negative charge.** In *Investigation 12-1,* the charge on the acetate strip rubbed with cotton was positive, while the charge on the vinyl strip rubbed with wool was negative.

Since the electric charges on electrified (charged) objects are not moving, they are referred to as **static charges** or **static electricity**. The word static means *not moving.*

As you saw in *Investigation 12-1,* a charged object will attract an uncharged (neutral) body, such as a piece of hair or dust. A charged object will also attract an oppositely charged body, but it will repel another body carrying the same charge.

Some Basic Rules of Static Electricity

1. **Bodies with the same charge repel each other.**
2. **Bodies with opposite charges attract each other.**
3. **A neutral body is attracted to either a positively charged body or a negatively charged body.**

12.3 The Electrical Atom

Prior to the present century, matter was thought to be made up of tiny, indivisible particles called atoms. The Atomic Theory of **John Dalton** assumed the atom had no internal structure. That is, it had no 'smaller bits'. **Sir Ernest Rutherford (1871-1937)** was the first person to show that the atom had, in fact, a **nucleus** where there was a concentration of positive charge. Since the atom was apparently neutral, there had to be negative charge somehow distributed around the nucleus. (Rutherford's experiment used newly identified particles called **alpha particles**, which are emitted from radioactive elements, as probes to reveal the internal structure of gold atoms.)

Rutherford was born in New Zealand. He came to McGill University in Montreal, Quebec, where he worked for seven years and contributed immensely to the understanding of the nature of the atom and of radioactivity. Rutherford is credited with the discovery of the nucleus of the atom, and he gave the positively charged **protons** within the nucleus their name. Credit for discovery of the negatively charged **electron** goes to **J. J. Thomson**, of Cambridge University in England. Rutherford worked with J. J. Thomson prior to coming to McGill University. **Robert A. Millikan**, an American physicist, was able to show experimentally that there is a 'smallest amount' of electric charge (the elementary charge) associated with electrons. The work of Thomson and Millikan provided information on both the mass and the charge associated with a single electron!

Rutherford's Theory of the Atom's Structure

Rutherford pictured the atom as a tiny planetary system, with electrons orbiting a positive nucleus. The positively charged particles in the nucleus are called protons. **Figure 12.3** includes **neutrons** in the nucleus. **James Chadwick**, one of Rutherford's contemporaries, discovered these neutral particles in 1932.

Neutrons carry no electrical charge. Their mass is just slightly greater than that of a proton, which is 1.67×10^{-27} kg. This is 1836 times greater than the mass of an electron, which is 9.11×10^{-31} kg.

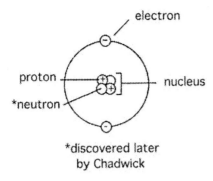

Figure 12.3

The smallest atom is that of hydrogen. Hydrogen atoms normally consist of a one-proton nucleus, with a single electron orbiting the proton. The proton by itself has a radius of about 10^{-15} m, while the radius of the whole atom is approximately 10^{-10} m. Rutherford believed that the hydrogen nucleus just might be the fundamental unit of positive charge, and it was Rutherford who first used the term **proton** for the hydrogen nucleus.

What Happens When an Object Is 'Charged'?

Atoms are normally neutral. Atoms can **gain electrons** or **lose electrons,** in which case they become electrically charged **ions**. Negative ions are atoms with extra electrons, while positive ions are atoms that are short of electrons. Protons are not directly involved in electrification, since they are locked in nuclei of the atoms and are not transferred from one material to the other during simple electrification.

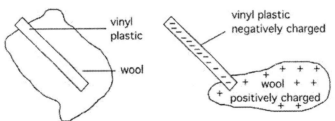

Figure 12.4

Figure 12.4 shows what happens when a vinyl strip is rubbed on wool. Vinyl has a stronger affinity for electrons than wool. When vinyl comes in contact with wool, electrons leave the wool and go to the surface of the vinyl. This leaves the vinyl with an excess of electrons, so it has a negative charge. The wool, having lost electrons, has a positive charge.

There is no 'creation' or 'destruction' of electric charge during this process of electrification. All that happens is that electrons are transferred from one body to another.

The Law of Conservation of Electric Charge

Experiments show that electric charge is never created and is never destroyed. Electric charge is a conserved quantity, like momentum and total energy.

Exercises

1. How could you find out whether the electric charge on your comb is positive or negative, after you comb your hair?
2. A rod made of ebonite, when rubbed with fur, repels a vinyl strip that was also rubbed with fur. What charge is on the ebonite?
3. What effect would a glass rod rubbed with silk have on an acetate rod rubbed with cotton?
4. A ping-pong ball hung by a string is attracted to *both* an electrified vinyl strip *and* an electrified acetate strip. What charge is probably on the ping-pong ball?
5. What are the three basic particles within the atom, and what electric charge does each carry?
6. Who discovered (a) the electron? (b) the nucleus? (c) the neutron?

Investigation 12-2 The Van de Graaff Generator

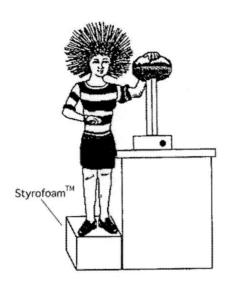

Styrofoam™

Figure 12.5

Purpose: To demonstrate static electrical effects on a large scale, using a static electric generator (a model Van de Graaff generator).

Procedure

1. Turn on the generator. Bring a graphite-painted ping-pong ball on a string close to the dome. If the dome is charged, the neutral ball should be attracted, then repelled as it picks up the same charge as the dome. *Do not discharge the ball.* It will be used to find out what charge is on the dome of the generator.
2. Find out whether the ball (and therefore the dome) is positive or negative, by bringing (a) a positively charged acetate strip (+) and (b) a negatively charged vinyl strip (-), near the ball. *Remember that like-charged objects repel each other.*

3. Turn off the room lights. Your teacher will demonstrate the discharging spark from the dome, by bringing a second, **grounded*** dome near the Van de Graaff generator dome. How long a spark can be obtained from the generator?
   [***Grounded** means '*connected to a large, conducting surface, such as the earth.*']
4. Turn off the generator and ground it. *Predict* what will happen to a handful of puffed rice placed on the dome, when the generator is charged up. Try it!
5. Turn off the generator and ground it. Place a stack of about 10 inverted, medium-sized aluminum pie plates on the dome. *Predict* what will happen to the pie plates when the generator is charged up. Try it!

6. Place a rabbit's fur (or a human wig?) on the discharged dome. **Predict** what will happen when the generator is charged up. Try it!

7. Discharge the dome of the generator. Your teacher will select a 'volunteer' for a hair-raising experience. The volunteer will stand on an insulating support, which might be a sturdy wooden chair, or a stack of Styrofoam plastic insulating sheets. The volunteer will place one hand on the dome of the generator. *The generator is turned on only after the volunteer is ready and in position.*

8. **Predict** what will happen if the ping-pong ball 'charge detector' is touched to the dome, and then brought near the subject holding on to the charged Van de Graaff generator. Try it!

Concluding Questions

1. What charge is on the Van de Graaff generator dome you used in this demonstration? How do you know this?

2. Why was the ping-pong ball first attracted, *then* repelled by the generator dome?

3. How would you describe the hair of the subjects for whom the hair-raising experiment worked best? Were there any common factors?

Figure 12.6: The author is holding on to the dome of a Van de Graaff generator. Fine sawdust gathers on his fingertips, illustrating the electric force field around his fingers.

12.4 Electrically Charged Objects

Conductors and Insulators

Electrical **conductors** are materials that allow charged particles (usually electrons) to pass through them with ease. Silver, copper and aluminum are excellent conductors, but all metals conduct well.

Atoms of metals have one or more outer electrons that are so loosely bound to their nuclei that they are classed as **free electrons**. It is these free electrons that are conducted through a metallic conductor when a suitable force is applied.

In electrical **insulators,** the electrons are tightly bound either to their parent atoms or to their neighbours, in a sharing arrangement. Electrons are not free to wander from atom to atom within the material. Surface electrons may, however, be transferred to another material with which the first material is in contact. For example, if wool and vinyl come in contact, some electrons will be attracted from the surface of the wool over to the surface of the vinyl. Then the vinyl will have an excess of negative charge. The wool will have a shortage of electrons and be positively charged. Since neither the vinyl nor the wool conducts electricity, both may hold on to their excess charge for quite some time.

Investigation 12-3 Charging by Conduction and Induction

Purpose: To learn how to charge objects (a) with and (b) without contact.

Part 1 Charging by Conduction

When you charge an object by touching it with another charged object, so that electrons can be conducted directly to it, you are charging it by **conduction**.

Procedure

1. Set two aluminum pop cans on or in Styrofoam™ cups, as in **Figure 12.7**. (Styrofoam is an excellent insulator, so it will keep any static charge you place on the cans from escaping to the bench.)

Figure 12.7

2. Place a **negative charge** on one of the cans as follows:
   (a) Rub a vinyl strip with wool or fur. You may hear a crackling sound if the vinyl is being charged. The vinyl will have a negative charge on it.
   (b) Rub the charged vinyl strip over one of the insulated pop cans. Excess electrons from the vinyl will flow onto the can, giving the can a negative charge.
   (c) Repeat the process several times, to make sure there is a lot of excess negative charge on the can.
3. Place a **positive charge** on the other can, as follows:
   (a) Rub an acetate strip with cotton. This will make the acetate positively charged, since electrons flow from the acetate onto the cotton.
   (b) Rub the acetate strip onto the second can. The positively charged acetate strip will attract electrons from the second metal pop can, making it positively charged.
   (c) Repeat this process several times, to make sure the second can has ample positive charge.
4. *Do not touch the metal cans!* Move the cans toward each other, touching only their insulated Styrofoam bases, until the cans are about 3 cm apart.
5. Carefully lower a graphite ball electroscope (**Figure 12.7**) between the two oppositely charged cans. Write down what you see happen.

Concluding Questions

1. What charge was on
   (a) the first can (touched with a charged vinyl strip)?
   (b) the second can (touched with a charged acetate strip)?
   (c) the graphite ball *before it was lowered between the cans?*

2. Explain what happened to the graphite ball during the experiment. Describe what happened to the **electrons** going to and from the three objects involved. Why does the action eventually stop?

Part 2 Charging by Induction

Imagine you have a negatively charged rod, but you wish to place a positive charge on another object. If you *touch* the other object with the negatively charged rod, you will charge it negatively (by conduction). However, if you use a method called **induction**, you can give it a charge that is *opposite* to the charge on the charging body.

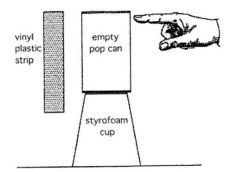
vinyl
plastic
strip

empty
pop can

styrofoam
cup

Procedure

1. Mount a pop can on (or in) a Styrofoam ™ cup.
2. Charge a vinyl strip negatively, by rubbing it with wool or fur.
3. Bring the vinyl strip *near and parallel to the pop can*, as in **Figure 12.8**, but *do not let the vinyl touch the can!*

Figure 12.8

4. ***Briefly touch the can with your finger, and then remove it and the vinyl strip completely. Predict* what charge is on the can.**

5. Work out a procedure to test for yourself whether the charge on the can is positive, negative or neutral. (Repeat **Procedures 2** to **4** several times if necessary, to establish what actually happened.)

Concluding Questions

1. Before you brought your finger near the can, what charge was on
   (a) the vinyl strip?
   (b) the side of the can near the vinyl strip?
   (c) the other side of the can?

2. Your finger can conduct electrons to or from your body. In this experiment, were electrons conducted to the can from your body, or from the can to your body?

3. (a) What was the final charge on the can?
   (b) Was this charge 'conducted' from the vinyl strip?
   (c) How did the can obtain this charge?

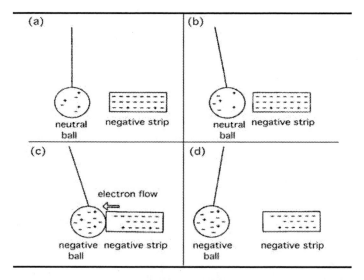

Figure 12.9

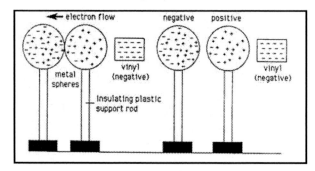

Figure 12.10

What Happens During Charging by Conduction?

Figure 12.9(a) shows a negatively charged vinyl strip being brought near a neutral ball. The vinyl strip has a huge surplus of negative **electrons**. As the negative strip approaches the ball [**Figure 12.9(b)**], electrons on the ball are repelled as far away as they can go, which is the far side of the ball. Positively charged protons are locked in their nuclei, so they 'stay put'. The near side of the ball has an **induced positive charge**, which is attracted to the negative charge of the vinyl strip. When the ball comes in contact with the vinyl strip as in **Figure 12.9(c)**, hordes of electrons flow over to the ball, attracted by the induced positive charge of the side of the ball near the vinyl strip. Now the ball has an excess of negative charge, so it is repelled by the vinyl strip [**Figure 12.9(d)**], which still has an excess of electrons. The ball, which was at first charged by **induction**, is now charged by **conduction**.

What Happens During Charging by Induction?

An object can be given a charge without even touching it. When this happens, it is called **charging by induction**. In **Figure 12.10**, a negatively charged vinyl strip has been brought *near, but not touching* a pair of metal spheres, which are insulated from the ground by a plastic support. The negative charge on the vinyl strip repels electrons away from it. Free electrons on the near sphere will tend to accumulate on the far sphere. If the two spheres are now separated (without removing the vinyl strip), the far sphere will have an excess of electrons and, therefore, a negative overall charge. The near sphere, having a shortage of electrons, will be positively charged. Once the spheres are separated, the vinyl strip can be removed from the scene. The two spheres have been given opposite charges by **induction**.

Note that charge has not been 'created' or 'destroyed' in this process. Charge has simply been re-distributed. The Law of Conservation of Charge has not been violated.

Challenge

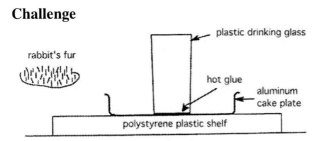

Charge a polystyrene plastic bookshelf, by rubbing it with wool or fur. This shelf will then be an excellent source of **negative** charge.

Attach an insulating handle to a rectangular aluminum cake tin. A plastic drinking glass can be used as the insulating handle. Use hot glue to attach it.

Figure 12.11

Set the cake tin down on top of the charged plastic shelf. Touch the cake tin briefly, and then lift the cake tin off the shelf. **Test** what charge is on the cake tin as follows: (a) Touch the charged tin with an electroscope ball. (The ball will have the same charge as the tin.) (b) Bring the ball near a charged vinyl strip (-), then a charged acetate strip. Which strip *repels* the ball? What charge is on the ball? What charge is on the cake tin?

Charge the shelf again. Place the cake tin on the charged shelf. This time, discharge the cake tin through a small fluorescent lamp or neon light (held in your hand). Lift the cake tin, and touch it with the lamp again! How often can you repeat this process?

Exercises

1. Replace the vinyl rod in **Figure 12.9** with a positive acetate rod, and redraw the sketches to show what happens with a positive charging strip.

2. Replace the vinyl rod in **Figure 12.10** with a positive acetate rod, and redraw the sketches to show what happens with a positive charging strip.

Inducing a Charge by *Grounding*

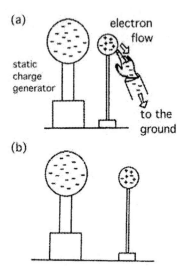

Figure 12.12

The earth is a fairly good conductor. It is also very, very large. It can give or receive a lot of charge without having its own total charge changed noticeably. If a charged object is connected to the ground by a good conductor, the charged object will lose essentially all its charge to the ground and become neutral. If the object is negatively charged, it will *lose* electrons to the ground. If the object is positively charged, it will *gain* electrons from the ground. In both situations, we say the object has been *grounded.*

Temporary grounding can be used to place a charge on an object that is *opposite to the charge on the charging body.* In **Figure 12.12**, a negatively charged static charge generator has been brought near a metal sphere on an insulating stand. If one touches the sphere, the negative charge on the generator repels electrons into your hand (and from there to **ground**). As soon as you take your hand away, the sphere will be left with a *shortage* of electrons; it now has a positive charge!

Exercise

If the static charge generator in **Figure 12.12** was **positively charged**, show what would happen to the charge on the sphere.

Chapter Review Questions

1. Who was the first to show that there are two kinds of electricity?

2. Who introduced the terms **positive** and **negative** with respect to electricity?

3. Which English scientist did the first true experiments with static electricity?

4. Who is credited with the discovery of the nucleus of the atom?

5. Who is credited with discovering the electron?

6. Who discovered the neutron?

7. What happens when a glass rod is rubbed with silk? (Explain why the glass develops a positive charge.) Is electric charge 'conserved' during this procedure? Explain.

8. Your comb attracts pieces of dust but repels a piece of vinyl plastic suspended from a string. What charge is on your comb? Explain.

9. What makes a metal a good conductor?

10. Why can insulators not conduct electricity as easily as metals?

11. A charged balloon will stick to a wall. Is the wall charged by conduction or by induction? Explain.

12. A single pop can is sitting on an insulating stand.
    (a) How can you give the pop can
       (i) the same charge as an acetate strip?
       (ii) the opposite charge but still using the acetate strip to charge it?
    (b) In which case are you charging by conduction, and in which case are you charging by induction?

13. What does **grounding** mean in electricity?

Test Yourself!

1. Negative is to electron as positive is to
   A. atom.
   B. neutron.
   C. molecule.
   D. proton.
2. What is the neutral particle found inside the core of the atom?
   A. electron
   B. neutron
   C. nucleus
   D. proton
3. An acetate plastic strip rubbed with cotton *repels* a glass rod rubbed with silk. What is the charge on the glass rod?
   A. neutral or negative
   B. neutral or positive
   C. definitely positive
   D. definitely negative
4. Where is the safest place to be during a lightning storm?
   A. inside your car
   B. on top of a tall tree
   C. on top of your car
   D. in a boat on a lake
   E. under a tall tree
5. Why is it difficult to place a static electrical charge on a hand-held copper rod, by rubbing it with other materials?
   A. Copper has too few electrons in it.
   B. Copper is too good a conductor.
   C. Electrons will not move through the copper.
   D. Copper is too good an insulator.
6. What happens when a positively charged rod is brought near a metal ball?
   A. Protons on the ball are attracted to the positive rod.
   B. Electrons on the ball move to the side of the ball closest to the positive rod.
   C. Electrons on the ball move to the side of the ball farthest from the positive rod.
   D. Protons on the ball are repelled to the side of the ball farthest from the rod.
7. Static electricity can best be detected with
   A. an ammeter.
   B. an electroscope.
   C. an ohmmeter.
   D. a galvanometer.

Open-Ended Question

You are given a metal pop can sitting on an insulating plastic cup. You are also given a vinyl plastic strip and some wool fabric.
 (a) Describe how you would place a **negative charge** on the pop can.
 (b) Describe how you would place a **positive charge** on the pop can.

Chapter 13 Current Electricity

13.1 What Is Electric Current?

An **electric current** exists when charged particles move from one place to another. In most situations you will encounter, a current consists of a flow of electrons in wires made of metals such as copper or aluminum. Electric currents can and do exist in water solutions of acids, bases and salts, and in gas discharge tubes such as neon lights, fluorescent lights, and sodium street lights. In these situations, the current may consist of positively charged ions and/or negatively charged ions, as well as electrons.

Figure 13.1

In **Figure 13.1**, a current of positively charged ions is causing the candle flame to be blown to the right. The **Van de Graaff** generator dome on the left is positively charged, and the dome on the right is negatively charged. The strong electric field between the two domes ionizes the air molecules in the space between them. Positive ions go to the right, and negative electrons go to the left.

Current is the amount of electric charge that passes a point in a circuit in one second.

If an amount of charge Q passes a point in a conductor in time t, then the average current I through that point is:

$$I = \frac{Q}{t}.$$

Since **charge** is measured in units called **coulombs**, current could be measured in **coulombs per second** (C/s), but one coulomb per second is called an **ampere**.

$$1 \text{ A} = 1 \text{ C/s}.$$

The ampere is named after **André Ampère (1775-1836)**, a French physicist.

One ampere is the magnitude of current that exists in a 100 W light bulb in your home. (A 100 W light bulb in a 110 V circuit draws approximately 0.9 A.) In terms of electrons, a current of one ampere means there are 6 240 000 000 000 000 000 electrons passing a point in a conductor every second!

$1 \text{ A} = 6.24 \times 10^{18}$ electrons per second

In many applications an ampere is too large a unit of current to use. Smaller units include the milliampere (mA) and the microampere (μA).

$$1 \text{ mA} = \frac{1}{1000} \text{ A} = 0.001 \text{ A} = 10^{-3} \text{ A}$$

$$1 \text{ } \mu\text{A} = \frac{1}{1\,000\,000} \text{ A} = 0.000\,001 \text{ A} = 10^{-6} \text{ A}$$

'Current Events' in History

Until 200 years ago, the idea that one could produce a steady current of electricity and put it to use was nonexistent. The discovery of a way to produce a flow of electric charges was, in fact, accidental. In the year 1780, at the University of Bologna, Italian professor of anatomy **Luigi Galvani (1737-1798)** was dissecting a frog. First he noticed that when a nearby static electricity generator made a spark, the frog's legs would jump as its muscles contracted, *if a metal knife was touching the frog's nerves!* Galvani proceeded to look for the conditions that caused this behaviour.* In the course of his investigations, Galvani discovered that if two different metal objects (such as a brass hook and an iron support) touched each other, while also touching the frog's exposed flesh, the same contractions of the frog's legs were observed. Galvani thought that the source of the electricity was in the frog itself, and he called the phenomenon 'animal electricity'.

Another scientist, physics professor **Alessandro Volta (1745-1827)**, of the University of Pavia, set about to test Galvani's 'animal electricity' theory for himself. Before long, Volta discovered that the source of the electricity was in the contact of two different metals. The animal (frog) was incidental. Any two different metals, if they are immersed in a conducting solution (acid, base or salt) will produce an electric current. Volta was able to show that some pairs of metals worked better than others. Of course, there were no ammeters or voltmeters to compare currents and voltages in those days. One of the ways that Volta compared currents was to use the response of muscle tissue of dead frogs. Volta actually invented the first practical electric battery. Zinc and silver disks, separated by paper pads soaked with salt water, acted as electric cells. Stacked one on top of another, these cells became a 'battery' that yielded more current than a single cell.

Ehren Stillman

*Neither Galvani nor Volta explained this observation. (There is no truth to the rumour that the frog's leg jumped because 1780 was a 'leap year'.) Many years later it was learned that **radio waves** generated by the sparking generator induced a current in the metal scalpel that was penetrating the frog, even though the scalpel was some distance from the generator!

13.2 Cells and Batteries

There are many types of electric cell in existence today. Usually when you purchase a 'battery' in a store, you are actually buying a single **cell.** Strictly speaking, a battery is made of two or more cells connected together. Nine-volt batteries used in transistor radios, tape recorders, calculators and smoke alarms are true 'batteries'. Inside a 9 V battery, there are six small 1.5 V cells connected together, one after the other (in series).

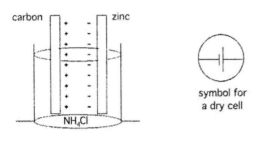

Figure 13.2

symbol for a dry cell

Figure 13.2 shows one type of **voltaic cell** (after Volta). The two rods (**electrodes**) are made of carbon and zinc, as in the traditional **'dry cell'**, but they are immersed in a solution of ammonium chloride (NH_4Cl). In a real dry cell, a paste made of NH_4Cl, sawdust and other ingredients is used. The chemistry of voltaic cells will be left to your chemistry courses.

The reaction that occurs, however, has the effect of *removing electrons* from the carbon electrode (making it **positive**) and adding them to the zinc (making the zinc negative). In a real dry cell, the outer casing of the cell is made of zinc. The zinc is dissolved away as the cell is used, and may eventually leak its contents.

There are many kinds of cells and batteries. Rechargeable 'batteries' use combinations such as nickel and cadmium, molybdenum and lithium, or lead and lead oxide (as in the standard car battery). There are many other kinds of cells on the market today, but they all produce electric current when connected to a conducting path!

13.3 Current Direction

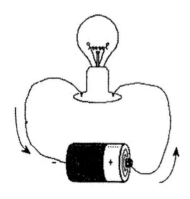

Figure 13.3

French physicist **André Ampère** was interested in the relationship between electric current and magnetism. At the time he did his experiments, he had no way of knowing just what electric current really was. As far as he knew, it might have consisted of positive charges moving one way through a conductor, *or* negative charges moving in the opposite direction, or both! Ampère decided *arbitrarily* to assume that the direction of electric current was the direction that **positive charges** would move between two points where there is a potential difference.

In **Figure 13.3**, **conventional current direction** is shown. If positive charges *could* move in a solid conductor, they would move from the positive terminal of the cell, through the wire and lamp, and back to the negative terminal of the cell.

In solid conductors, it is negative charges (electrons) that actually move. In solid conductors, the positive charges (protons) are locked in the nuclei of atoms, which are relatively fixed in their locations in the crystal. Loosely attached conduction electrons (free electrons) can, however, move from atom to atom.

Why is the direction of positive charges still used as the conventional current direction? There are many situations where the flow of charges *may* consist of positively charged ions as well as negatively charged ions or electrons. In liquids and gases, it is quite possible for both positive and negative ions to flow.

Some electronics books use the direction of electrons for current direction. Most physics textbooks stay with conventional current direction; that is, the direction that positive charges *would* take if they could move (whether they can move in a given situation or not).

Exercises

1. Change these currents to amperes (A).
   (a) 540 mA   (b) 21 mA   (c) 1500 mA   (d) 1.2 mA   (e) 56 μA   (f) 350 μA
2. Express these currents in milliamperes (mA).
   (a) 0.0024 A   (b) 2.5 A   (c) 0.078 A   (d) 0.49 A   (e) 0.00068 A
3. Express these currents in microamperes (μA).
   (a) 0.0000056 A   (b) 0.000048 A

Investigation 13-1 Measuring Electric Current

Purpose: To learn how to use and read the scale on an ammeter, which is designed specifically to measure electric current.

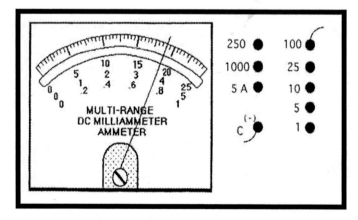

Figure 13.4

Procedure

1. Examine the scales on your ammeter. **Figure 13.4** shows the various ranges of current measured by one commonly used laboratory ammeter. It should be remembered that the number beside the binding post you choose to use is the *highest* current reading of the ammeter scale. In **Figure 13.4**, the 100 mA range is being used. There are three sets of numbers on the meter. The bottom set ends with **[1]**. If you are using the **100 mA** binding post, you will read the **[1]** as **100 mA**. The needle is between 70 mA and 80 mA. Since it is 3/5 of the way between 70 mA and 80 mA, the correct reading is **76 mA**.
2. Familiarize yourself with the other ranges. With the needle just where it is, what current would the meter be reading if the wire was connected to each of these binding posts?
   (a) 5 A (b) 1000 mA (c) 250 mA (d) 25 mA (e) 10 mA (f) 5 mA (g) 1 mA

> You will be supplied with a freshly charged nickel-cadmium battery, a milliammeter, connecting wires, three identical 1.5 V light bulbs in sockets. Make a copy of **Figure 13.5** in your record book.

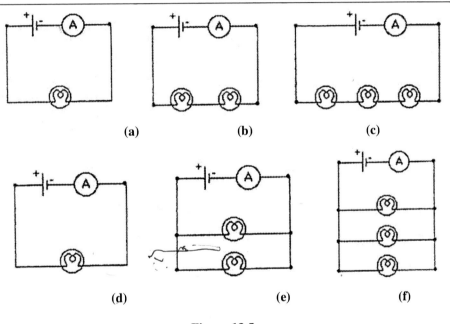

Figure 13.5

3. In turn, set up each of the circuits shown in **Figures 13.5(a)** to **13.5(f)**. Connect the negative terminal of the battery to the black (-) terminal of the milliammeter. Start by using the **5 A** range of the milliammeter, and adjust as necessary.
4. As you complete each circuit, read the current in mA, and record it on your copy of **Figure 13.5**.
5. For each circuit with more than one bulb in it, try loosening one bulb for a moment. What effect does this have on the other light bulbs, and on the current?

Concluding Questions

1. In circuits **13.5(a)** to **13.5(c)**, all the light bulbs are connected in one continuous path. These are **series circuits**. How did the current change when you added more and more light bulbs 'in series'?
2. In circuits **13.5(d)** to **13.5(f)**, the light bulbs were connected in parallel paths. These were **parallel circuits**. What happened to the current when you added more and more light bulbs 'in parallel'?

13.4 Electromotive Force (emf)

In a carbon-zinc dry cell, forces resulting from the chemical reaction within the cell drive charges to the terminals, doing work to overcome the repulsive forces. The work done on the charges increases their potential energy. The difference in potential energy between the terminals amounts to 1.5 J for every coulomb of charge separated. We say the **potential difference** (P.D.) is 1.5 J/C, or 1.5 V. For a cell or battery that is not supplying current, the potential difference is at its peak value, which is called the **electromotive force (emf)**. It is given the symbol $\mathcal{E}$.

For a dry cell, the emf is 1.5 V. A nickel-cadmium cell is usually labelled 1.25 V, but a freshly charged nickel-cadmium battery will have a higher emf than its labelled rating. The cells in a lead storage battery have emf's of 2 V each. Six of these cells connected in series within the battery give a total emf of 12 V.

13.5 Voltage in Circuits

What Is Battery Voltage?

When you buy a battery, you must be sure to get one with the proper **voltage** for its intended purpose. The voltage of a battery tells you how much **energy** that battery supplies each unit of charge (**coulomb**) it delivers.

The voltage of a battery is one volt (V) if one joule (J) of energy is supplied to each coulomb (C) of charge delivered by the battery.

$$1 \text{ volt} = 1 \frac{\text{joule}}{\text{coulomb}} \text{ , or } 1 \text{ V} = 1 \text{ J/C}$$

Sources of Potential Difference (Voltage)

A **current** exists only if there is a **voltage** between the ends of the conductor in which the charges are moving. To obtain a steady current (as opposed to a brief spark that you might get between your finger and a metal tap after you have walked over a carpet), you need a **voltage source**, such as a chemical cell or a generator. A photocell is another possible voltage source, providing there is light to shine on it.

A chemical cell has two different metals, and a conducting solution between them. A chemical reaction occurring inside the cells tends to *remove* electrons from one metal (making it positive) and add them to the other metal (making it negative). Because of the work done on the electrons in moving them from one electrode to the other, a **potential (energy) difference** develops between the two terminals attached to the metals. The **voltage** of the cell or battery tells you how much potential energy per coulomb is available from the charges in the cell. In a standard zinc-carbon dry cell, the potential difference, or **voltage**, between the terminals is 1.5 J/C, or 1.5 V. This is the **terminal voltage**, or **source voltage**. (The source voltage is equal to the **electromotive force**, or **emf** *when the cell is not providing current.*) The cell's voltage depends on the combination of metals in it. (A nickel-cadmium cell, for example, is rated 1.25 V.)

Generators are a major source of potential difference. The generator changes mechanical energy (of water, steam or perhaps wind) into electrical energy. Large generators can produce a potential difference of 500 000 V. By the time electricity is delivered to your home, transformers have reduced the voltage to 120 V or 240 V.

Investigation 13-2   Measuring Voltage

Purpose: To learn how to use and read a voltmeter, and to learn what a potential divider (potentiometer) does.

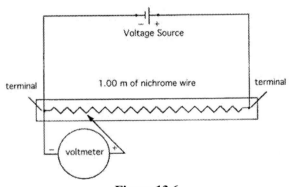

Figure 13.6

Procedure

1. Set up the apparatus in **Figure 13.6**. A voltage source (either 1.5 V or 3.0 V) is connected to the two ends of a 1.00 m nichrome wire, which is attached to a metre stick. (Nichrome is an alloy of iron, nickel and chromium.)

2. Connect the negative terminal of your voltmeter (black binding post) to the negative terminal of your battery. Connect the positive terminal of your voltmeter (red binding post) to the positive terminal of your battery. Measure the potential difference (voltage) between the two terminals of the battery. This potential difference is called the **terminal voltage** of the battery.

3. Remove the voltmeter from the battery. Connect the terminals of the battery to the terminals of the nichrome wire. Connect the negative terminal of the voltmeter to the end of the nichrome wire that is connected to the negative end of the battery. Touch the positive lead from the voltmeter to the nichrome wire at the 10.0 cm mark and record the voltage. Repeat at the 20.0 cm, 30.0 cm, 40.0 cm and up to 100.0 cm mark. Organize your data as in **Table 13.1**.

Table 13.1

Length of Wire L (cm)	0	10.0	20.0	30.0	40.0	50.0	60.0	70.0	80.0	90.0	100.0
Voltage V (V)											

4. Plot a graph with Voltage (V) on the Y-axis and Length of Nichrome Wire (L) on the X-axis.

Concluding Questions

1. Determine the slope of your graph of Voltage vs Length of Wire. Express your slope in appropriate units.

2. Write an equation for your line, with V as the subject of the equation. Include proper units for the slope in your equation relating V and L.

3. Explain why the arrangement you have just used is called a **potential divider**. Describe what would happen if you replaced the voltmeter with (a) a light bulb and (b) a small electric motor.

4. Examine a laboratory potential divider. Make a sketch of the coil of nichrome wire in its backside, and describe how it is (a) similar to and (b) different than the 'slide-wire' potential divider you used in this investigation.

Voltage in a Part of a Circuit

When you measure the **voltage** of a battery, you measure *how much energy is gained* in the battery *by each coulomb of charge*. You can measure voltage with a **voltmeter**. In *Investigation 13-3,* you will measure the voltages of several batteries.

If a battery is connected in a circuit, and a complete path is provided in which the electrons can flow, then the electrons will *lose* energy as they pass through the circuit. *Since energy is a conserved quantity, the energy lost in the circuit should equal the energy gained in the battery.* This can be checked out using a voltmeter.

A voltmeter is connected between the two ends of the part of the circuit that you are testing, so that it is *parallel* to that part of the circuit. The voltmeter will measure how much energy each coulomb of charge loses in that part of the circuit. In this situation, voltage is *loss of energy per coulomb* instead of gain of energy per coulomb.

Investigation 13-3 Voltage in Circuits

Purpose: To learn how to measure voltage, and to compare battery voltage (energy gain) with external voltage (energy loss).

Part 1 **Measuring Battery Voltages**

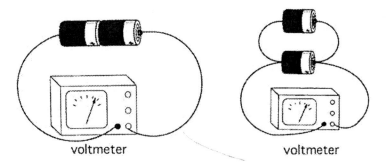

| **Figure 13.7** | **Figure 13.8** |

Procedure

1. You are supplied with 4 rechargeable nickel-cadmium cells. Connect the red connecting lead (wire) of your voltmeter to the positive (+) terminal of one of the cells. Connect the black lead to the negative (-) terminal of the cell. Write down the **voltage** of the cell, in **volts** (V). In parentheses beside it, write down what the manufacturer says the voltage *should* be. [**Example: 1.35 V (1.25 V)**]

2. Connect two of the cells in **series**, as in **Figure 13.7**. Write down the voltage of a battery of two cells in series. (Use a copy of **Table 13.2**.)

3. Measure the voltage of 3 cells in series, then 4 cells in series. Record your measurements in **Table 13.2**.

Table 13.2   Voltage of Cells in Series

Number of Cells in Series	Voltage of Battery (V)
1	
2	
3	
4	

4. Connect two of the cells in **parallel**, as in **Figure 13.8**. Measure and write down the voltage of two cells in parallel. Use a copy of **Table 13.3**.

5. Measure the voltage of 3 cells in parallel, then 4 cells in parallel. Record your measurements in **Table 13.3.**

Table 13.3   Voltage of Cells in Parallel

Number of Cells in Parallel	Voltage of Battery (V)
1	
2	
3	
4	

Part 2   Measuring Voltages in a Complete Circuit

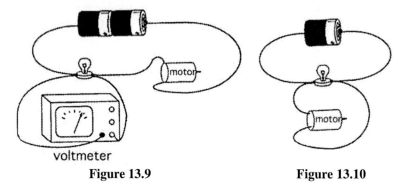

Figure 13.9   Figure 13.10

Procedure

1. Connect a circuit like the one in **Figure 13.9**. It has a battery of two or more cells in series, a light bulb, and a small motor. Use the smallest number of cells that will keep the bulb lit and the motor turning. Notice that all the components of this circuit are connected in one, uninterrupted conducting path. This is a **series circuit**.
2. (a)   Measure the battery voltage with your voltmeter, and write it down.
   (b)   Measure the voltage across the lamp, by connecting the voltmeter to the two terminals of the lamp. Write it down.
   (c)   Measure the voltage across the motor, and write it down.
3. Connect the light bulb and motor **in parallel** with each other and with one cell. See **Figure 13.10**.
4. Measure the voltage across (a) the cell, (b) the light bulb, and (c) the motor.

Concluding Questions

1. What happens to the voltage of a battery when you add more cells in series?
2. (a) What happens to the voltage of a battery when you add more cells in parallel?
   (b) What is the advantage to connecting cells in parallel inside a battery?
3. In a **series circuit**, how does the battery voltage compare with the sum of the voltages across the parts of the external circuit?
4. In a **parallel circuit**, how does the battery voltage compare with the voltage of the external parts of the circuit?
5. In a **parallel circuit**, what special feature did you notice about the voltages of the branches of the circuit?

13.6 Drift Velocity

How fast do electrons move in a wire carrying a current of, say 1 A? When a switch is closed in a circuit, the effect of the current can be detected immediately throughout the entire circuit. This might lead one to conclude that the electric charges (usually electrons) travel at very high velocity through the circuit. In fact, this is not so! The average **'drift velocity'** of electrons in a given set of circumstances can be calculated.

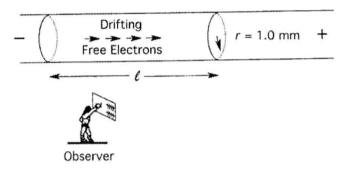

Figure 13.11

Within a length of metal wire, there are many, many loosely attached electrons (sometimes called 'free electrons'), which move about much as the molecules in a container of gas might move. Silver is an excellent conductor. Let us assume there is one free electron for every silver atom in a piece of wire. When the wire is connected to a source of emf, the potential difference (voltage) will cause electrons to move from the negative terminal of the source of emf toward the positive terminal. This movement is *superimposed* upon the random motion of the electrons that is going on all the time with or without a source of emf.

The 'trip' the electrons make from the negative to the positive terminal is not a smooth one. Electrons in the metal wire collide with positive silver ions on the way, and transfer some of their kinetic energy to the silver ions. The increased thermal energy of the silver ions will show up as an increase in temperature of the silver conductor.

Assume current in the silver wire in **Figure 13.11** is **1.0 A**.

Then there are **6.24 x 10^{18} electrons** passing the 'observer' each second. This is because

$$1.0 \text{ A } = 1.0 \text{ C/s } = 6.24 \text{ x } 10^{18} \text{ e/s.}$$

To calculate the average **drift velocity** of the electrons, we start by again assuming that there is *one free electron for every silver atom,* a reasonable assumption, since chemists tell us that silver usually forms ions with a charge of +1.

All we need to know is what **length** of the silver wire in **Figure 13.11** would contain 6.24 x 10^{18} silver atoms (and therefore 6.24 x 10^{18} **free electrons**). We can find this out in three steps, as follows:

(1) The **mass** of silver needed to have 6.24×10^{18} free electrons is:

$$\textbf{mass} = \frac{6.24 \times 10^{18} \text{ atoms}}{6.02 \times 10^{23} \text{ atoms/mole}} \times 108 \text{ g/mole} = 1.12 \times 10^{-3} \text{ g}.$$

(2) The **volume** of silver wire needed to have 6.24×10^{18} free electrons is:

$$\textbf{volume} = \frac{\text{mass}}{\text{density}} = \frac{1.12 \times 10^{-3} \text{ g}}{10.5 \text{ g/cm}^3} = 1.07 \times 10^{-4} \text{ cm}^3 .$$

(3) The radius of the silver wire in **Figure 13.11** is 1.0 mm, or 1.0×10^{-1} cm. Its cross-sectional area is πr^2, so the **length**, ℓ, can be found as follows:

$$\textbf{length, } \ell = \frac{\text{volume}}{\text{area}} = \ell \frac{1.07 \times 10^{-4} \text{ cm}^3}{\pi\{1.0 \times 10^{-1} \text{ cm}\}^2} = 3.4 \times 10^{-3} \text{ cm} .$$

Since a length of 3.4×10^{-3} cm contains 6.24×10^{18} electrons, and this many electrons pass the observer in 1 s, the **average drift velocity** of the **conducting electrons** is 3.4×10^{-3} cm/s, or 0.034 mm/s! This is true only for the stated conditions, of course. If the amount of current, the nature of the material in the conductor, or the dimensions of the conductor changes, then the drift velocity will change accordingly.

When you turn on a switch to light a lamp using a battery, the change in the electric field may travel at the speed of light, but the electrons themselves drift ever so slowly through the wire, under the influence of the electric field.

Investigation 13-4 Measuring Current Using Electroplating

Purpose: To measure current by counting copper atoms deposited on a carbon rod in a measured amount of time.

$$\mathcal{E} = 1.5 \text{ V}$$

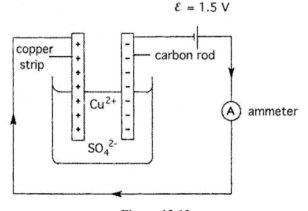

Figure 13.12

Introduction

A solution of copper II sulfate contains two kinds of ions: Cu^{2+} ions, which give the solution its blue colour, and SO_4^{2-} ions, which are colourless. If two electrodes are immersed in the copper II sulfate solution, and connected to a source of emf, the electrode connected to the positive terminal of the cell will attract SO_4^{2-} ions, and the electrode connected to the negative terminal of the cell will attract Cu^{2+} ions.

Cu^{2+} ions attracted to the negative electrode pick up two electrons, and deposit themselves on the negative electrode as **copper atoms, Cu^0.**

$$Cu^{2+} + 2e^- \rightarrow Cu^0$$

Meanwhile, at the positive electrode, which is made of copper, copper atoms *lose* two electrons and become copper ions, thus replenishing the Cu^{2+} ions in the solution.

$$Cu^0 \rightarrow Cu^{2+} + 2e^-$$

The two electrons return to the source of emf, the cell.

In this experiment, you allow the copper atoms to **plate** on to a negatively charged carbon electrode. If you measure the **increase in mass** of the carbon electrode after, say, twenty minutes of copper-plating, you can calculate the mass of copper plated, thus the number of copper atoms plated, and from this the number of electrons that were transferred in the twenty minutes. Finally you can calculate the **current** in amperes. You can also compare your calculated current with the current measured with an ammeter placed in the same circuit.

Procedure

1. Measure as precisely as you can the **mass** of a dry, clean carbon rod.
2. Set up the circuit in **Figure 13.12**. Make sure the carbon rod is connected to the negative terminal of the dry cell or other DC power source. The red binding post of the ammeter should be connected to the positive terminal of the cell, and an appropriate current range chosen as quickly as possible when the current is turned on. *Let the current run for a carefully measured time, such as 20 minutes.* Record current frequently, and *average* it.
3. As soon as the current is turned off, carefully remove the carbon electrode. Dip it in a beaker of methyl hydrate, and allow it time to dry. A heat lamp can be used to speed drying.

Caution! Methyl hydrate is flammable!

4. Measure the mass of the plated carbon rod precisely, and calculate the amount of **copper** that has plated on its surface. Record the mass of copper.
5. To remove the copper, set up the circuit once more, but *reverse the connections to* the cell so that the copper plates back on to the copper strip.

Concluding Questions

1. One mole of copper atoms (63.5 g) contains 6.02 x 10^{23} atoms. Using this information and the mass of copper plated on the carbon rod, calculate
   (a) the *number of copper atoms plated;*
   (b) the *number of electrons transferred;* and
   (c) the *number of coulombs transferred in 20 min.*
2. If 1 A = 1 C/s, what was the current in A?
3. Compare your calculated current with the measured current, by calculating the percent difference between the two currents.

Exercises

1. If the current in a wire is 5.0 A, how many coulombs of charge pass a point in the wire in one minute?
2. What is the current if 6.0 x 10^3 C pass a point in a circuit in 10.0 min?
3. If the current in a circuit is 12 A, how many electrons pass a point in one hour?
4. The drift speed of electrons in a copper wire running from a battery to a light bulb and back is approximately 0.020 mm/s. The battery is at the front of a classroom and wires run around the perimeter of the room to the light bulb. The total length of wire is 40.0 m. How long would it take a single electron to drift from the negative terminal of the battery back to the positive terminal? Express your answer in days.
5. How much copper would be plated by a current of 1.5 A in a time of 1.0 h?
6. How much silver is deposited by a current of 1.000 A in 1.000 h? The mass of one mole of silver atoms is 107.9 g.

$$Ag^+ \ + \ 1e^- \ \rightarrow \ Ag^0$$

13.7 Electrical Resistance

The **current** that exists in a conductor depends on two factors:

(1) The potential difference (**voltage**) that exists between the ends of the conductor. If the conductor is the only conductor connected to the voltage source, this potential difference will just be the terminal voltage of the source.

(2) The amount of resistance that the conductor offers to the flow of charges through it. This property, called **resistance**, depends in turn on:
   (a) how thick the conductor is;
   (b) how long the conductor is;
   (c) the material used to make the conductor; and
   (d) the temperature of the conductor.

In *Investigation 13-5,* you will do an experiment similar in nature to one first done by **Georg Simon Ohm (1787-1854).** The result of experiments like this was a general rule for metallic conductors, called **Ohm's Law.**

Investigation 13-5   Ohm's Law

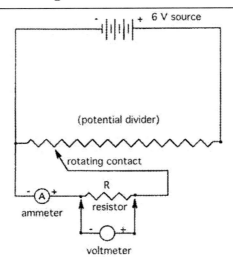

Figure 13.13

Purpose: **To see how the current in a conductor varies with the potential difference (voltage applied to its ends).**

Procedure

1. Connect a 6 V D.C. power supply to the two end terminals of a laboratory potentiometer, as in **Figure 13.13**. Connect an ammeter (on its *least* sensitive range) and a carbon resistor to the end post and centre post of the potentiometer, as shown in the figure. Connect a voltmeter to the two ends of the resistor. The ammeter will measure the current in the resistor, and the voltmeter will read the potential difference (voltage) between the two ends of the resistor.

2. Using the rotating contact, vary the potential difference across the resistor in steps ranging from 0 V up to, say, 5.0 V. Choose a range on the ammeter which will permit you to read all the currents on the same range, and record the current for each of the voltages in **Table 13.4**.

Table 13.4 Data for *Investigation 13-5*

Voltage V (V)	0	0.50	1.00	1.50	2.00	2.50	3.00	3.50	4.00	4.50	5.00
Current I (A)											

3. Plot a graph with voltage (V) on the Y-axis and current (I) on the X-axis.

4. Calculate the slope of your graph. The units for the slope will have the dimensions of [V/A]. This slope is the electrical **resistance** (R) of your resistor and is measured in **ohms (Ω).**

5. Repeat **Procedures 1-4** using a different resistor. Plot a graph on the same sheet as the first graph and determine its slope.

Concluding Questions

1. According to your data, how does the voltage across a resistor vary with the current in the resistor?
2. What were the resistances, in ohms, of your two resistors?
3. **Table 13.5** tells you how to figure out the manufacturer's estimate of the resistance of your resistors using a colour code. Use the table to figure out what the resistances of your resistors is supposed to be according to the manufacturer, then see if your measured values fall within the range given by the colour codes.
4. What would be the major sources of error in this investigation?

Table 13.5 Resistor Colour Code

Band Colour	Number	Multiplier	Tolerance
black	0	$10^0 (= 1)$	
brown	1	10^1	
red	2	10^2	
orange	3	10^3	
yellow	4	10^4	
green	5	10^5	
blue	6	10^6	
violet	7	10^7	
gray	8	10^8	
white	9	10^9	
gold			5%
silver			10%
(No colour)			20%

Resistor Colour Code: Resistors are either labelled with their resistance or colour-coded with four coloured bands, each of which has significance. The first coloured band gives the first digit in the resistance, and the second coloured band gives the second digit. The third coloured band gives the power of ten multiplier (the number of zeros following the first two digits). The fourth coloured band, if there is one, gives the manufacturer's tolerance. A gold band means the resistance of the resistor is accurate to within 5%. A silver band means the resistance is accurate to within 10%. If there is no fourth band, the resistance is only accurate to within 20%.

Example

A resistor has these coloured bands: brown, black, orange, silver. What is the resistance?

Solution

The first digit is 1 (brown); the second digit is 0 (black) and these digits are followed by three zeros (orange). The resistance is 10 000 Ω with a tolerance (uncertainty) of 10% (silver band). The resistance can be written 10 000 ± 1 000 Ω. The manufacturer therefore claims that the resistance of the resistor is between 9 000 Ω and 11 000 Ω.

Resistors

Under normal circumstances, every conductor of electricity offers some resistance to the flow of electric charges, and is therefore a **resistor.** In any resistor, electrical energy is transformed into thermal energy. (There are some materials which, if cooled to temperatures approaching 0 K, offer no resistance to the flow of charges. These materials are called **superconductors**.) Usually when we use the term resistors we refer to devices manufactured specifically to control the amount of current in a circuit.

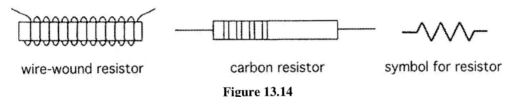

wire-wound resistor   carbon resistor   symbol for resistor

Figure 13.14

There are two main kinds of resistor: (1) **wire-wound resistors**, made of a coil of insulated, tightly wound fine wire and (2) **carbon resistors**. See **Figure 13.14**. Carbon resistors consist of a cylinder of carbon, with impurities added to control the amount of resistance. Metal wire leads are attached to each end of the carbon cylinder, and the whole assembly is enclosed in an insulating capsule. A colour-coded resistance is often painted on the capsule. (See **Table 13.5**.)

The electrical resistance (R) of a resistor depends on a number of variables:

(1) **Length** (ℓ): The longer the wire (or carbon resistor), the more resistance there will be to charges flowing through it.

(2) **Cross-sectional Area** (A): A thick wire offers *less* resistance than a thin wire, just as a fat hose lets water go through it more easily than a thin hose. In fact, resistance is inversely proportional to cross-sectional area!

(3) **The Material**: Resistance of a conductor of given length and cross-sectional area depends on the nature of the material of which it is made.

(4) **Temperature**: In general, resistance increases with temperature, though there are exceptions. Carbon resistors show a *decrease* in resistance with increasing temperature.

Resistivity

Consider a conductor made of a certain material, at a fixed temperature. The resistance of the conductor will be proportional to its length and inversely proportional to its cross-sectional area.

$$R \propto \frac{\ell}{A} \quad \text{or} \quad R = \rho . \frac{\ell}{A} .$$

The proportionality constant is called the **resistivity** (ρ) of the material. (The symbol ρ is the Greek letter *rho*.) The resistivity depends only on the material being used and on its temperature.

Solving for resistivity, $$\rho = \frac{RA}{\ell}.$$

The dimensions of resistivity must be: $\dfrac{\Omega m^2}{m} = \Omega m.$

A table of resistivities tells you at a glance how the resistances of various materials of given size, shape and temperature compare. See **Table 13.6**.

Table 13.6 Approximate Resistivities at 20°C of Common Materials
(Values depend on purity of sample.)

Material	Resistivity, ρ, in $\Omega \cdot m$	Classification
silver	1.6×10^{-8}	conductor
copper	1.7×10^{-8}	conductor
gold	2.4×10^{-8}	conductor
aluminum	2.8×10^{-8}	conductor
tungsten	5.6×10^{-8}	conductor
iron	10×10^{-8}	conductor
mercury	98×10^{-8}	conductor
nichrome	150×10^{-8}	conductor
carbon	3.5×10^{-5}	semiconductor
silicon	10^3	semiconductor
wood	$10^8 - 10^{11}$	insulator
glass	$10^{10} - 10^{14}$	insulator
sulfur	10^{15}	insulator
mica	10^{15}	insulator
fused quartz	10^{17}	insulator

Example

What would be the resistance of a kilometre of pure gold wire, of diameter of 1.0 mm?

Solution: $$R = \rho \frac{\ell}{A} = \frac{(2.27 \times 10^{-8} \ \Omega \cdot m)(1.0 \times 10^3 \ m)}{(\pi)(0.50 \times 10^{-3} \ m)^2}$$

$$R = \frac{2.27 \times 10^{-5} \ \Omega \ m^2}{7.85 \times 10^{-7} \ m^2} = 29 \ \Omega.$$

Exercises

1. You need a resistor with a resistance of 4700 Ω. What coloured bands should you look for on the resistors in your collection?

2. What is the resistance of a resistor with these coloured bands? (Give the manufacturer's tolerance, as well as the rated resistance.)
   (a) red, brown, black, gold
   (b) brown, black, brown, silver
   (c) green, black, green, silver
   (d) brown, black, green, gold
   (e) brown, black, orange, silver

3. A 4.0 m length of wire has a resistance of 16.0 Ω. If you cut the wire into four pieces of equal length, then bundle them into one conducting cable 1.0 m long, what will the resistance of the cable be?

4. What would be the resistance, at 20°C, of a kilometre of silver wire with a radius of 1.0 mm?

5. You have a spool of nichrome wire of diameter 0.50 mm. What length of this wire would you need, at 20°C, to make a 5.0 Ω resistor?

6. What is the resistance, at 0°C, of 500 km of aluminum wire, which has a cross-sectional area of 5.0 cm^2 and a resistivity at 0°C of 2.6 x 10^{-8} Ω·m?

7. A resistor designer wants some nichrome wire to have a resistance at 20°C of 1.0 Ω/m. What must the diameter of the wire be?

13.8 Ohm's Law

Georg Simon Ohm experimented with current in wires using variations in potential difference (voltage) to produce different currents in the conducting wires. He found that for metal conductors at a given temperature, the current is directly proportional to the voltage between the ends of the conductor. That is, $I \propto V$, and

$$\frac{V}{I} = \text{constant.}$$

The constant of proportionality is the resistance, R, of the conductor. The relationship among current I, voltage V, and resistance R can be written: $\frac{V}{I} = R$. Ohm's Law can be written in other forms, but all three forms are equivalent.

$$I = \frac{V}{R} \qquad V = IR \qquad R = \frac{V}{I}$$

Example 1

The heating element in a kettle carries a current of 12.5 A when plugged into a 120 V source. What is the resistance of the element?

Solution: $$R = \frac{V}{I} = \frac{120 \text{ V}}{12.5 \text{ A}} = 9.6 \text{ }\Omega.$$

Example 2

The current in a portable stove's heating element is 12.0 A when the potential difference between the ends of the element is 120 V. What is the resistance of the stove element? (Or, "How many ohms on the range?")

Solution: $$R = \frac{V}{I} = \frac{120 \text{ V}}{12.0 \text{ A}} = 1.0 \times 10^1 \text{ }\Omega$$

Exercises

1. A current of 1.2 mA exists in a resistor when a potential difference of 4.8 V is applied to its ends. What is the resistance of the resistor? Express your answer in **kilohms**. (1 kΩ = 10^3 Ω)
2. A current of 3.25 mA exists in a 2.2 kΩ resistor. What is the voltage between the ends of the resistor?
3. What current will exist in a 24 Ω resistor if a 120 V voltage is applied to its ends?
4. A piece of wire 0.500 m long and 0.010 mm² in cross-sectional area has a resistance at 20°C of 1.2 Ω. What is the metal in the wire? (See **Table 13.6.**)
5. A resistor allows 1.0 mA to exist in it when a potential difference of 1.5 V is applied to its ends. What is the resistance of the resistor, in kilohms?
6. If a 10.0 Ω kettle element is plugged into a 120 V outlet, how much current will it draw?
7. A current of 1.25 mA exists in a 20.0 kΩ resistor. What is the potential difference between the ends of the resistor?

Limitations to Ohm's Law

Ohm's Law applies to metallic conductors and metal-like conductors such as carbon. The ratio of V / I for these materials is constant providing the temperature of the conductor remains essentially constant. One *cannot* apply Ohm's Law to a conducting solution or to a gas discharge tube, however. Ohm's Law applies only to metallic or metal-like conductors at a specific temperature.

Special Resistors

In *Investigation 13-6,* you will work with two special types of resistor: a **photoresistor** and a **diode**. Both have interesting and very useful properties.

Investigation 13-6 Special Resistors

Purpose: To investigate resistance with (a) a **photoresistor**, and (b) **a diode**.

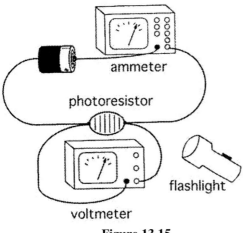

ammeter

photoresistor

flashlight

voltmeter

Figure 13.15

Procedure

Part 1   A Photoresistor

1. Connect a single cell to a milliammeter and a photo resistor, in a simple series circuit, as in **Figure 13.15**. Connect a voltmeter between the ends of the photo resistor.

2. Cover the photo resistor with your finger, so that no light can reach its light-sensitive surface. Measure I and V, and calculate the resistance, R, of the darkened photo resistor, using **Ohm's Law**. Record the resistance, in **ohms**.

3. Let room light fall on the photo resistor, and repeat **Procedure 2**. Record I and V, and calculate R.

4. Use an artificial light source (ray box, flashlight, or lamp) or direct sunlight to illuminate the photo resistor. Determine the value of R when the photo resistor is fully illuminated.

Part 2   A Diode

Replace the photo resistor in your circuit with a **diode**. Diodes are special resistors, which because of their composition, allow more current in one direction than in the other. (The details of how they work can be found in elementary electronics books.)

1. With the diode in the circuit, measure V and I, and calculate R using Ohm's Law. Record your measurements and your calculated value of R.

2. Disconnect the diode, and turn it around. Repeat the measurements you made in **Procedure 1**. Record the value of R when the diode is reversed.

Part 3   Light-Emitting Diodes

Obtain a few samples of light-emitting diodes (LED's) and experiment with these interesting and useful devices. Try connecting a photo resistor and a light-emitting diode in series with a 3.0 V battery. When you change the intensity of light falling on the photo resistor, what happens to the brightness of the LED?

Concluding Questions

1. What effect does light have on the resistance of a photo resistor?

2. Think of a practical use for a photo resistor. How might one be used in a streetlight?

3. What were (a) the lowest resistance and (b) the highest resistance you measured for your diode?

4. Household electricity is alternating current (A.C.). The electron current changes direction in a cyclical manner, with a frequency of 60 Hz. What effect would a **diode** have on alternating current?

5. Investigate and find out the names of several devices that use diodes. Why are diodes needed in these devices?

6. Name at least five devices that use light-emitting diodes.

Ehren Stillman Cartoon

Superconductors

A **superconductor** is a material which, when cooled to a temperature called the **transition temperature**, loses all resistance to electric current. The first superconductor was discovered in 1911 by Dutch physicist **Kamerlingh Onnes (1853-1926).** Onnes was the first scientist to successfully liquefy helium, a process that requires the extremely low temperature of 4.2 K. During further investigations of the effects of very low temperatures on materials, Onnes made the amazing discovery that mercury loses all its resistance to electric current when it is cooled to 4 K! Soon after, he showed that tin and lead displayed the same property of superconductivity. A current was started in a closed loop of such a conductor, which was kept below the transition temperature in a bath of liquid helium. The conductor was then isolated from the source of the current. A year later, the current still existed in the superconductor!

Until recently, superconductors have required extremely low temperatures, and liquid helium, which is costly and difficult to work with, was the only suitable coolant. Superconductors have therefore found only limited use up to now. One reason that physicists are excited about superconductors at present is the recent discovery of a whole new family of superconductors with transition temperatures high enough that liquid nitrogen can be used as the coolant. Nitrogen is far less expensive than helium. Nitrogen makes up approximately 80% of the atmosphere, and so is readily available. It liquefies at 77 K.

Even more promising is the discovery of ceramic (clay-like) materials with even higher transition temperatures. These new superconductors are combinations of oxides of metals such as barium, copper and lanthanum. The discovery of ceramic superconductors has opened up a whole new and puzzling area of physics.

Why all the excitement about superconductors? Consider some of the possible applications. For example, electricity from hydroelectric generators could be delivered with essentially no loss of energy. Smaller and more powerful motors, generators and computers will become possible. Hydrogen fusion might quickly become a practical reality. Expensive and large medical imaging devices may become small enough to be portable and more easily affordable. High-speed trains levitated and driven by powerful superconducting electromagnets could become an everyday part of our transportation system. Magnetic levitation might be used for personal transportation as well. The possibilities for using room-temperature superconductors are endless.

Challenges

1. Find out what the highest transition temperature achieved with ceramic superconductors is as of today's date.
2. How does magnetic levitation work? How might it be put to use in the future?

13.9 Electric Circuits

A circuit is any uninterrupted path through which electric charges (usually electrons) can flow. When the path is complete and uninterrupted so that charges can flow, the circuit is said to be **closed**. If there is an interruption in the circuit, such as when a switch is opened, the circuit is said to be **open**.

A circuit often has more than one component or element to it. If two elements are connected along the same path, we call the circuit a **series circuit**. If the elements are connected in such a way that they form branches, which provide separate paths for charges to move through, then the circuit is a **parallel circuit**.

In the next two investigations, you will experiment first with series circuits, then with parallel circuits.

Investigation 13-7 Series Circuits

Part 1

Problem: What happens to the current when you add identical resistors to a series circuit?

(a)   (b)

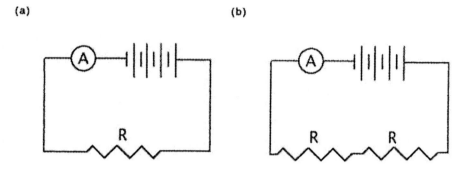

Figure 13.16

Procedure

1. Set up the circuit in **Figure 13.16(a)**. Use 3 or 4 cells (4.5 V or 6.0 V on your power pack if you are using one) and select a range on your ammeter that gives a nearly full-scale reading with the single carbon resistor. Write down the current in amperes and also the source voltage.

2. *Predict* what the current will be when you add a second *identical* resistor in series with the first, as in **Figure 13.16(b)**. Now set up this circuit and measure the current. The source voltage should be the same as before.

3. *Predict* what the current will be with (a) three identical resistors and (b) four identical resistors in series. Now test your predictions.

Concluding Questions

1. For each resistor combination, including the single resistor, calculate the resistance of the combination by dividing the source voltage by the current in the resistors.

2. What happens to the resistance of the resistor combinations when you add more resistors in series? What would be the easiest way to calculate the resistance of the combination of resistors?

Part 2

Problem: A series circuit has only one conducting path. What happens to the magnitude of the current as charges flow along the length of the path?

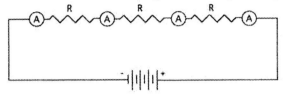

Figure 13.17

Procedure

1. *Predict* what will happen to the magnitude of the electric current as charges move from the source through the three resistors and back to the source.
2. (Several teams of students could set up this arrangement since it requires four ammeters.) Set up the circuit in **Figure 13.17**, and then measure the current at each of the locations indicated in the diagram.

Concluding Question: How does the current change as charges go through the elements of a series circuit?

Part 3

Problem: How does the source voltage compare with the voltage in the resistors of a circuit?

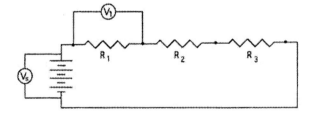

Figure 13.18

Procedure

1. Use a voltmeter to measure the terminal voltage V_s of the source. This is a measure of the *gain* in potential energy per unit of charge by the charges flowing through the battery.

2. Measure the potential difference between the two ends of the first identical resistor R_1. Then measure the potential difference between the ends of resistor R_2. Repeat with resistor R_3.
[Each of these three voltages represents a *loss* of potential energy per unit of charge going through the resistor. (In what form of energy is the electrical potential energy going to appear after it is transformed by the resistor?)]

3. Add up the three voltages across the resistors to get the total loss of potential energy per coulomb in the series circuit.

4. Replace the three identical resistors with three *different* resistors. Repeat **Procedures 1, 2** and **3.**

Concluding Questions

1. (a) How does the source voltage V_S compare with the sum of the voltages across all the resistors?
   (b) Calculate the percent difference between V_S and the sum of $V_1 + V_2 + V_3$ for both the circuits that you used.
2. What general principle of physics would suggest that the source voltage should equal the sum of the voltages across the resistors?
3. What are some sources of error in this investigation?

General Conclusions for *Investigation 13-7*

1. In a series circuit, what can be said of the current in various parts of the circuit?
2. In a series circuit, how does the source voltage compare with the sum of the voltages across the resistors in the circuit, allowing for experimental error?
3. If you know the resistance of each element in a series circuit, how do you calculate the resistance of the entire circuit?
4. In an old set of Christmas tree lights, eight lamps are connected in series and plugged into a 120 V outlet. What is the voltage across each individual lamp?

Investigation 13-8   Parallel Circuits

Part 1

Problem: **What happens to the current in a circuit when more identical resistors are added in parallel with each other?**

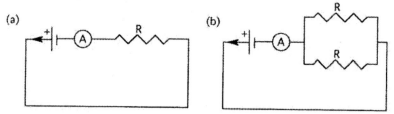

Figure 13.19

Procedure

1. Set up the circuit in **Figure 13.19(a)**. Only one cell or a 1.5 V DC source is needed. Measure the current and record it in amperes. Also record the source voltage.
2. *Predict* what the current in the ammeter will be when you add a second parallel *identical* resistor, as in **Figure 13.19(b)**. Now test your prediction. Record the current.
3. *Predict* what the current in the ammeter will be when you have three identical parallel resistors. Test your prediction. Record the current.
4. *Predict* what the current would be with four identical parallel resistors, and then test your prediction.

Concluding Questions

1. What happens to the current in a parallel circuit as identical resistors are added in parallel?
2. Has adding these resistors increased the resistance of the circuit or decreased it? Explain.

Part 2

Problem: What rules govern the currents and voltages in a parallel circuit?

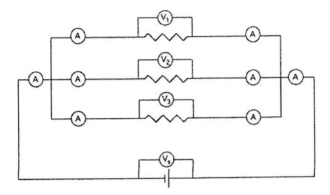

Figure 13.20

Procedure

1. Set up the circuit in **Figure 13.20**. The experiment can be done by one group, placing the meters at each indicated location one step at a time, or by a large group placing meters at all the locations simultaneously. Use different resistors at each of the three locations. For simplicity in setting ammeter ranges, use resistors with similar orders of magnitude, such as 100 Ω, 330 Ω and 150 Ω.
2. Record the **currents** at each of the locations shown on the diagram. A good way to do this is to draw the circuit diagram and record the currents right on the diagram. Express currents in **milliamperes (mA)**.
3. Remove the ammeters from the circuit. Measure and record the **voltages** across each resistor. Also, measure the voltage across the source.

Concluding Questions

1. In a parallel circuit, what do you conclude about the voltage in the branches of the circuit?

2. If you know the current in each branch of a parallel network, how can you find the total current entering and leaving the parallel network of resistors?

3. What determines the current in each branch of a parallel network?

4. Examine the currents entering and leaving each **junction** in your circuit. How does the total current *entering* each junction compare with the total current *leaving* each junction?

Chapter Review Questions

[1 coulomb = 6.24 x 10^{18} electrons]

1. Define **electric current**.

2. What is one **ampere**?

3. What is the direction of **conventional current**?

4. What is (a) a **milliampere**? (b) a **microampere**?

5. Express these currents in amperes:

    (a) 3.4 mA   (b) 450 mA   (c) 652 μA   (d) 2.1 μA

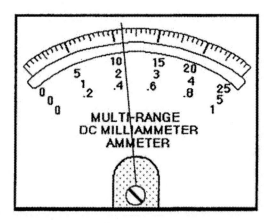

Figure 13.21

6. What is the current according to the ammeter in **Figure 13.21** if the ammeter is being used on each of these ranges?
   (a) 0-10 mA
   (b) 0-25 mA
   (c) 0-100 mA
   (d) 0-5 mA
   (e) 0-5 A

7. What current exists in a wire if 2.4 x 10^3 C of charge pass through a point in the wire in a time of 6.0 x 10^1 s?

8. The current through an ammeter is 5.0 A. In one day, how many electrons will pass through the ammeter?

9. How much silver will be electroplated by a current of 0.255 A in one day?

10. What is the difference between the terminal voltage of a battery and its emf?

11. What are four factors that affect the **resistance** of a resistor?

12. How is **resistivity** related to resistance of a conductor?

13. If you need a resistor with a rating of 10 000 Ω, what coloured bands should you look for on the resistor?

14. What is the resistance and tolerance of a resistor with coloured bands of green, green, black and silver?

15. A 9.0 m length of wire has a resistance of 81 Ω. If you cut the wire into nine equal lengths and form a single cable with the pieces, what is the resistance of the cable?

16. What is the resistance at 0°C of 10.0 m of pure gold wire of diameter 1.0 mm, if the resistivity of gold at that temperature is 2.27 x 10^{-8} Ωm?

17. What is **Ohm's Law**? Name all the variables.

18. To which type of conductors does Ohm's Law apply?

19. A set of eight decorative lights is plugged into a 120 V wall receptacle. What is the potential difference across each light bulb filament, if the eight lights are connected (a) in series? (b) in parallel?

20. What is the resistance of a resistor if a potential difference of 36 V between its ends results in a current of 1.20 mA?

21. What is the potential difference (voltage) between the ends of a resistor if 24.0 J of work must be done to drive 0.30 C of charge through the resistor?

Test Yourself!

1. Current is to ampere as potential difference is to
   A. volt .   B. ohm.   C. watt.   D. joule.   E. coulomb.

2. Which of the following is the largest current?
   A. 10 000 electrons/second   B. 20 mA   C. 10,000 μA   D. 1.5 A

3. Four 2.0 V cells are connected in series. What is voltage of the battery?
   A. 0.5 V   B. 2.0 V   C. 4.0 V   D. 8.0 V

4. Four 2.0 V cells are connected in parallel. What is voltage of the battery?
   A. 0.5 V   B. 2.0 V   C. 4.0 V   D. 8.0 V

5. To measure the true **emf** of a battery, what condition must be satisfied?
   A. There must be a maximum load connected to the battery.
   B. There must be a voltmeter connected in parallel with the battery.
   C. There must be no current drawn from the battery.
   D. The battery must be brand new.

6. Voltage is a measure of
   A. energy gained or lost per coulomb of charge.
   B. energy gained or lost per second.
   C. amount of charge passing a point in a circuit per second.
   D. resistance offered to moving charges in a conductor.

7. The ratio of potential difference between the ends of a resistor to the current in the resistor is a measure of
   A. the voltage across a resistor.
   B. the energy consumed per second in the resistor.
   C. the resistance of the resistor.
   D. the commercial value of the resistor.

(8-10) Match the equivalent resistance with the *letter* of the resistor combination that would produce that resistance. All resistors have identical resistance, **R**.

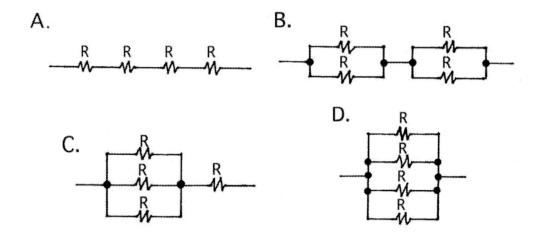

8. Which resistor combination has an equivalent resistance of **R**?   A   B   C   D

9. Which resistor combination has an equivalent resistance of **4R**?   A   B   C   D

10. Which resistor combination has an equivalent resistance of $\frac{1}{4}$**R**?   A   B   C   D

Chapter 14 Circuit Theory

14.1 EMF, Terminal Voltage and Internal Resistance

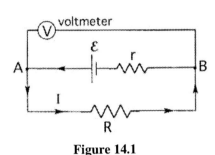

Figure 14.1

In **Figure 14.1** the dry cell has a rated electromotive force (emf) of 1.50 V. If you use a high quality voltmeter to measure the potential difference between the terminals A and B of the cell, when essentially no current is being drawn from the cell other than a tiny amount going through the voltmeter itself, the voltage between the terminals will be nearly equal to the ideal value of the emf. That is, *with no current, the terminal voltage of the battery,* V_{AB}, will equal the emf, $\mathcal{E}$.

If, however, the cell is connected to a resistor R so that a current I exists in the simple circuit *including the cell itself,* then it will be observed that the terminal voltage is *less than* the cell emf.

$$V_{AB} < \mathcal{E}$$

This is because the cell itself has an **internal resistance** of its own, symbolized by r. According to Ohm's Law, the loss of potential energy per coulomb between the terminals is Ir. The measured terminal voltage of the cell will be less than the ideal emf by an amount Ir.

$$V_{AB} = \mathcal{E} - Ir$$

Example

A dry cell with an emf of 1.50 V has an internal resistance of 0.050 Ω. What is the terminal voltage of the cell when it is connected to a 2.00 Ω resistor?

Solution: Apply Ohm's Law to the circuit as a whole, and consider the internal resistance r to be in series with the external resistance, R.

$$I = \frac{\mathcal{E}}{R + r} = \frac{1.50 \text{ V}}{2.05 \ \Omega} = 0.732 \text{ A}$$

Now the terminal voltage $V_{AB} = \mathcal{E} - Ir$

$$V_{AB} = 1.50 \text{ V} - (0.732 \text{ A})(0.050 \ \Omega) = 1.50 \text{ V} - 0.037 \text{ V} = 1.46 \text{ V}.$$

Exercises

1. A dry cell with an emf of 1.50 V and an internal resistance of 0.050 Ω is 'shorted out' with a piece of wire of resistance only 0.20 Ω. What will a voltmeter read if it is connected to the terminals of the dry cell at this time?

2. A battery has an emf of 12.50 V. When a current of 35 A is drawn from it, its terminal voltage is 11.45 V. What is the internal resistance of the battery?

3. A battery with an emf of 6.00 V has an internal resistance of 0.20 Ω. What current does the battery deliver when the terminal voltage reads only 5.00 V?

14.2 Resistors in Series

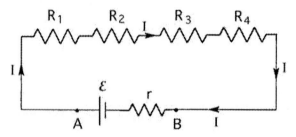

Figure 14.2

In **Figure 14.2**, four resistors are connected end-to-end so that there is one continuous conducting path for electrons coming from the source of emf, through the resistors and back to the source. Electrons move through the resistors, one after the other. The same current exists in each resistor. Resistors arranged like this are said to be **in series** with each other. **Figure 14.2** shows a typical **series circuit**.

Within the cell, the gain in potential energy per unit charge is equal to the emf, $\mathcal{E}$. When a current I exists, energy will be lost in resistors R_1, R_2, R_3, R_4 and r. The loss of potential energy per unit charge in each resistor is the voltage, V, across that resistor.

From Ohm's Law we know that $V = IR$. The Law of Conservation of Energy requires that the total *gain* in energy in the cell(s) must equal the total *loss* of energy in the resistors in the circuit. It follows that *the total gain in energy per unit charge ($\mathcal{E}$) must equal the total loss of energy per unit charge in the circuit.*

$$\mathcal{E} = Ir + IR_1 + IR_2 + IR_3 + IR_4$$

$$\therefore \mathcal{E} - Ir = IR_1 + IR_2 + IR_3 + IR_4$$

Recalling that **terminal voltage** $V_{AB} = \mathcal{E} - Ir$,

$$V_{AB} = IR_1 + IR_2 + IR_3 + IR_4 = V_S,$$

where V_S is the *sum of voltages across the resistors in the external part of the circuit.*

Another way of writing this is:

$$V_{AB} = V_1 + V_2 + V_3 + V_4 = V_S$$

In summary, here are the rules for a **series circuit**:

Series Circuits

(1) Current is the same everywhere in a series circuit.

(2) The terminal voltage of the source equals the sum of the potential differences (voltages) across the resistors in the series circuit.

$$V_{AB} = V_1 + V_2 + V_3 + \ldots + V_n$$

(3) The equivalent resistance, R_s, of a series circuit is the sum of all the resistances in the circuit.

$$R_s = R_1 + R_2 + R_3 + \ldots + R_n$$

Example

Three resistors of resistance 5.0 Ω, 12.0 Ω and 8.0 Ω are connected in series with a 50.0 V power source.

(a) What is the equivalent resistance of the circuit?

(b) What is the current in the circuit?

(c) What is the potential difference between the ends of the 12.0 Ω resistor?

Solution:

(a) $R_S = R_1 + R_2 + R_3$

$R_S = 5.0\,Ω + 12.0\,Ω + 8.0\,Ω = 25.0\,Ω.$

(b) $I = \dfrac{V_S}{R_S} = \dfrac{50.0\ V}{25.0\ Ω} = 2.00\ A.$

(c) $V = I_S R$

$V = (2.00A)(12.0\,Ω) = 24.0\ V.$

14.3 Resistors in Parallel

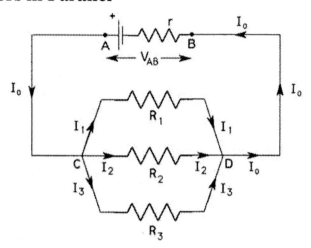

Figure 14.3

The resistors in **Figure 14.3** are in **parallel.** The current divides into three branches. Electrons coming from the cell take one of three paths, which meet at a **junction** where the electrons all converge to one path again and return to the battery.

   Electric charge is a conserved quantity. The electrons do not get 'created' or 'lost' during their epic journey through the parallel network of resistors. The number of electrons entering a junction (such as **D**) per second will equal the number of electrons leaving that junction per second. Likewise, the number of electrons entering junction **C** per second will equal the number of electrons leaving **C** per second. (The direction of electron flow is opposite to the conventional current direction shown on **Figure 14.3**.) If we express current in C/s or in A, as is normally the case,

$$I_0 = I_1 + I_2 + I_3.$$

   The net gain in potential energy per unit charge in the cell, which is V_{AB}, is equal to the loss in potential energy per unit charge between **C** and **D**. If you think of **C** as an extension of terminal **A**, and **D** as an extension of terminal **B** of the cell, you can see that the difference in potential between **C** and **D** is the same no matter which of the three paths the electrons take to get from one terminal to the other. In fact,

$$V_{AB} = V_1 = V_2 = V_3.$$

where V_{AB} is the terminal voltage of the cell, and V_1, V_2 and V_3 are the voltages across resistors R_1, R_2 and R_3 respectively.

   Since the voltages are the same in each branch, we shall use the label V_p for the voltage in *any* branch of the parallel network.

Equivalent Resistance

What single resistance could be used in place of the parallel network of resistors, and draw the same total current? Call this the **equivalent resistance**, R_p.

If the voltage across the parallel network is V_p, and the equivalent single resistance is R_p, we can apply Ohm's Law as follows to find the total current I_0 entering the network:

$$I_0 = \frac{V_p}{R_p}.$$

However, $I_0 = I_1 + I_2 + I_3$.

Using Ohm's Law again, $\qquad \dfrac{V_p}{R_p} = \dfrac{V_p}{R_1} + \dfrac{V_p}{R_2} + \dfrac{V_p}{R_3}.$

Eliminating V_p, $\qquad \dfrac{1}{R_p} = \dfrac{1}{R_1} + \dfrac{1}{R_2} + \dfrac{1}{R_3}$

The rules for a parallel circuit are summarized below.

Parallel Circuits

(1) Voltage is the same across each branch of a parallel network.

(2) The total current entering a junction of a parallel network is equal to the total current leaving the same junction. As a result, the total current entering a parallel network of resistors or leaving the same network is equal to the sum of the currents in the branches.

(3) The reciprocal of the single equivalent resistance that will replace all the resistances in a parallel network and draw the same current is equal to the sum of the reciprocals of the resistances in the branches.

$$\frac{1}{R_p} = \frac{1}{R_1} + \frac{1}{R_2} + \frac{1}{R_3} + \ ... \ + \frac{1}{R_n}.$$

Example: Resistors of 25 Ω, 50 Ω and 150 Ω are connected, in parallel, to a 3.0 V source.

(a) What is the equivalent resistance of the parallel network?

(b) What is the voltage across each of the three branches of the circuit?

(c) What is the current in and out of the source?

(d) What is the current in the 50-Ω resistor?

Solution: (a) $\frac{1}{R_p} = \frac{1}{R_1} + \frac{1}{R_2} + \frac{1}{R_3}$

$\frac{1}{R_p} = \frac{1}{25\ \Omega} + \frac{1}{50\ \Omega} + \frac{1}{150\ \Omega} = \frac{6+3+1}{150\ \Omega} = \frac{10}{150\ \Omega}$

Therefore, $R_p = \frac{150\ \Omega}{10} = 15\ \Omega.$

(b) Each branch has a voltage of 3.0 V, since they are parallel with the source.

(c) $I_0 = \frac{V_p}{R_p} = \frac{3.0\ \text{V}}{15\ \Omega} = 0.20\ \text{A}\ (200\ \text{mA}).$

(d) $I = \frac{V_p}{R} = \frac{3.0\ \text{V}}{50\ \Omega} = 0.060\ \text{A}\ (60\ \text{mA}).$

14.4 Combined Series and Parallel Circuits

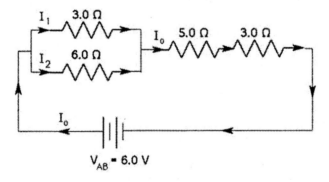

Figure 14.4

Figure 14.4 shows a combined **series-parallel** circuit. The rules you have learned for series and parallel circuits can be applied to this problem. A logical approach for finding the equivalent resistance and current for the circuit in **Figure 14.4** is to first reduce the parallel network to a single equivalent resistance, then treat the circuit as a series circuit.

Example

(a) What is the equivalent resistance of the circuit in **Figure 14.4**?

(b) What is the voltage across the 6.0 Ω resistor?

Solution: First, reduce the parallel network to an equivalent single resistance.

$$\frac{1}{R_p} = \frac{1}{3.0 \ \Omega} + \frac{1}{6.0 \ \Omega} = \frac{2 + 1}{6.0 \ \Omega} = \frac{3}{6.0 \ \Omega} = \frac{1}{2.0 \ \Omega} \ ;$$

$$\therefore \ R_p = 2.0 \ \Omega.$$

Next, add the three resistances that are in series with one another.

$$R_s = 2.0 \ \Omega + 5.0 \ \Omega + 3.0 \ \Omega = 10.0 \ \Omega.$$

Thirdly, find the current using Ohm's Law with the total equivalent resistance and the battery terminal voltage.

$$I_o = \frac{V_{AB}}{R_s} = \frac{6.0 \ \text{V}}{10.0 \ \Omega} = 0.60 \ \text{A}.$$

Finally, the voltage across the parallel network is found by using Ohm's Law on the parallel network by itself.

$$V_p = I_o R_p = (0.60 \ \text{A})(2.0 \ \Omega) = 1.2 \ \text{V}.$$

The voltage across both branches of the network is 1.2 V.

Exercises

1. Draw a simple series circuit with a 1.5 V cell connected to a 12 Ω resistor, a 15 Ω resistor and a 33 Ω resistor. Calculate (a) the equivalent resistance and (b) the current in the circuit.

2. Draw a simple parallel circuit with a 3.0 V battery connected to a 3.0 Ω resistor, a 5.0 Ω resistor and a 7.5 Ω resistor. Calculate:
   (a) the equivalent resistance,
   (b) the total current,
   (c) the current in the 5.0 Ω resistor.

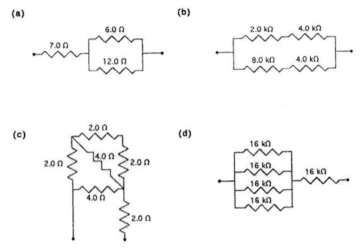

Figure 14.5

3. Calculate the equivalent resistance of each network of resistors in **Figure 14.5**.

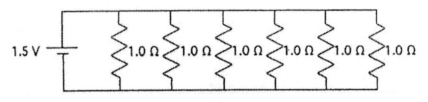

Figure 14.6

4. What is the current in the battery in **Figure 14.6**?

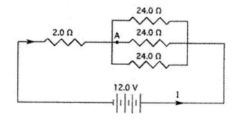

Figure 14.7

5. (a) What is the equivalent resistance of the circuit in **Figure 14.7**?
   (b) What is the current in the battery?
   (c) What is the current at point A?
   (d) What is the potential difference across the 2.0 Ω resistor?
   (e) The wire at A is cut. When this happens, predict whether the current in the battery will (i) stay the same, (ii) increase, or (iii) decrease. Check your prediction by calculating the new current in the battery.

14.5 Joule's Law

James Prescott Joule (1818-1889) did experiments to measure the amount of heat released by various resistors under different conditions. He found that, for a particular resistor, *the amount of thermal energy released in a unit of time by a resistor is proportional to the square of the current.* Since the rate at which energy is released with respect to time is called **power**, Joule's results can be expressed as follows:

$$P \propto I^2,$$

$$\text{or, } P = \text{constant} \cdot I^2.$$

The constant in this equation will have units with the dimensions W/A^2, since constant $= P/I^2$. Consider the following simplification of these measuring units (W/A^2):

$$1 \frac{W}{A^2} = 1 \frac{J/s}{C^2/s^2} = 1 \frac{J/C}{C/s} = 1 \frac{V}{A} = 1\,\Omega$$

The **ohm** (Ω) is the unit for **resistance!** In fact then, the constant of proportionality in the relationship discovered by Joule is the same constant of proportionality that is in Ohm's Law. The ratio P/I^2 is the **resistance** of the resistor.

Joule's Law can be written as follows: $P = R \cdot I^2$. By combining Joule's Law with Ohm's Law for resistors, other expressions for electrical power can be derived.

$$P = RI^2 = \frac{V}{I} \cdot I^2 = VI$$

Also, $$P = VI = V \cdot \frac{V}{R} = \frac{V^2}{R}.$$

In summary,

$$P = RI^2 = VI = \frac{V^2}{R}$$

Examples

1. What is the resistance of the element of a 1500 W kettle, if it draws 12.5 A?

Solution $$R = \frac{P}{I^2} = \frac{1500 \text{ W}}{\{12.5 \text{ A}\}^2} = 9.6\,\Omega.$$

2. How much thermal energy is released by a 1500 W kettle in 5.0 minutes?

Solution

Thermal energy released $= P\,t = (1500\,\frac{J}{s})(5.0 \text{ min})(60.0\,\frac{s}{\text{min}}) = 4.5 \times 10^5 \text{ J}.$

Exercises

1. What is the resistance of a 60.0 W lamp, if the current in it is 0.50 A?

2. A 600-W coffee percolator is operated at 120 V.
   (a) What is the resistance of the heating element of the percolator?
   (b) How much thermal energy does it produce in 6.0 min?

3. A 1.0 kΩ resistor is rated $\frac{1}{2}$ W. (It will be destroyed if the rate of heat dissipation is greater than $\frac{1}{2}$ W.) What is the maximum voltage you can apply to this resistor without damaging it?

4. A light bulb operating at 120 V draws 0.50 A. What is its power?

5. What is the resistance of a 100 W bulb operating at 120 V?

6. What is the current in a 1500 W kettle operating at 120 V?

7. How much power is dissipated by an electric kettle that has a resistance of 9.60 Ω, if it operates at 120 V?

8. A 120 V circuit is protected by a 15 A fuse. What is the maximum power of the appliance that can be used in this circuit?

9. A 1500 W kettle and a 600 W toaster are plugged into the same 120 V outlet.
   (a) What total current will they draw?
   (b) If the circuit is protected by a 15 A circuit breaker, will the circuit breaker be activated?

14.6 The Kilowatt·Hour

The usual measuring unit for energy is the joule (J). This is a very small amount of energy compared with what the average householder uses in a month or two. Consider just one appliance — an electric range. The range has a power rating of perhaps 12,000 W. This means that if it is being used on full power, it uses 12,000 J every second! In one hour it will use

$$12,000 \text{ J/s} \times 3,600 \text{ s/h} = 43,200,000 \text{ J!}$$

When your electric power company bills you each month (or every two months), it bills you for the **energy** you have used, not for power. It could charge you by the joule, but it is such a small unit that to bill you by the joule would be rather impractical. Instead, a much larger unit, the kilowatt-hour is used.

What is a kilowatt-hour? Since power is a measure of how much energy is used in a unit of time, $P = \frac{E}{t}$, therefore $E = Pt$.

When calculating household energy use, the **kilowatt** is used for power and the **hour** for time. Thus, energy can be expressed in **kilowatt-hours (kWh)**. A kilowatt-hour is equivalent to a very large number of joules!

$$1 \text{ kWh} = (1{,}000 \text{ W})(3{,}600 \text{ s}) = 3{,}600{,}000 \text{ Ws} = 3{,}600{,}000 \; \frac{J}{s} \cdot s.$$

$$1 \text{ kWh} = 3{,}600{,}000 \text{ J}.$$

Your hydroelectric bill is based on how many kilowatt-hours of energy you have used since your last billing.

Exercises

1. If you use your television set an average of 3.0 h per day for a 30-day month, and its power rating is 200.0 W, then how much energy will it use during that period? Express your answer (a) in joules and (b) in kWh. If electrical energy costs 6¢/kWh, what will it cost to use your TV that month?

2. How much does it cost to operate a 400 W block heater for your car for one 30-day month, if you use it 10.0 h/day on average? Assume electrical energy costs 6¢/kWh.

3. A 60 W porch light is left on for an average of 12 h/day for a 30-day period. If the lamp is only 5% efficient, how much of the energy that you are paying for was used simply to heat the environment around the lamp?

Chapter Review Questions

1. A mercury cell has an emf of 1.35 V and an internal resistance of 0.041 Ω. If it is used in a circuit that draws 1.50 A, what will its terminal voltage be?

Figure 14.8

2. What is the value of the unknown resistance **R** in **Figure 14.8**?

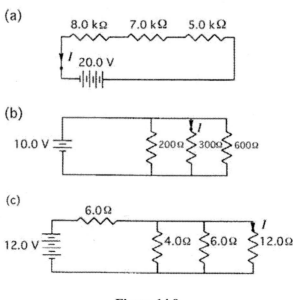

Figure 14.9

3. (i) Find the **equivalent resistance** of each of the circuits in **Figure 14.9**, and the current at the point indicated by "*I*".

(ii) In **Figure 14.9(a)**, what is the **voltage** across the 8.0 kΩ resistor?

(iii) In **Figure 14.9 (b)**, what is the **voltage** across the 300 Ω resistor?

(iv) In **Figure 14.9 (c)**, what is the **voltage** across the 4.0 Ω resistor?

4. What are three versions of the power equation?

5. What is the power rating of a toaster that draws 8.33 A when plugged into a 120 V source?

6. How much current is drawn when a 1500 W kettle and a 1000 W waffle iron are plugged into the same 120 V circuit?

7. What is the resistance of the element of a 600 W coffee percolator if it operates on 120 V?

8. A wall clock of the 'plug-in' variety is rated at 4 W. If electrical energy costs 7¢/kWh, how much does it cost to run the clock for one year (365 d)?

9. You are given four resistors, each 24 Ω. Using one or more of these at a time, how many different equivalent resistances can you obtain using these identical resistors?

10. A 2.2 kΩ resistor is rated at $\frac{1}{2}$ W. What is the highest voltage you could safely apply to the resistor without risking damage to it from overheating?

Test Yourself!

$\mathcal{E} = 1.5\ \text{V} \qquad r = 0.50\ \Omega$

$R = 0.10\ \Omega$

1. The cell in the above diagram is short-circuited with a wire of resistance 0.20 Ω. What is the terminal voltage under these conditions?

2. A storage battery has an emf of 12.0 V. What is the terminal voltage if a current of 150 A is drawn just as the starter motor is turned on, if the internal resistance is 0.030 Ω?

3. A wire has length ℓ and resistance R. It is cut into four identical pieces, and these pieces are arranged in parallel. What will be the resistance of the parallel network thus created?

4. Calculate the equivalent resistance of each of the following networks of resistors.

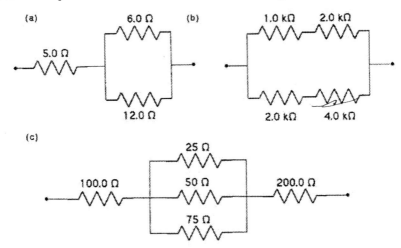

(a)   6.0 Ω   (b)   1.0 kΩ   2.0 kΩ

5.0 Ω

12.0 Ω   2.0 kΩ   4.0 kΩ

(c)   25 Ω

100.0 Ω   50 Ω   200.0 Ω

75 Ω

5. (a) How many kWh of energy will a 400 W television set use in one 30-day month, if it is turned on for an average of 5.0 h per day?

(b) What will it cost you at $0.07/kWh?

Chapter 15   Special Relativity

15.1 Albert Einstein (1879-1955)

Albert Einstein's reputation as one of the greatest, most creative thinkers in all recorded history is well established. His ideas were truly of a revolutionary nature. For example, he suggested that mass and energy were equivalent. He predicted that mass could be converted into energy, and energy into mass. Einstein was a pacifist. He abhorred war and its destruction. Ironically, it was the application of his mass-energy equation ($E = mc^2$, where E is energy, m is mass and c is the speed of light) that contributed to the development of the atomic and hydrogen bombs.

Einstein was born in Ulm, Germany in 1879. He did not complete school in Germany. He did later, in Zurich, Switzerland. After graduating in 1900 from the Polytechnic Academy, he worked in the Swiss patent office in Bern. In 1905, he published several important scientific papers, which were to change the way scientists look at the universe. One of these explained Brownian motion (the random motion of particles suspended in liquids). Another suggested that light comes in **photons**, and that light behaves not only as if it was a wave motion, but also as if it consisted of particles. He developed what is now called the **Special Theory of Relativity**, and established the mass-energy equivalence equation, $E = mc^2$.

In 1916 Einstein, working at the University of Berlin, published his General Theory of Relativity. In this theory, Einstein perceived gravity differently than Isaac Newton. To Einstein, gravity was not a force but a curved field in space and time, created by the presence of mass. With his theory he successfully predicted the amount of deflection of light from distant stars as it passed close to our own massive sun. (This deflection could only be measured during an eclipse. In 1929, Einstein's predictions were verified photographically during a total eclipse of the sun.)

Einstein spent his later years trying to develop a mathematical connection between electromagnetism and gravity (a 'unified field' theory). He was not successful in that quest.

In 1933, Albert Einstein left Germany and went to the United States, where he became a valued member of the Institute of Advanced Study at Princeton, New Jersey. Einstein died in 1955 in Princeton.

15.2 Frames of Reference

Imagine you are rowing a boat downstream in a river where the water is moving with a velocity of 5.0 km/h. Someone tells you that your boat is travelling with a velocity of 10.0 km/h. You can see that there is a problem here! Does the observer mean that you are travelling 10.0 km/h *relative to the earth (perhaps a point on the river bank)* or does the observer mean 10.0 km/h *relative to the water?*

If the observer means 10.0 km/h relative to the water, then your velocity relative to the earth is 10.0 km/h + 5.0 km/h = 15.0 km/h! It is important when dealing with velocities to specify the **frame of reference** in which the velocity was measured.

Figure 15.1 Frames of Reference

Exercises

The following questions are based upon **Figure 15.1**.

1. What is the velocity of the people in the boat relative to: (a) the water? (b) the earth?
2. What is the velocity of the bird relative to: (a) the air? (b) the water? (c) the earth?
3. What is the velocity of the water relative to the bird?
4. What is the velocity of the people in the boat relative to the bird?
5. What would all the velocities in the diagram appear to be, relative to a camera in a spy satellite in geosynchronous orbit? (Its position is 'fixed' relative to a point on the rotating earth.)

15.3 Relative Motion

The preceding exercises have no doubt made it clear that an object can have two velocities at the same time, each one correct relative to a different frame of reference. To measure a velocity, we generally choose a frame of reference and *pretend* that the frame of reference is absolutely still. If your speedometer says your car is travelling 80 km/h, then your speed relative to the earth below your car is 80 km/h. Relative to the centre of the planet, your car's speed might be several hundreds of kilometres per hour, since the earth is rotating on its axis and your car is moving with the earth's surface. Relative to the sun, your speed is even greater (over 100 000 km/h) since the earth is revolving around the sun that fast. And then there is always the centre of our galaxy to consider as a possible frame of reference!

Figure 15.2: Two **Snowbird** jets approach each other 'head-on' before doing a 'level roll'. Each aircraft is travelling approximately 600 km/h *relative to the ground*. What is the speed of either plane *relative to the other plane?*

15.4 The Relativity Principle

Einstein's Special Theory of Relativity is based upon two fundamental assumptions that he made. These fundamental assumptions are called **postulates.** The first of these postulates is the **relativity principle:**

The First Postulate of the Relativity Principle

If two frames of reference move with constant velocity relative to each other, then the laws of physics will be the same in both frames of reference.

It is important to remember that the Special Theory of Relativity deals only with frames of reference that are moving at *constant velocity relative to each other.* (There is no acceleration involved.) In relativity theory, there is no 'preferred' frame of reference. For example, rather than saying your car is moving 80 km/h relative to the road below it, you could just as easily and correctly say the car is still and the road is moving 80 km/h relative to your car. (See **Figure 15.3**. Your less informed friends may suggest an appointment with a psychiatrist, but relatively speaking, you would be correct.)

Figure 15.3

Figure 15.4

Figure 15.4 illustrates how observers in two different frames of reference, both of whom are moving at constant velocity, would observe the same result for a simple experiment: throwing a ball into the air and catching it. If the person standing on the road and the person in the van both throw the same ball up in the same way, both will observe the same result. Also, an observer outside the van (which has a clear glass side window, of course) will find that the same natural laws can be used to predict the path of the ball, even though the path of the ball will look different. (It will be an elongated parabola because the van, and therefore the ball in the van, has a steady horizontal velocity.)

Exercises

1. In the text, it is stated that both observers in **Figure 15.4** are moving at constant velocity. What is the velocity of observer A relative to the road?

2. Sketch what the path of the ball thrown in the van would look like to an observer standing on the road looking into the van as it passes.

15.5 The Speed of Light Is a Constant

Is there any frame of reference that might be considered as truly 'fixed'? Such a frame of reference would be the **absolute reference frame**, relative to which all velocities might be measured. In ancient times, it was believed that the earth itself was at rest and that all other celestial bodies moved around the earth. If this were true, then the earth would be the absolute reference frame. When Copernicus showed that the earth actually orbited the sun (and not the other way around), the idea of using the earth as a fixed reference frame became outdated. The sun cannot be used as an absolute reference frame because it is moving around the centre of the galaxy. And our galaxy itself moves relative to distant galaxies. It seems that everything in nature moves relative to something else.

Might space itself be a useful absolute reference frame?

The Michelson-Morley Experiment

In the late nineteenth century, two Americans **A. A. Michelson (1852-1931)** and **E. W. Morley (1838-1923)** conducted a vital experiment in search of the absolute frame of reference. Scottish physicist **James Clerk Maxwell (1831-1879)**, in his theory of electromagnetic radiation, had predicted that the velocity of light would be 300 000 km/s (presumably 'relative to the absolute reference frame').

The theory at the time was that light was a wave motion. What was it that was vibrating in space? After all, light will travel through a vacuum. It was thought that there was a mysterious 'something' called the **ether,** and that light waves were really vibrations in the ether. Perhaps the ether could serve as a fixed reference frame?

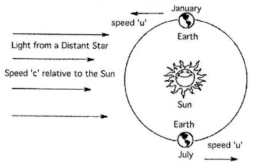

Figure 15.5

Michelson and Morley did numerous experiments, measuring the speed of light with the help of an instrument called an **interferometer,** which permitted detection of very tiny changes in the speed of light. **Figure 15.5** shows one of the key experiments done by Michelson and Morley.

In January of 1887, Michelson and Morley measured the speed of light coming from a distant star. In *January,* the earth was moving *toward* the star with a speed *u* relative to the sun.

The speed of light relative to the sun was assumed to *be 'c'*. The measured speed of light relative to the earth was *predicted* to be $c + u$. In *July,* the earth was moving *away* from the distant star and the *predicted* measurement for the speed of light was $c - u$. The careful measurements done by Michelson and Morley *failed to detect any difference* in the speed of light relative to the earth for the two situations. ***The measured speed of light relative to earth was the same whether the earth (the observers' frame of reference) was moving toward the source of light or away from it.***

The result of the Michelson-Morley experiment and other follow-up experiments was quite surprising. Our everyday experience would not lead us to expect the speed of light to be independent of our frame of reference. Consider this example: You are driving north on a road, moving 70 km/h. A car approaches you travelling 80 km/h south. The speed of the other car relative to your car is

$$80 \text{ km/h} + 70 \text{ km/h} = 150 \text{ km/h}.$$

That is what you expect, and that is what really happens. Similarly, if you are travelling north at 70 km/h, and the faster car is travelling in the same direction at 80 km/h, the speed of the faster car relative to your car is

$$80 \text{ km/h} - 70 \text{ km/h} = 10 \text{ km/h}.$$

If, however, you replace the 'faster car' by **light**, you find that the speed of light relative to your car is 300 000 km/s whether your car is moving toward the light or away from it!

The Michelson-Morley experiment is famous for its *negative* result. It showed experimentally that *the speed of light in space is the same for all observers regardless of their velocity or the velocity of the source of the light. The speed of light simply does NOT depend on your frame of reference at all!* No evidence could be found that space (or the 'ether' that some believed pervaded space) could be used as a fixed frame of reference.

This experimentally verified fact was *predicted theoretically* by **Albert Einstein.** Einstein, who was not even aware of the work that Michelson and Morley had done, never did believe that there was such a thing as a 'fixed frame of reference' or an 'ether'. In fact, he summed up what he thought about the velocity of light in his second fundamental postulate of relativity.

The Second Postulate of the Relativity Principle

The speed of light in space is the same for any observer no matter what the velocity of the observer's frame of reference is, and no matter what the velocity of the source of the light is.

The two fundamental postulates of relativity were used by Einstein to derive some extremely interesting predictions.

15.6 Time Dilation (Your Time ≠ My Time, ... Necessarily)

[*Dilate: 'To Make Wider Or Larger'.*]

According to Einstein's Special Theory of Relativity, *a clock that is moving will run slow*. This 'stretching' of time by a moving object is called **time dilation.**

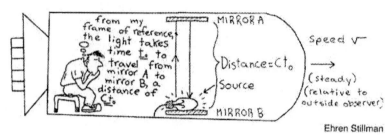

Ehren Stillman

Figure 15.6

Is it possible that in two different frames of reference, identical clocks might run differently, and that time might pass differently? In fact, this is one of the predictions of Albert Einstein's **Special Theory of Relativity**!

Figure 15.6 illustrates an observer inside an imaginary, custom-made glass-walled spaceship, made especially so that an outside observer can watch an experiment done by an inside observer. The inside observer is watching an event consisting of an imaginary oscillating light beam. (Think of it as 'light entertainment'.)

The oscillating light beam acts like a clock. The beam goes from the source up to mirror A and back to mirror B. The inside observer measures the time for the light to travel from A to B and finds that the time is t_o . Since distance = speed x time, the distance that the inside observer sees the light beam travel is $d = ct_o$.

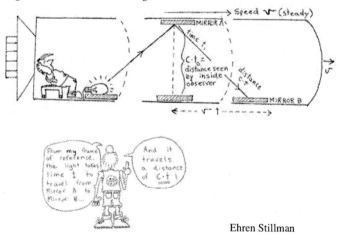

Ehren Stillman

Figure 15.7

Figure 15.7 illustrates what an observer in a different frame of reference sees. The outside observer is *not* moving at speed *v!* He sees the spaceship going by at speed *v, relative to him*. To the outside observer, the light beam in the spaceship takes a time *t* to travel a distance *ct* while the spaceship moves forward a distance *vt*. A right-angled triangle is formed with sides ct_o, vt, and *ct*. According to Pythagoras' Theorem,

$$[ct]^2 = [ct_o]^2 + [vt]^2$$

Therefore,
$$[ct]^2 - [vt]^2 = [ct_o]^2$$

and
$$c^2t^2 - v^2t^2 = c^2t_o^2$$

or,
$$t^2[c^2 - v^2] = c^2t_o^2.$$

Dividing both sides of the equation by c^2,

$$t^2[1 - \frac{v^2}{c^2}] = t_o^2.$$

Rearranging terms,
$$t^2 = \frac{t_o^2}{[1 - \frac{v^2}{c^2}]}.$$

Taking the square root of both sides of the equation, we obtain an equation for *t* (as observed by the outside observer):

$$t = \frac{t_o}{\sqrt{1 - v^2/c^2}}.$$

Example

By how much is time 'expanded' (or the clock 'slowed') from a fixed observer's point of view if the spaceship in **Figure 15.7** is moving at one-half the speed of light? ($v = 1/2\ c$.)

$$t = \frac{t_o}{\sqrt{1 - \frac{[0.5c]^2}{c^2}}} = \frac{t_o}{\sqrt{1 - 0.25}} = \frac{t_o}{\sqrt{0.75}} = 1.15t_o.$$

(Time is dilated or 'stretched' by 15%.)

Exercise

An observer in a 'fixed' frame of reference is watching an event that takes time t_o to occur according to an observer in a frame of reference moving at speed *v* relative to the fixed observer. Calculate the time the fixed observer will measure if t_o is 5.0 s, and the speed of the moving frame of reference (a spaceship) is:

(a) $0.65c$ (b) $0.866c$ (c) $0.995c$ (d) $0.999c$

Experimental Evidence for the Prediction of Time Dilation

Elementary particles called **mu-mesons** (or muons) are known to exist and to have an average 'life-time' of 2.0×10^{-6} s. Mu-mesons created about 6 to 8 km above the earth during collisions of cosmic rays with nuclei of atoms in air molecules have been observed to travel with a very high speed of $0.988c$! The mu-mesons decay into electrons at the end of their short 'lifetime'.

Consider a mu-meson formed at high altitude and travelling downward at a speed of $0.988c$. How far will it travel during a lifetime of 2.0×10^{-6} s?

$$d = vt = (0.998 \times 3.0 \times 10^5 \text{ km/s})(2.0 \times 10^{-6} \text{ s}) = 0.60 \text{ km}.$$

According to this calculation, *none* of the mu-mesons formed 6 to 8 km above the ground should *reach* the ground. The mu-mesons, however, *are* detected at ground level! To see why, consider the time of travel of the mu-mesons *in the frame of reference of a stationary observer on earth.*

$$t = \frac{t_o}{\sqrt{1 - v^2/c^2}} = \frac{2.0 \times 10^{-6} \text{s}}{\sqrt{1 - [(0.998c)^2/c^2]}} = \frac{2.0 \times 10^{-6} \text{s}}{\sqrt{1 - 0.996}} = \frac{2.0 \times 10^{-6} \text{s}}{\sqrt{0.004}}$$

$$t = 3.2 \times 10^{-5} \text{ s}.$$

In a time of 3.2×10^{-5} s, the mu-meson could travel a distance of:

$$d = vt = (0.998 \times 3.0 \times 10^5 \text{ km/s})(3.2 \times 10^{-5} \text{ s}) = 9.6 \text{ km}.$$

Thus, when the effects of time dilation are taken into account, the mu-meson *does* have time to reach earth's surface! This is why mu-mesons created 6 to 8 km above the earth can reach earth during their average lifetime. The average lifetime is 2.0×10^{-6} s from the frame of reference of the mu-meson, but it is 3.2×10^{-5} s (*sixteen times as long*) from *our* frame of reference on a fixed earth.

A Thought Experiment

Imagine your age is 30 a and that you have a daughter who is 6 a old. You leave on a space trip in the year 2 000 and travel at a speed of $0.99c$ for a time of 5.0 a (as measured by you in the spaceship). In other words, from the space traveller's frame of reference, $t_o = 5.0$ a.

How much time will have elapsed when you return, from the frame of reference of your young daughter who was left behind on earth? To find out, use the time dilation formula:

$$t = \frac{5.0 \text{ a}}{\sqrt{1 - [0.99c]^2/c^2}} = \frac{5.0 \text{ a}}{\sqrt{1 - 0.980}} = \frac{5.0 \text{ a}}{\sqrt{0.020}} = \frac{5.0 \text{ a}}{0.14} = 36 \text{ a}.$$

What this means is this: Having left earth in the year 2 000 A.D., you will return to earth in the year 2036 A.D. Your daughter, whom you left at home, will be 6a + 36 a = **42 a** old.

You will be 30 a + 5a = 35 a old! Yes! Your daughter will be *older* than you are! As a high-speed space traveller, you only age by 5 a as measured from the spaceship frame of reference. To earth observers, their clocks tell them that 36 a have gone by since you left on your journey.

15.7 Length Contraction

Einstein's Special Theory of Relativity makes other predictions about objects moving at speeds greater than zero. Without going into mathematical detail, we shall simply state the prediction relating to the **length** of a moving object.

The length of an object is *measured* to be shorter when it is moving than when it is at rest. (This shortening is only seen in the dimension of its motion.)

If the length of an object when it is standing still is L_O, the theory of relativity predicts that the object's length L when it is moving at speed v will be *measured* to be:

$$L = L_o\sqrt{1 - \frac{v^2}{c^2}}$$

Example

How long would a metre stick *appear* to be if it was moving past you with a speed of 0.995c?

Solution:
$$L = L_o\sqrt{1 - \frac{v^2}{c^2}}.$$

$$L = 1.00 \text{ m}\sqrt{1 - (0.995c)^2/c^2} = 1.00 \text{ m}\sqrt{1 - 0.990} = 1.00 \text{ m}\sqrt{0.010}.$$

$$L = 0.10 \text{ m (or 10 cm!)}$$

Exercise

Calculate the *apparent* length of a 100 m futuristic spaceship when it is travelling at these speeds:

(a) 0.63c   (b) 0.866c   (c) 0.999c

(Note: If you are *in* the spaceship, you will perceive its length to be 100 m at all times at any speed!)

15.8 Relativistic Momentum

The definition of **momentum** given earlier ($p = mv$) does *not* apply to objects travelling at relativistic speeds. The expression for relativistic momentum is:

$$p = \frac{mv}{\sqrt{1 - \frac{v^2}{c^2}}}.$$

For lower speeds, one can see that as $v \to 0$, the ratio $v/c \to 0$, and momentum $p \to mv$. In other words, the Newtonian definition of momentum 'works' for lower speeds. You will recall that Newton's Second Law can be written in terms of momentum: $F = \frac{\Delta p}{\Delta t}$. Newton's Second Law can be used at relativistic speeds, *but only in this form, where p is **relativistic momentum.***

Exercises

1. Let the mass of an electron be m. The speed of light is c. Calculate what the momentum of an electron would be at each of the following speeds, according to the **Newtonian** equation for momentum, $p = mv$.
   (a) 0.10 c (b) 0.50 c (c) 0.87 c (d) 0.9999 c (e) c

2. Calculate what the **relativistic momentum** of an electron would be at these speeds:
   (a) 0.10 c (b) 0.50 c (c) 0.87 c (d) 0.9999 c (e) c

3. Calculate the unbalanced force that would be needed to accelerate an electron from rest up to the speed of light, c, in a time t.

15.9 Speed Limit for the Universe: The Speed of Light

Can a body be accelerated to the speed of light? Consider what would happen to the momentum (p) of, say, an electron. (The same argument applies to *any* object having mass.) If the velocity v were in some fashion increased until it equaled c, then the momentum of the object would become:

$$p = \frac{mv}{\sqrt{1 - c^2/c^2}} = \frac{mv}{0} = \infty.$$

The **momentum** of an object approaches *infinity* as the speed of an object approaches the speed of light. The unbalanced force needed to accelerate it to speed c would also be infinite! Therefore an object cannot be accelerated to the speed of light.

Ehren Stillman

Could a particle have a velocity *greater* than *c?* If this were so, the magnitude of $(1 - v^2/c^2)$ would be less than zero, and the square root of a negative number does not exist in the real number system. (The momentum would be imaginary!)

It does appear, then, that the speed of light truly is the speed limit for the universe. A precise value for the speed of light is: $c = 2.99792458 \times 10^8$ m/s. For most applications, the speed of light is rounded off to 3.00×10^8 m/s. This is for light travelling through a vacuum. In air, the speed is only slightly lower.

15.10 Mass-Energy Equivalence

Einstein was able to show mathematically that, as a consequence of his Special Theory of Relativity, mass and energy are different aspects of the same thing. They are equivalent to one another. The **total energy** in a body is related to its mass by the following formula:

$$E = \frac{mc^2}{\sqrt{1 - v^2/c^2}}$$

When the body is at rest, $v = 0$, and the **total energy** equation reduces to:

$$E = mc^2.$$

This is one of the most famous equations in physics. It says, for example, that a body at rest has energy because of its mass. Einstein predicted that mass could be changed into energy and that energy could be changed into mass. Both predictions have been verified experimentally. Mass is changed into energy during the nuclear processes that occur in reactors and in atomic and hydrogen bombs. The first evidence that energy could be changed into mass was found in 1932, when American physicist **C.D. Anderson** observed, in a photographic emulsion, evidence that a gamma photon (very high energy light) had changed into two particles: an **electron** and a *positive electron* (**positron**). The positron is an anti-particle of an electron; it has the same mass as an electron but the opposite charge.

Example

If one kilogram of mass were completely changed into energy, how much energy would be produced?

Solution: $E = mc^2 = (1.0 \text{ kg})(3.0 \times 10^8 \text{ m/s})^2 = 9.0 \times 10^{16} \text{ kg} \cdot \text{m}^2/\text{s}^2.$

Note! **1 kg·m²/s² = 1 Nm =1 Joule.**

One kilogram mass is equivalent to 9.0×10^{16} J, or *90 000 000 000 000 000 J*. That's a huge amount of energy!

Challenges

1. Find out from your hydroelectric bill how many joules of electrical energy you use each month. If you could somehow convert 1 **gram** of mass directly into electrical energy, with how many months worth of electrical energy would this provide you?

2. The **Special Theory of Relativity** deals only with frames of reference moving at uniform velocity. Find out what the **General Theory of Relativity** is concerned with in the realm of gravity, space and time.

Chapter Review Questions

1. Upon what two postulates is the Special Theory of Relativity based?
2. You are approaching a star in a spaceship that is travelling at half the speed of light. How fast will the light from the star go past you?
3. An astronaut makes a trip in a spaceship travelling at a speed of $0.65c$.
   (a) The astronaut's calendar and clocks indicate the trip lasts 10 a. How long does the trip last according to observers on a 'fixed' earth?
   (b) The spaceship is 50.0 m long when at rest. How long does it appear to be to an observer in a fixed position on a line parallel to the path of the spaceship?

4. How fast must a Greyhound 'space bus' travel in order for its length to appear to contract to one-half its full length?

5. A man is 25 a old. He expects to live to an age of 75 a. He plans to make a trip in a spaceship, leaving earth in 2 000 A.D. He would like to return to earth in the year 2 500 A.D. Is this possible? How fast would the spaceship have to travel?

6. If one milligram (1 mg = 10^{-6} kg) of mass were converted into pure energy, how many joules of energy would be produced?

Test Yourself!

1. What are the two **postulates** of the **Relativity Principle?**

2. An event takes t_o seconds to occur, according to the occupants of a space bus that is moving at one-half the speed of light ($\frac{1}{2}$ c). To a fixed observer outside the space bus, how long will the event take to occur?

3. From a fixed reference point, you observe a space bus pass by at a very high speed, v. The occupants say the space bus is 10 m long. If the space bus appears to be only 5 m long from *your* frame of reference, how fast is the space bus moving? Express your answer as a decimal fraction of the speed of light, c.

4. When you look at a distant star in the night sky, do you see the star
   (a) as it appears now?
   (b) as it will look sometime in the future, or
   (c) as it looked sometime in the past?
   Discuss why you chose this answer.

5. Discuss what happens to the momentum, *p,* of an electron, if it is accelerated to a speed approaching the speed of light. Discuss whether the electron can be made to travel at the speed of light.

6. (a) If the mass of a golf ball (46 g) could be converted entirely into energy ($E = mc^2$), how much energy would be released?
   (b) Imagine your residence uses an average of 16 kWh of electrical energy per day. If you could convert the energy from the mass of a golf ball directly into electrical energy (and store it), how many *years* supply would you be able to store away? (1 kWh = 3.6 x 10^6 J)

Chapter 16   The Nuclear Atom

16.1 The Beginnings of Modern Atomic Theories

In the nineteenth century, experiments conducted by chemists convinced them that matter consisted of tiny particles called **atoms.** The concept was not a new one. Early Greek philosophers such as **Democritus** had suggested the idea centuries before English chemist **John Dalton (1766-1844)** proposed his **Atomic Theory.** Dalton's solid evidence suggested that each chemical element was made up of unique atoms. Different elements had different atoms. Dalton could not say in what way the atoms were different. Dalton believed that atoms were indivisible and had no inner structure. Until the end of the last century, there was no evidence to suggest that Dalton's ideas might be incomplete or wrong. At the end of the nineteenth century and the beginning of the twentieth century, many exciting discoveries were made about matter. It took great discoveries and great minds to interpret the new evidence.

The Mystery of Cathode Rays

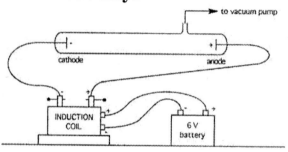

Figure 16.1

Michael Faraday (1791-1867) is a name often mentioned in chemistry and physics books. He was a brilliant experimental scientist. One of his more important inventions is the **induction coil.** The induction coil is similar to the ignition coil in a car. It changes low voltage electricity into very high voltage (high energy) electricity. It produces sufficiently high voltage to cause electrical discharges several centimetres long in air. Michael Faraday set up the apparatus as illustrated in **Figure 16.1**. A vacuum pump is used to gradually remove the air in the glass tube. A high voltage is applied to the two electrodes by the induction coil. The positive electrode (+) is called the **anode** (from the Greek word *ana,* which means *up*) and the negative electrode (-) is called the **cathode** (from the Greek *cata,* which means *down*). (Electricity was presumed to travel 'down' from the anode to the cathode; that is, from positive to negative.)

At normal air pressure, nothing happens in the tube. At moderately low air pressure, pink, lightning-like sparks can be seen between one electrode and the other. As more air is removed, a uniform pink glow fills the discharge tube. Then, as even more air is removed, the pink breaks up into distinct layers. With a really good vacuum pump, which can remove just about every trace of air from the discharge tube, the pink colour can be made to disappear, and the glass is observed glowing with a green fluorescence.

The source of the green fluorescence was a mystery. Another English physicist-chemist, **Sir William Crookes (1832-1919)**, pursued Faraday's discovery further. He designed several modifications of the discharge tube first used by Faraday.

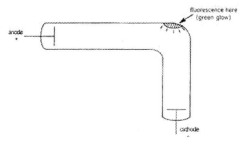

Figure 16.2

Figure 16.2 illustrates one of Crookes' tubes. This tube is highly evacuated and, when connected to an induction coil, the green glow is most noticeable at the region of glass opposite from the **cathode**. It appeared that the source of the fluorescence was something that came from the cathode. Eventually, the mysterious 'something' was called **cathode rays**.

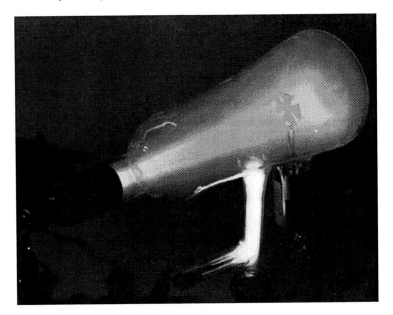

Figure 16.3(a)

Crookes continued his investigation of cathode rays. In one of his tubes, he inserted a metal object shaped like a Maltese Cross (**Figure 16.3(a)** and **(b).** When cathode rays passed through the tube, they cast a shadow of the Maltese Cross on the far end of the tube. This shadow was very sharp, the sort of shadow you might expect from a point source. The cathode, however, was really quite large. If the cause of the shadow was light from the cathode, then the shadow should have been quite blurred, as are all shadows cast by large light sources nearby.

Crookes was aware of work Faraday had done with electric fields. If the cathode rays were **particles** following electric lines of force, which are perpendicular to the cathode, then the shadow would be sharply defined. Could the cathode rays be electrical in nature?

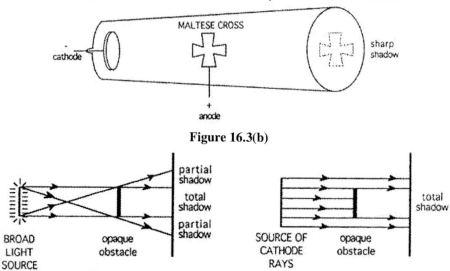

Figure 16.3(b)

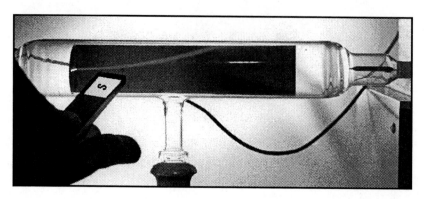

Figure 16.4

German physicists were very interested in cathode rays. **Johann Wilhelm Hittorf** performed the same experiment as Crookes, showing that an opaque object would cast a sharp shadow when placed between a source of cathode rays and the end of the cathode ray tube. Hittorf actually published his result before Crookes did. Improved vacuum tubes were made possible by the invention of a better pump by **Heinrich Geissler (1814-1879)**. Geissler, a glassblower, manufactured a variety of Geissler tubes containing exceptionally high vacuums. Physicist **Julius Plucker (1801-1868)** used one of Geissler's high vacuum tubes to show that cathode rays, whatever they were, *were deflected by a magnetic field*. No form of *light* is deflected by a magnetic field.

Figure 16.5

Figure 16.5 illustrates a cathode ray tube designed to demonstrate the magnetic deflection of cathode rays. If the magnetic poles are reversed, the deflection of the cathode rays is also reversed. Notice that the deflection is *perpendicular* to the direction in which the magnet is aligned.

Many physicists experimented with cathode rays, trying to identify what they were. Some thought that cathode rays were a form of light. Others thought that they were electrically charged particles, perhaps 'atoms of electricity'.

In 1887, brilliant English physicist **Joseph John Thomson (1856-1940)** was able to show that cathode rays, if passed between oppositely charged plates, *were deflected away from the negative plate and toward the positive plate.* Others had failed to observe this effect, but Thomson was convinced the reason they had not seen the electric deflection was the lack of sufficiently good vacuum. With a cathode ray tube having an exceptionally good vacuum, Thomson succeeded. This was a critical experiment. Knowing that cathode rays were deflected by both a magnetic field and an electric field, Thomson concluded with some confidence that *cathode rays were particles carrying a negative charge!*

Thomson is credited with discovering what some considered to be the 'atoms of electricity'. Years earlier, an Irish physicist named **George Johnstone Stoney (1826-1911)** had suggested the name **electron** for the as-yet undiscovered smallest bit of electricity. The name electron was quickly adopted for the negatively charged particles discovered by Thomson.

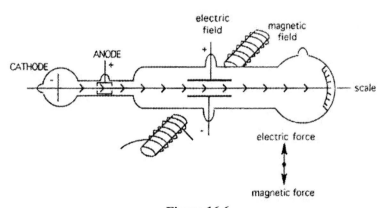

Figure 16.6

Thomson did more than show that cathode rays were electrons. He used combined electric and magnetic fields to actually calculate the *ratio* of the electron's charge to its mass (e/m). **Figure 16.6** illustrates the apparatus Thomson used to determine the charge-to-mass ratio of the electron. Electric fields were used to balance magnetic fields in his procedure.

Experiments done with **hydrogen ions** (hydrogen atoms minus an electron) indicated that the charge-to-mass ratio for a hydrogen ion was approximately 1/1836 that of the electron. Evidence suggested that the charge on a hydrogen ion was equal in magnitude, but opposite in sign, to the charge on an electron. This meant that the mass of an electron was 1/1836 the mass of a hydrogen atom.

Since the electron was much lighter than the lightest atom known (hydrogen), it appeared that electrons were smaller than atoms. Electric forces could remove electrons from the metal atoms in cathodes, and it seemed quite certain that electrons were therefore **subatomic particles.** Dalton's idea that atoms were indivisible particles was thus disproved.

The Discovery of X-Rays

German physicist **Wilhelm Konrad Röntgen (1845-1923)** was interested in cathode rays. He also had a special interest in the phenomenon of **fluorescence.** Certain minerals were known to fluoresce when cathode rays struck them. Röntgen wanted to see the faint effect better, so he completely surrounded his cathode ray tube with thin black cardboard to keep out room light. When he turned on the cathode ray tube, he noticed that a sheet of paper covered with **barium platinocyanide**, which was near the cathode ray tube, was giving off light. The room lights were off, and the cathode ray tube was completely shielded with the black paper. Even when he took the barium platinocyanide into the next room and darkened the room, it would glow when the cathode ray tube was turned on next door!

Röntgen concluded that some form of radiation was coming from the cathode ray tube — a radiation that penetrated opaque black paper (and a wall). It was soon discovered that the **Röntgen rays** could even pass through thin pieces of metal! Röntgen called the mysterious new radiation **X-rays**. The discovery was made on November 5, 1895, and within a very short time, the usefulness of these penetrating rays was discovered by medical doctors and dentists.

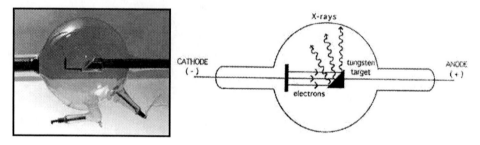

Figure 16.7

Figure 16.7 illustrates the parts of an X-ray tube. The X-rays are produced when the high-energy cathode rays (electrons) strike the tungsten target. A high voltage is applied to the electrodes to accelerate electrons to very high speed. Great care must be taken in using X-rays, since they are harmful to human tissue.

The Discovery of Radioactivity

The phenomenon called **fluorescence** has interested physicists for many years. Fluorescent substances absorb light of one wavelength, and then give off light at a longer wavelength. For example, the colouring on some posters will absorb ultraviolet light from a 'black light', and then emit bright colours in the visible range.

In 1896, French physicist **Antoine Henri Becquerel (1852-1908)** was investigating fluorescent materials. X-rays had just been discovered by Röntgen, and Becquerel was curious to know whether fluorescent materials might, in addition to visible light, give off these 'new' rays.

As fate would have it, one of the fluorescent compounds that Becquerel was working with was potassium uranyl sulfate $K_2UO_2(SO_4)_2$. Becquerel knew that if he exposed this compound to bright sunlight, and then took it into a dark room, it would **fluoresce**. (Delayed fluorescence like this is called **phosphorescence**.) To find out if the fluorescence included X-rays, he placed the sample above a photographic plate, which was completely wrapped in black paper so that no visible light could reach the plate.

When the plate was developed, it was fogged, indicating that radiation was penetrating the black paper. Was it X-rays that were exposing the film? Becquerel made a very important observation. If the uranium compound was left sitting on the paper-covered photographic plate, the plate was exposed whether the compound was fluorescing or not. The radiation that was causing the plate to fog was being emitted by the uranium compound *all the time*. This new radiation had nothing to do with fluorescence or phosphorescence. Its discovery was just good luck (and good observation) on the part of Becquerel.

No one knew what these new 'rays' were, but they were called **Becquerel rays.** Whatever they were, scientists found out that they had several properties that were similar to Röntgen rays.

Properties of Becquerel Rays

(1) They are very penetrating.
(2) They expose photographic plates.
(3) They are invisible to the eye.
(4) They cause air molecules to become ions.

The property that some substances have of emitting penetrating radiation, which ionizes the air, was called **radioactivity** by **Madame Marie Sklodowska Curie (1867-1934)**. Madame Curie showed that all uranium compounds are radioactive, and concluded that it was the uranium atom itself that was radioactive.

Other Radioactive Elements

Marie Curie made many extremely important contributions to the new science of radioactivity. Marie showed that the element **thorium** was also radioactive. She and her husband **Pierre Curie (1859-1906)** showed conclusively that radioactivity of an element originated in the atoms of the elements; it did not depend on any external factors or on compounds formed by the elements.

In their search for other elements that might be radioactive, Marie and Pierre examined pitchblende ore, a mixture containing uranium oxide. They found that the degree of radioactivity (measured with apparatus invented by Pierre Curie) was many times greater than one would obtain from uranium itself. It appeared there was an element in the ore that was even more radioactive than uranium. After carrying out lengthy chemical separations of the substances in pitchblende, they isolated a substance with 400 times the activity of uranium. They named the radioactive element in the isolated material **polonium**, after Marie's native Poland. In the same year, 1898, they discovered yet another radioactive element in the pitchblende and called it **radium.** Radium was even more radioactive than polonium.

Pierre and Marie Curie were awarded the 1903 Nobel Prize for physics, along with co-winner Henri Becquerel. Marie has the distinction of being the only scientist to win two Nobel prizes for science achievements. She won her second prize in 1911 for chemistry, for her discoveries of polonium and radium. (In addition to Marie's own achievements, her daughter **Irene Curie** won the 1935 Nobel Prize for chemistry.)

A Canadian Contribution

One of the truly great pioneers in atomic research did much of his important work while at McGill University in Montreal. **Ernest Rutherford (1871-1937)** was born in New Zealand. After earning his master's degree in physics in New Zealand, Rutherford went to Cambridge, England to work with **J. J. Thomson** (discoverer of the electron) from 1885 until 1898. In 1898, he accepted the position of physics professor at McGill University. He stayed at McGill University until 1907, and then returned to England.

Rutherford and Thomson studied the effect that X-rays have on air. The air is ionized, and thus rendered conducting by the passage of X-rays through it. When Becquerel rays were discovered, Rutherford was intensely interested in finding out more about them.

At McGill University, Rutherford and his graduate students investigated the penetrating ability of Becquerel rays. They let the rays from a sample of uranium metal pass through various thicknesses of aluminum foil and pass into a detector, which used the property of electrical conductivity of air. He found that the intensity of the radiation fell off as the thickness of the foil increased, but there was a 'discontinuity' when the thickness reached a certain value. The discontinuity suggested to him that Becquerel rays were of at least two types. One of those types was far more penetrating than the other. The less penetrating rays were labelled **alpha rays** and the more penetrating rays were labelled **beta rays**. Alpha (α) and beta (β) are the first two letters of the Greek alphabet.

The identification of two types of Becquerel rays by Rutherford in 1899 was followed shortly after by the discovery of a third type of Becquerel ray by French physicist **Paul Villard (1860-1934)**. In 1900, Villard found a form of radiation emitted by radium that was far more penetrating than either alpha or beta rays. This third form of radiation was labelled **gamma** (γ) radiation. Gamma radiation can pass through several centimetres of lead, or several metres of concrete, before being completely stopped. Gamma rays are more penetrating than X-rays.

Exercises

1. How did cathode rays get their name?

2. What was unusual about the shadow cast by the Maltese Cross inside a highly evacuated cathode ray tube?

3. Why was the discovery that cathode rays were deflected by a magnetic field so critical to understanding what they were (or were not)?

4. What are cathode rays? Who established this fact beyond a doubt?

5. Why is the electron called a *subatomic particle?*

6. (a) What was Röntgen actually looking for when he discovered X-rays by accident?
   (b) What was Becquerel looking for when he discovered radioactivity by accident?

7. (a) Who introduced the term, *radioactivity?*
   (b) Who first identified alpha particles? beta particles? gamma radiation?

What Are α, β, and γ Radiations?

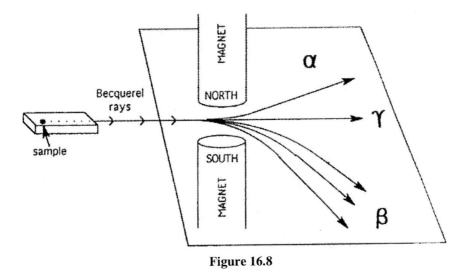

Figure 16.8

The task of figuring out what α, β and γ radiations were was taken on by numerous scientists, including Marie and Pierre Curie, Henri Becquerel and Ernest Rutherford. One of the clever ways they used to study their behaviour was to pass a narrow beam of Becquerel rays through a magnetic field. If the magnetic field was strong enough, it separated the three kinds of radiation quite definitely. **Figure 16.8** is a simplified diagram of the apparatus used and the results observed.

The alpha radiation was deflected in one direction, following a circular path while within the magnetic field. Beta radiation was deflected in the opposite direction, in circular paths of shorter radius. The gamma radiation was not affected by the magnetic field. Beta radiation was affected in the same way as cathode rays, which showed that beta radiation carried a negative charge. Since alpha radiation deflected in the opposite direction, it obviously carried a positive charge.

Becquerel used the technique of J. J. Thomson to measure the charge-to-mass ratio of beta radiation. The result he obtained was essentially the same as for electrons. Beta particles were electrons!

Experiments with alpha particles indicated they were much more massive than beta particles (electrons). The magnitude of charge on them was equal to or twice that of the electron. The magnetic field experiments suggested that the alpha particle might be (a) a hydrogen molecule with a single positive charge (H_2^+) or (b) a helium atom with a double positive charge (He^{2+}).

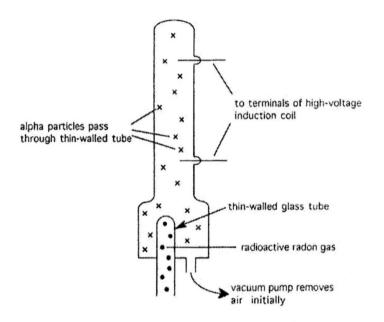

to terminals of high-voltage induction coil

alpha particles pass through thin-walled tube

thin-walled glass tube

radioactive radon gas

vacuum pump removes air initially

Figure 16.9

Rutherford and **T. S. Royds** carried out an ingenious experiment to find out whether alpha particles were, in fact, helium atoms missing two electrons (He^{2+}). Rutherford and Royds knew that radon gas was radioactive and gave off alpha particles. They passed radon gas into a very thin-walled glass tube, as in the schematic diagram in **Figure 16.9**. An outer glass tube surrounding the radon-filled tube was evacuated with a vacuum pump. The outer tube had two electrodes built into it. After several days enough alpha particles from the radioactive radon had escaped through the thin-walled inner container into the outer container, and the contents of the outer container could be tested. A high voltage was applied to the two electrodes, and the discharge that occurred was examined with a spectroscope. The spectral lines observed were identical with the spectrum of helium gas. Alpha particles, Rutherford and Royd concluded, were helium atoms with two electrons missing (that is, helium ions with a double positive charge, He^{2+}).

Gamma radiation was very penetrating, and was not deflected by magnetic or electric fields. Rutherford and a colleague, **E. N. da C. Andrade**, used a new technique involving diffraction by crystals to actually measure the wavelength of gamma radiation. This convinced Rutherford and Andrade that gamma radiation was similar to X-radiation. It was a form of electromagnetic radiation and travelled at the speed of light. Wavelengths of gamma radiation were shorter than the wavelengths of X-radiation. Thus, gamma rays, discovered in 1900 by Villard, were finally identified in 1914 by Rutherford and Andrade.

The work of many great scientists indicated that the atom could no longer be considered an indivisible particle with no internal structure. All the evidence gathered by Becquerel, the Curies, Thomson and Rutherford suggested that radioactive atoms literally threw off fragments of themselves. Eventually it was shown that these fragments came from an inner core of the atoms, called its **nucleus**. It was Ernest Rutherford who demonstrated that the atom had a nucleus.

Exercises

1. What effect does a magnetic field have on a beam of radiation containing a mixture of alpha, beta and gamma rays?

2. How did Rutherford and Royds show that alpha rays were actually helium ions?

3. Who showed that beta particles were actually electrons? How did he do it?

4. Who showed that gamma radiation was actually electromagnetic radiation like light and X-rays? What kind of experiment did this require?

What Happens to a Radioactive Atom?

Many scientists occupied themselves trying to figure out what actually happened during radioactive decay of atoms of elements such as uranium, thorium, polonium and radium. In 1900, William Crookes made a surprising discovery. When a uranium sample was *thoroughly purified,* its radioactivity actually *decreased!* This was indeed puzzling, and it was thought for a while that perhaps it was an impurity in uranium that was radioactive, rather than the uranium itself. Shortly after, however, Becquerel duplicated the experiment, obtained the same result, *but* found that if the originally pure sample was left standing it *regained* its activity. Eventually it became as radioactive as previous measurements of uranium had indicated.

In 1902, Rutherford and English physicist **Frederick Soddy (1877-1956)** found that thorium showed the same behaviour as uranium. Purified, its activity initially became very low, but on standing the sample recovered its activity.

Rutherford and Soddy drew a startling conclusion from these observations. What was happening, they said, was that when a radioactive atom such as uranium gave off radioactive particles, the uranium atom changed into an atom of a different element altogether! This new atom gave off radioactive particles and became yet another element. The increasing radioactivity of the uranium sample was due to the growing concentration of these radioactive 'daughter elements'. The 'daughter elements' were more radioactive than the parent uranium atoms, so the radioactivity increased from the time the pure uranium was left standing.

Natural Transmutations

The idea that one element could change into another element was absolutely revolutionary. (The alchemists had tried unsuccessfully for centuries to find ways to change common metals into gold. Of course, there is still no *chemical* way to change one element into another, but radioactive decay is not a chemical reaction.) The process of changing one element into another through radioactive decay is called **transmutation.** The work by Rutherford and Soddy, which verified that transmutation did, in fact, occur when alpha and beta particles were given off by a radioactive element, was done at McGill University. The discovery resulted in Rutherford winning the Nobel prize in chemistry in 1908. By that time, Rutherford had returned to England where he was associated with the University of Manchester.

Probing Atoms with Alpha Particles

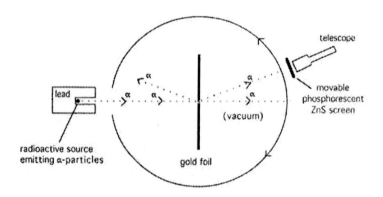

Figure 16.10

Alpha particles were among Ernest Rutherford's favorite tools for his atomic research. While at McGill University, he had observed that a beam of alpha particles, if made to pass through a thin metal foil, was scattered from its path. Presumably, the deflection was caused by atoms in the foil. This scattering effect of atoms on alpha particles was explored further by two of Rutherford's physics students at the University of Manchester in England. **Hans Geiger (1882-1945)** and **Ernest Marsden** used a zinc sulfide screen as a detector of alpha particles. Zinc sulfide *phosphoresces* when struck by alpha particles. **Figure 16.10** is a schematic diagram of the apparatus, all of which was enclosed in an evacuated container so that air molecules would not be a factor in scattering the alpha particles.

Hans Geiger had earlier observed that the amount of scattering of the alpha particles by a metal foil increased if either (a) a thicker foil or (b) heavier atoms were used. However, most of the alpha particles went through the foil with little deflection, suggesting that the atoms might be composed largely of empty space.

Rutherford suggested that Marsden (a young undergraduate student) find out whether any alpha particles were scattered through *large* angles. A few days later Geiger and Marsden reported to Rutherford that they had observed alpha particles coming *backwards* off the foil. This observation absolutely astounded Rutherford. After all, alpha particles, on the atomic scale, are very massive 'bullets', with approximately 7000 times the mass of an electron!

Apparently, the fast-moving (10^7 m/s), alpha particles were being repelled by a powerful, highly *centralized force* within the atoms of the gold foil. The foil used initially by Geiger and Marsden was approximately 400 atoms thick. According to their observations, approximately 1 alpha particle in 8 000 was turned back through an angle greater than 90°. What incredibly large force could turn around a massive alpha particle, travelling one tenth the speed of light, and send it back the way it came?

The Rutherford Model of the Atom

The scattering of alpha particles by atoms could be explained by assuming that:

(a) The atom is mostly empty space.
(b) Within the atom there is a tiny core carrying a positive charge where most of the mass of the atom is concentrated. This 'core' is the **nucleus** of the atom.
(c) Surrounding the nucleus are the negatively charged **electrons**. The mass of one electron is only 1/1836 times the mass of a normal hydrogen nucleus.

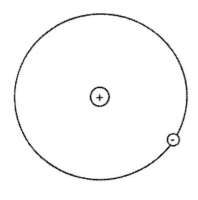

Figure 16.11

Figure 16.11 illustrates how Rutherford pictured the hydrogen atom: a dense core with a positive charge forming the nucleus of the atom. Around it, a negatively charged electron orbits the nucleus, much as a planet orbits the sun. The atom as a whole is electrically neutral.

The nucleus of a hydrogen atom is apparently simple. A single, positively charged particle carries most of the mass of the atom. In 1920, the nucleus of a hydrogen atom was given the name **proton.** By this time, it was becoming apparent that the proton might be a fundamental building block of all atoms. In fact, the number of protons in the atom of an element determines the number of electrons orbiting the nucleus, and the number and arrangement of these electrons determines the chemical properties of the element. The number of protons in the nucleus of an element's atoms is the element's **atomic number.**

Discovery of the Neutron

In 1932, a third subatomic particle was discovered by the English physicist **James Chadwick (1891-1947)**. The existence of the *neutron* had been predicted years before by Rutherford and others. The neutron has no charge and has nearly the same mass as a proton. The nucleus appeared to have two kinds of 'building blocks'. The protons and neutrons, called **nucleons,** together account for the **mass** of the nucleus of an atom. Protons alone account for the **charge** of the nucleus.

The proton-neutron model of the nucleus is still used. However, some questions naturally arise about this model. If there are no electrons in the nucleus, then where do beta particles, which are electrons, originate? Unlike protons and electrons, which are **stable** particles (as far as is known) and do not 'break down', neutrons are **unstable**.

Outside the nucleus, a neutron breaks down into a proton and an electron.

$$n^o = p^+ + e^-$$

Within the nucleus, neutrons are stabilized in some atoms. But in **radioactive atoms,** neutrons are unstable. When the neutron breaks down, the electron comes off as a beta particle, but the proton stays in the nucleus. Notice that *this raises the atomic number of the atom by one. It is no longer the same element!*

Another question raised by the proton-neutron model of the nucleus is: What keeps the positively charged protons together? Positively charged particles should *repel* each other, especially when at such close range. It turns out there is another force called the **strong force.** The nuclear strong force is only effective over *very short ranges.* Even the nuclear strong force cannot alone keep two isolated protons from flying apart. The presence of electrically neutral neutrons seems to be necessary to keep nuclei with more than one proton together. The nuclear strong force acts equally between two neutrons as it does between two protons. It is only effective over a very short range (10^{-16} m). Having neutrons in the nucleus makes the strong force better able to compete with the **electrostatic force** trying to pull apart the nucleus.

Exercises

1. (a) What is natural transmutation?
   (b) For what achievement was Rutherford awarded the Nobel Prize in chemistry?
2. What was the main accomplishment of the alpha-particle scattering experiment done by Geiger and Marsden in Rutherford's laboratory?
3. Describe the Rutherford model of the hydrogen atom.
4. What is a proton? What is the atomic number of an element?
5. Who discovered the neutron?
6. Is a neutron stable outside the nucleus? Explain.
7. What is special about the nuclear strong force? Over what distance is it effective?

16.2 Nuclear Reactions

Chemical reactions involve whole atoms, with some rearranging of electrons in the process. Nuclear reactions involve changes in the atomic nucleus. Radioactivity is due to nuclear reactions that involve the decay of a nucleus with the emission of particles or electromagnetic radiation. Radioactivity is beyond our control. It happens spontaneously and results in the formation of a new nucleus with a different atomic number. In other words, a new element forms. **Natural transmutation** occurs.

In order to write down what happens in nuclear reactions, certain symbols are used to represent subatomic particles. In the following chart, the **subscript** indicates the **electric charge** carried by the particle; the **superscript** indicates the number of **nucleons** (neutrons plus protons) in the particle.

Particle	*Symbol*
proton	$_1^1 H$
neutron	$_0^1 n$
electron (beta)	$_{-1}^0 e$
helium nucleus (alpha)	$_2^4 He$
gamma ray	γ

The charge and nucleon number system is also used for symbols of larger atomic nuclei. For example, the symbol for uranium-238 is $_{92}^{238}U$. The atomic number (nuclear charge) is 92. There are 238 nucleons in the nucleus. Since there are 92 protons, there must be 238 - 92 = 146 neutrons.

An example of a nuclear reaction is when uranium-238 undergoes radioactive decay and gives off an alpha particle. Here is how this nuclear reaction is written:

$$_{92}^{238}U \rightarrow _{90}^{234}Th + _2^4 He.$$

Because it ejected an alpha particle (helium nucleus), the atomic number of the new atom is two less (90). This is no longer uranium but **thorium**. The nucleon number is reduced to 234. Notice that there has been no overall loss of mass or charge! This reaction is an example of **alpha decay.**

The thorium formed from alpha decay of uranium-238 is also radioactive. It, however, undergoes **beta decay.** When thorium decays, one of its neutrons breaks down into a proton and a beta particle (electron). The proton stays in the nucleus and the beta particle is ejected. Here is how the net reaction is written:

$$_{90}^{234}Th \rightarrow _{91}^{234}Pa + _{-1}^0 e.$$

The **nuclear mass** has not been changed appreciably by the loss of an electron, but the **nuclear charge** has *increased* by one, and the new element is **protactinium.** Again, there is no overall loss of mass or charge.

The protactinium is also radioactive and undergoes beta decay as well:

$$^{234}_{91}\text{Pa} \quad \rightarrow \quad ^{234}_{92}\text{U} + ^{0}_{-1}\text{e} .$$

As you can see, the series of radioactive decays has lead us back to **uranium!** The atomic number of 92 tells us the element is uranium, but notice that the nucleon number is 234, not the original 238. This form of uranium has a different number of neutrons, 234 - 92 = 142 to be exact. There must be two forms of uranium! In fact, there are several forms of uranium. Different forms of the same element having different numbers of neutrons are called **isotopes.**

Isotopes

Isotopes of an element are chemically the same, but since the nuclei of the atoms have different numbers of neutrons, the atomic masses will differ. Three isotopes of hydrogen are illustrated in **Figure 16.12.**

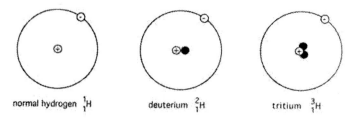

normal hydrogen $^{1}_{1}\text{H}$ deuterium $^{2}_{1}\text{H}$ tritium $^{3}_{1}\text{H}$

Figure 16.12

The most common isotope of hydrogen has one proton in the nucleus. This isotope is designated $^{1}_{1}\text{H}$. Hydrogen with a neutron in the nucleus does exist, and because it has two nucleons, this isotope, called **deuterium,** is designated $^{2}_{1}\text{H}$. A third isotope, **tritium,** has two neutrons in the nucleus along with the proton. Since it has *three* nucleons, it is designated $^{3}_{1}\text{H}$. The number of nucleons in the nucleus is called the **mass number.** The mass number of normal hydrogen is 1; of deuterium, 2; and of tritium, 3. (Deuterium oxide is **'heavy water'**, used in nuclear reactors.)

Isotopes exist of every chemical element. Some isotopes are stable and others are radioactive. Normal hydrogen and deuterium are stable, while tritium is radioactive, giving off beta particles as it decays and forms an isotope of helium.

$$^{3}_{1}\text{H} \quad \rightarrow \quad ^{3}_{2}\text{He} + ^{0}_{-1}\text{e}$$

Helium has three isotopes, designated $^3_2$He, $^4_2$He and $^5_2$He. The third element in the periodic table, lithium, has these isotopes: $^5_3$Li, $^6_3$Li, $^7_3$Li, $^8_3$Li and $^9_3$Li. Most naturally occurring lithium is Li-7 (92.5%) and Li-6 (7.5%). The other isotopes are artificially made **radioisotopes**. A radioisotope is an isotope that is unstable and therefore radioactive. Radioisotopes have many uses, such as in: medicine, biology, nuclear reactors, pacemakers, rock dating, and weapons.

Most carbon in nature is the isotope carbon-12, $^{12}_6$C. Small amounts of the radioactive carbon-14, or $^{14}_6$C, are found wherever carbon is found, including the gas carbon dioxide (CO_2). Because the amount of carbon-14 in a given sample of carbon dioxide is well-known, and the rate at which the C-14 'decays' is also well known, it is possible to 'date' ancient objects that contain carbon compounds using the amount of carbon-14 remaining. The technique of radioactive 'dating' has been used to determine how old the Dead Sea Scrolls are, and when the ice ages occurred (from the ages of trees knocked over by the glaciers).

Uranium has several isotopes, and all of them are radioactive. The most abundant isotope of uranium is $^{238}_{92}$U. Other isotopes of uranium include $^{233}_{92}$U, $^{234}_{92}$U and $^{235}_{92}$U.

Exercises

1. Explain in detail what this symbol means: $^{238}_{92}$U.

2. Complete these nuclear reactions:

(a) $^{226}_{88}$Ra $\rightarrow$ $^{222}_{86}$Rn + _____

(b) $^{214}_{82}$Pb $\rightarrow$ $^{214}_{83}$Bi + _____

(c) $^{218}_{84}$Po $\rightarrow$ _____ + $^4_2$He

(d) $^{210}_{83}$Bi $\rightarrow$ _____ + $^0_{-1}$e

3. What are isotopes? How are they the same? How are they different?

4. What is a radioisotope?

The 'Half-Life' of Radioisotopes

The rate at which a radioisotope decays can be measured. It is expressed in terms of *the time it takes for half the radioactive atoms to decay.* The time it takes for half the atoms in a radioactive sample to decay is called the **half-life** of the isotope. For example, uranium-238 has a half-life of 4.5 billion years. If a sample of uranium-238 had, say, 1 000 atoms to begin with, then after 4.5 billion years, 500 of these atoms will have decayed to thorium-234 (which, in turn, decays into protactinium-234, which in turn decays into uranium-234, and so on).

Uranium-238 has an exceptionally long 'half-life'. Uranium-235 has a half-life of 7.1 x 10^8 years, which is also very long. Uranium-237's half-life is only 6.63 *days!* Thorium-234, formed when U-238 decays, has a half-life of only 24.1 days. Protactinium-234 has a half-life of just over one minute! There are radioisotopes with half-lives of less than one millionth of a second.

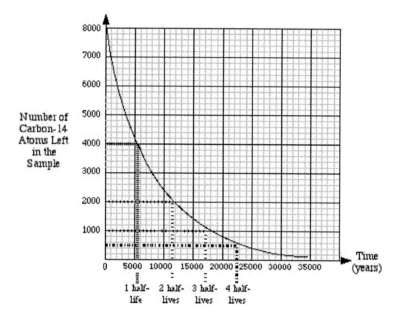

Figure 16.13

**Graph Illustrating the Decay Rate of Carbon-14, a
Radioisotope with a Half-Life of Approximately 5700 Years**

Figure 16.13 illustrates how an imaginary sample of 8 000 carbon-14 atoms decays over a period of many, many years. Every half-life (5700 years), the number of carbon-14 atoms left is reduced by one-half the number that existed at the start of the half-life. **Table 16.1** lists half-lives of some important radioisotopes.

Table 16.1   Half-Lives* of Some Isotopes

Isotope	*Half-Life* (a = year)
$^{3}_{1}$ H (tritium)	12.5 a
$^{14}_{6}$ C	5700 a
$^{15}_{8}$ O	2.1 min
$^{60}_{27}$ Co	5.2 a
$^{131}_{63}$ I	8.1 d
$^{90}_{43}$ Tc	6.0 h
$^{235}_{92}$ U	7.1 x 10^8 a
$^{238}_{92}$ U	4.5 x 10^9 a

Example: How long will it take for the number of radioactive $^{131}_{63}$ I atoms in a sample to be reduced to 1/16 of the initial number?

Solution: 1/16 = 1/2 x 1/2 x 1/2 x 1/2.   Four half-lives are required, and the half-life of this radioisotope is 8.1 d (**Table 16.1**), so the sample will be reduced to 1/16 the number of I-131 atoms in a time of 4 x 8.1 d = 32.4 d.

Exercises

1. What is meant by the half-life of an isotope?
2. Thorium-234 has a half-life of 24 d. How many atoms from a 4 000 atom sample will still be Thorium-234 after a period of 144 d?
3. After 26 a, the number of radioactive cobalt-60 atoms in a sample is reduced to 1/32 of the initial count. What is the half-life of the isotope?
4. A solution containing a radioactive isotope is injected into your blood stream just prior to conducting a brain scan. Should the radioisotope used have a short half-life or a long half-life? Explain.
5. Why is carbon-14 useful for dating ancient items containing carbon?

---

* The half-life of a sample is determined by measuring the activity of the sample, in emissions per second, over a period of time. One emission per second is one **becquerel** (Bq). Higher activities are measured in **kilobecquerels** (kBq) and **megabecquerels** (MBq).

Investigation 16-1
Simulating Radioactive Decay

Purpose: To simulate radioactive decay and half-life.

Procedure:

1. Your instructor will provide you with 100 'dice-size' wooden cubes, one side of which is coloured or marked in some way. (Dice can be used, but you must choose one number to represent 'decayed' atoms.)

2. Roll the cubes the way you would roll dice, each time recording the number of decayed atoms and the number of radioactive atoms still left after each roll. (The 'decayed' atoms are removed from the set after each roll.) Do this until all the atoms have 'decayed'.

3. Collect all class data, and prepare a master table listing combined class results. Plot a graph of **radioactive atoms** still left vs. **number of rolls.**

Concluding Question

From the graph, determine the **half-life** of your 'radioactive atoms', and express it in 'number or rolls'.

Radioactive Series

Recall that uranium-238 decays to thorium-234, and that thorium-234 decays to protactinium-234. In turn, protactinium decays to uranium-234. The series of decays does not end there. As **Figure 16.14** illustrates, the series of decays results ultimately in stable lead-206. This is an example of a **radioactive series.** When an alpha particle is emitted during radioactive decay, atoms of a new element are formed, with an atomic number two less than the original element and a mass number four less. When a beta particle (electron) is emitted, the new element has the same mass number but an atomic number one higher. During radioactive decay, gamma rays are often emitted as well, but they do not affect either the atomic number or the mass number.

Exercises

1. Write the nuclear reaction for the decay of radium into radon (**Figure 16.14**).

2. Write the nuclear reaction for the decay of Pb-214 into Bi-214.

3. How many different **elements** are involved in the radioactive series in **Figure 16.14**? How many different **isotopes** are involved?

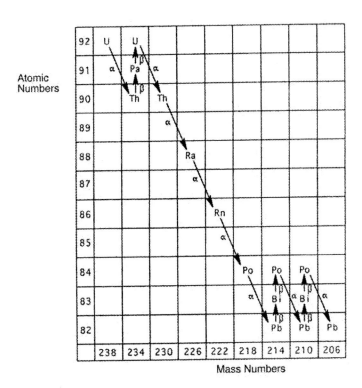

Figure 16.14: A radioactive series of naturally occurring radioisotopes, with $^{238}_{92}U$ as the parent. Atomic numbers are on the left, and mass numbers are along the bottom of the chart.

Artificial Transmutation of Elements

Artificial transmutation is a routine matter to modern-day physicists. The first physicist to succeed in changing one element into another element was **Ernest Rutherford**, who achieved this landmark reaction in 1919.

Rutherford filled a sealed container with pure **nitrogen** gas. He then bombarded the nitrogen with alpha particles. After the bombardment, he detected **oxygen** and **hydrogen** in the container. He explained this as being due to the **transmutation** of nitrogen into oxygen and hydrogen, according to this reaction:

$$^{14}_{7}N \quad + \quad ^{4}_{2}He \quad \rightarrow \quad ^{17}_{8}O \quad + \quad ^{1}_{1}H$$

nitrogen atom	alpha particle	oxygen atom	hydrogen atom (proton)

Since Rutherford's experiment, artificial transmutation has become a common procedure for today's nuclear physicists. In the early days, transmutation was achieved by bombarding atoms with particles from radioactive minerals. Later, physicists began to use particles accelerated by high-energy accelerators.

Research

1. Investigate how radioactive dating with radioisotopes such as carbon-14 and uranium isotopes is accomplished.
2. Read about ways that radioisotopes are used in medicine and biological investigations. Prepare a report on radioisotopes and tracers.
3. Is it possible to totally avoid being subjected to radiation?
4. How much did early researchers such as Rutherford and the Curies know about the dangers of radioactivity?
5. How is radioactivity detected? How is it measured?

16.3 Fission and Fusion

In 1932, English physicist **John Douglas Cockcroft (1897-1967)** and Irish physicist **Ernest Thomas Sinton Walton (1903-1995)** used a particle accelerator to produce high-speed (and therefore high kinetic energy) protons. These protons were made to collide with lithium nuclei. The high-speed protons were able to penetrate and disrupt the lithium nuclei, resulting in an artificially induced nuclear reaction:

$$\,^{7}_{3}\text{Li} \;+\; \,^{1}_{1}\text{H} \;\rightarrow\; \,^{4}_{2}\text{He} \;+\; \,^{4}_{2}\text{He}.$$

In this nuclear reaction, caused by accelerated protons, the lithium nucleus was, in effect, 'split', and the net result was two new nuclei, both helium. The newspapers reported that Cockcroft and Walton had 'split the atom' for the first time.

An important observation from this experiment, however, was the fact that when the kinetic energies of the two helium nuclei (alpha particles) were added up, *the total kinetic energy was greater than the kinetic energy of the proton that caused the reaction to occur!*

However, the combined **mass** of the alpha particles was found to be *less* than the masses of the proton and lithium atom combined.

This experiment actually confirmed a prediction made by **Albert Einstein (1879-1955)** that mass could be changed into energy. He related mass to energy with his famous equation, $E = mc^2$.

What actually happened in the nuclear reaction induced by Cockcroft and Walton was that *mass was converted into energy!* (Mass-energy, however, was conserved.)

The same year as Cockcroft and Walton carried out the first artificial nuclear reaction, **Chadwick** bombarded beryllium with alpha particles that had been accelerated. The helium nucleus was absorbed by the beryllium nucleus, carbon atoms were formed along with a 'new' particle — the **neutron**. Energy was released in this reaction as well. (This is how Chadwick discovered the neutron.)

$$\,^{9}_{4}\text{Be} \;+\; \,^{4}_{2}\text{He} \;\rightarrow\; \,^{12}_{6}\text{C} \;+\; \,^{1}_{0}\text{n} \;+\; \text{Energy}$$

This and other nuclear reactions can be used to produce free neutrons, which are now used as nuclear 'bullets'. Unfortunately, fast-moving neutrons are not too useful in nuclear bombardment experiments. Fast-moving neutrons go right through nuclei without having much effect. Slow-moving neutrons are another matter! They can actually be absorbed by nuclei, with very important results. Fast-moving neutrons can be slowed down by passing them through **deuterium oxide** (heavy water) or **graphite** (carbon). These substances slow down the neutrons enough to let them react with other nuclei. Heavy water and graphite used in this way are called **moderators**.

If a slow-moving neutron is captured by an atom of the most common isotope of uranium, uranium-238, here is what happens:

$$^{238}_{92}U + ^{1}_{0}n \rightarrow ^{239}_{92}U.$$

The uranium-239 is unstable and emits a beta particle.

$$^{239}_{92}U \rightarrow ^{239}_{93}Np + ^{0}_{-1}e.$$

Neptunium is radioactive, with a short half-life of only 2.3 days. It decays by emitting a beta particle to become Plutonium-239.

$$^{239}_{93}Np \rightarrow ^{239}_{94}Pu + ^{0}_{-1}e.$$

Both neptunium and plutonium are elements with atomic numbers higher than 92. They are just two of the many artificially produced elements beyond uranium in the periodic table. All are radioactive and have short half-lives. (Examine a periodic chart and see how many of these **transuranium elements** have been made by scientists.)

Nuclear Fission

A small fraction of natural uranium is the isotope uranium-235. When this atom absorbs a slow neutron, its nucleus undergoes an unusual transformation.

Recall that the strong nuclear force keeps the nucleus together, while electrical forces between like-charged protons tend to make it fly apart. In the uranium-235 nucleus, the balance between the normally dominant nuclear strong forces and the electrical forces is a fragile one. According to a nuclear model proposed by **Neils Bohr** (1885-1962) (called the **liquid drop model**), the addition to the nucleus of one more neutron might cause the nucleus to oscillate (**Figure 16.16**) and, if the electrical forces overcome the nuclear forces, the nucleus could break apart. This process can, in fact, occur. It is called **nuclear fission**, and it was discovered by two teams of scientists working independently, within days of each other. German chemists **Otto Hahn** and **Fritz Strassman** observed this reaction in 1939:

$$^{235}_{92}U + ^{1}_{0}n \rightarrow ^{144}_{56}Ba + ^{90}_{36}Kr + 2^{1}_{0}n + Energy.$$

Working in Denmark, two Austrian physicists made similar observations. **Lise Meitner** and **Otto Frisch** compared the process with the division of living cells and coined the label 'fission' to describe what happened to the uranium nucleus. The most striking feature about nuclear fission is the release of very large amounts of nuclear energy (due to conversion of mass into energy, according to Einstein's equation, $E = mc^2$). The amount of energy released during fission is extremely large compared with normal chemical reactions. The source of the energy is conversion of mass from the nuclei involved in the fission. Now, one nucleus undergoing fission may not be too significant, but keep in mind that for every fission that occurs, two or three neutrons are released. These neutrons can initiate more fissions which, in turn, produce more neutrons and more fissions. The possibility of a **chain reaction** occurring is very real!

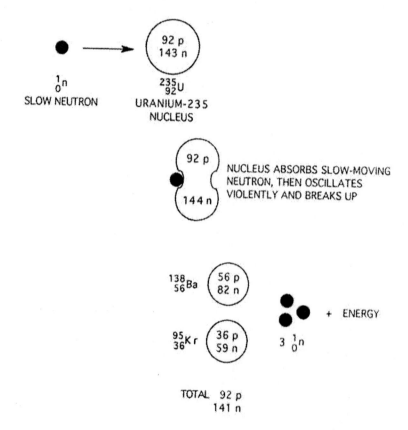

Figure 16.15: The Liquid Drop Model of One Possible Fission Reaction

A slow-moving neutron is momentarily absorbed by a **uranium-235** nucleus. The nucleus, according to Bohr's liquid drop model, oscillates wildly then divides into two smaller 'drops' — a **barium-138** nucleus, and a **krypton-95** nucleus. Three neutrons are also released!

Nuclear fission does not occur in naturally occurring uranium because uranium-235 makes up less than 1% of natural uranium metal. If fission did occur in a sample of naturally occurring uranium, neutrons from the uranium-235 would be safely absorbed by uranium-238 nuclei, which do not normally undergo fission. Even with pure uranium-235, a certain minimum mass called the **critical mass** is needed before a chain reaction can be realized. If the needed critical mass is achieved, an explosion of incredible force will occur. In a nuclear bomb, two or more sub-critical masses of uranium-235 are forced together abruptly by a conventional explosive, and the bomb explodes.

In a nuclear reactor, the uranium-235 is diluted with uranium-238 to an extent that a bomb reaction is impossible.

Research

1. Find out how the **Candu reactor** works. What are some of the safety precautions taken with this reactor? What are some of the concerns people have about obtaining energy from nuclear reactors?

2. What is a **breeder reactor**? What is it that is 'bred'? What is the advantage of a breeder reactor? What are the problems associated with the availability of plutonium?

Nuclear Fusion

Nuclear fusion is the opposite of fission. If light nuclei such as hydrogen, tritium and deuterium are forced to within a distance of approximately 10^{-16} m of each other, the strong nuclear force exceeds the electrical repulsive force, and **fusion** may occur.

As you might imagine, if two like-charged nuclei are to get very, very close to one another without repelling, they must be moving at extremely high speeds. High speed means high kinetic energy, which, in turn, means very high temperatures — the sort of temperatures found near the centre of the sun and other stars. Fusion is the source of the sun's energy.

Fusion occurring due to very high temperatures is called **thermonuclear fusion.** When light nuclei fuse, there is a loss of mass. This 'lost' mass is converted into energy. (Remember $E = mc^2$.) The sun actually loses millions of tonnes of mass every *second*. The energy produced from this mass leaves the sun as electromagnetic radiation (including visible light, infrared and so on).

Here is an example of a fusion reaction:

$$^2_1 H + {}^2_1 H \rightarrow {}^3_2 He + {}^1_0 n + \text{Energy}.$$

Two deuterium nuclei fuse to form helium-3, and a neutron is released in the process along with energy in the form of radiation.

The fusion process that takes place in the sun apparently involves a series of steps, but the net reaction is believed to be:

$$4\,{}^1_1 H \rightarrow {}^4_2 He + 2\,{}^0_{+1} e + \text{Energy}.$$

In the process, ordinary hydrogen nuclei are fused to helium with the emission of a **positive electron (positron)**. The positron is the **anti-particle** of an electron. It has the same mass as an electron, but the opposite charge. It is estimated that the loss of mass due to thermonuclear fusion in the sun is at the rate of *four billion kilograms every second!* Fortunately, the sun still has 2×10^{30} kg of mass left.

One of the great dreams of nuclear physicists is to master the process of fusion so that it can be controlled and used as a source of energy for humankind. Fusion is a 'clean' process whose products are not radioactive. (Helium is one of these products. Helium is the harmless gas used in toy balloons.) Research is going on at the present time. Fusion has been achieved, but as yet, scientists have not obtained a *sustained* reaction that releases more energy than is put into the reaction to get it started. The 'fuel' needed for a fusion reactor is simple hydrogen, which is available in plentiful supply from water (H_2O).

People have achieved fusion on a brief, horrendous scale in the development of the hydrogen bomb. The high temperatures needed are obtained by using a fission bomb (atom bomb) to force the reacting nuclei together.

Exercises

1. (a) Describe the landmark achievement of Cockcroft and Walton.
   (b) What was the source of the excess energy in this reaction?
2. What happens when a slow-moving neutron successfully encounters:
   (a) a uranium-238 nucleus?
   (b) a uranium-235 nucleus?
3. (a) What happens during nuclear fission?
   (b) What is the source of the large amount of energy released during fission?
4. What is it about the fission of U-235 that makes a chain reaction feasible?
5. What is meant by **critical mass**? How is it achieved when an atomic bomb explodes?
6. In a nuclear reactor, how is an explosion avoided when fission occurs?
7. What kind of nuclei can undergo fusion? What conditions are needed?
8. How is fusion initiated in a hydrogen bomb?
9. Why are scientists hopeful of achieving controlled fusion as a source of energy?

Chapter Review Questions

1. What experiments convinced J. J. Thomson that cathode rays consisted of particles carrying a negative charge? What are these particles called?
2. Look up the meaning of the word **serendipity**. Discuss the discovery of X-rays and the discovery of radioactivity in terms of serendipity.
3. Of what do alpha, beta and gamma radiation consist?
4. Why would one not expect alpha particles, on passing through gold atoms, to be deflected significantly by **electrons** in the gold atoms?
5. What was the essential conclusion made by Rutherford based upon the results of the alpha particle scattering experiment?
6. How was the neutron discovered? Who discovered it?

7. Write nuclear reactions for the following:
   (a) uranium-238 decaying to thorium-234
   (b) thorium-234 decaying to protactinium-234
8. How are the three isotopes of hydrogen similar? How are they different?
9. (a) What is meant by the **half-life** of a radioisotope?
   (b) Cobalt-60 has a half-life of 5.2 a. Describe what would happen to a sample of one million cobalt-60 atoms in a period of 52 a.
10. Describe the first artificial transmutation reaction. Who did it?
11. (a) What is nuclear fission? What is the most important consequence of fission?
    (b) Why is a chain reaction feasible in nuclear fission of uranium-235?
12. What is nuclear fusion? Give one example of a possible fusion reaction.

Research

1. What elements make up most of the stars?
2. Read about attempts to master **fusion**. What is a **plasma**? Explain the concept of **magnetic confinement**. How are **lasers** being used to initiate fusion?
3. What are the actual 'fuels' for nuclear fusion? What are the products?
4. Why would fusion scientists be particularly interested in the development of higher temperature superconductors?
5. What is meant by 'cold fusion'? What is the most current thinking on its possibilities?

Test Yourself!

Multiple Choice Questions

1. Which scientist is credited with showing that cathode rays are negatively charged subatomic particles (now called electrons)?
   A. Rutherford   B. J. J. Thomson   C. Röntgen   D. Faraday

2. While he was studying the fluorescent effect of cathode rays, X-rays were accidentally discovered by
   A. Röntgen.   B. Rutherford.   C. Becquerel.   D. Crookes.

3. Radioactivity was discovered accidentally by
   A. Röntgen.   B. Rutherford.   C. Becquerel.   D. Curie.

4. What is an alpha particle?
   A. a proton
   B. an electron
   C. electromagnetic radiation
   D. a neutron
   E. a helium nucleus

5. What is a beta particle?
   A. a proton
   B. an electron
   C. electromagnetic radiation
   D. a neutron
   E. a helium nucleus

6. Gamma 'rays' consist of
   A. protons.
   B. electrons.
   C. electromagnetic radiation.
   D. neutrons.
   E. helium nuclei.

7. Ernest Rutherford won the Nobel Prize in chemistry for discovering that
   A. the atom has a small positively charged nucleus.
   B. radioactive elements undergo natural transmutation.
   C. alpha particles can become helium atoms.
   D. the atom was mostly empty space.

8. One atom of $^{238}_{92}U$ has

   A. 238 protons.   B. 238 neutrons.   C. 92 neutrons.   D. 92 protons.

9. The symbol, $^{0}_{-1}e$, represents

   A. a gamma photon.
   B. a neutron.
   C. an alpha particle.
   D. a beta particle.

10. How is $^{235}_{92}U$ different than $^{238}_{92}U$?
    A. It has a different number of protons.
    B. It has a different number of electrons.
    C. It is chemically different.
    D. It has a different number of neutrons.

11. Technetium-90 has a half-life of 6.0 h. If there are 64 atoms of technetium-90 in a sample to start with, how many atoms of this radioisotope will be left in their original state after one full 24-hour day?

    A. 1
    B. 2
    C. 4
    D. 8
    E. 16

353

Complete the following nuclear reactions. A Periodic Table will be helpful.

12. $$^{226}_{88}Ra \rightarrow \, ^{222}_{86}Rn \, + \underline{\hspace{3cm}}$$

13. $$^{230}_{90}Th \rightarrow \, ^{4}_{2}He \quad + \underline{\hspace{3cm}}$$

14. $$^{234}_{90}Th \rightarrow \, ^{234}_{91}Pa \, + \underline{\hspace{3cm}}$$

15. $$^{14}_{6}C \quad \rightarrow \, ^{0}_{-1}e \, + \underline{\hspace{3cm}}$$

16. $$^{218}_{84}Po \rightarrow \, ^{214}_{82}Pb \, + \underline{\hspace{3cm}}$$

17. $$^{222}_{86}Rn \rightarrow \, ^{4}_{2}He \, + \underline{\hspace{3cm}}$$

18. $$^{210}_{82}Pb \rightarrow \, ^{210}_{83}Bi \, + \underline{\hspace{3cm}}$$

19. $$^{210}_{83}Bi \rightarrow \, ^{0}_{-1}e \, + \underline{\hspace{3cm}}$$

Open-ended Questions

20. What happens when uranium-235 undergoes **fission**? Describe what initiates the process, what happens during fission, and what the consequences are.

21. How is **fusion** different than **fission**? Give an example of a fusion reaction. Why is fusion difficult to achieve under controlled circumstances? Why is fusion favoured over fission as a future source of energy for human endeavours?

Answer Key

Chapter 1
Distance, Time and Speed
Page 11
2. 89 km/h
3. 0.76 h (46 min)
4. 4.6×10^2 km
5. (a) Total $d = 95$ km
(b) 88 km/h
6. (a) $v = \bar{v}$ at $t = 0.50$ s
   (b) $v_f = 2\bar{v} = 28$ m/s
7. $d = ct$
   (a) 1.80×10^7 km
   (b) 1.08×10^9 km
   (c) 2.59×10^{10} km
   (d) 9.46×10^{12} km
Page 15
1. 12.93 mm
2. 48.1 m^3
3. 12.01 mL
4. 0.9 mm
5. 12.5 g
6. 16.767 kg
Page 16
1. 0.31 m^2
2. 5.2 cm^2
3. 6.7 cm
4. 76.8 g
5. 4.1×10^2 g/mL
Page 18
1. (a) 5.72×10^{-3} kg
   (b) 5.2×10^{11} km
   (c) 3.0×10^8 m/s
   (d) 1.6×10^{-19} C
   (e) 1.1870004×10^2 g
2. (a) $10^{3+7+12} = 10^{22}$
   (b) $10^{23-5} = 10^{18}$
   (c) $10^{12+(-13)} = 10^{-1}$
   (d) $10^{-8+(-12)} = 10^{-20}$
   (e) $10^{5-(-7)} = 10^{12}$
   (f) $10^{-2-(-9)} = 10^7$
3. (a) 2.5×10^{-10}
   (b) 6.2×10^9
   (c) 4.69×10^7
   (d) 4.501×10^{-3}
4. 358 m^3 = 3.58×10^2 m^3
5. 11 g/mL
Page 19 Chapter Review Questions
1. (a) 2.84 s
   (b) 0.352 Hz
2. T will be ½ x 2.00 s, or 1.00 s.
   $f = 1/T = 1.00$ s^{-1} = 1.00 Hz.
3. 79 km/h
4. 0.64 km

5. 2.3 h
6. (a) 20.8 m
   (b) 55 s
   (c) 38 cm/s
7. 2.56 s
8. 1.4%
9. (a)

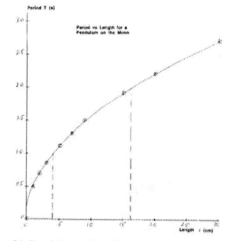

(b) (i) $\cong 4.1$ cm (ii) $\cong 16.5$ cm
(c) 4 times as long
(d) $\cong 2.48$ s

Chapter 2   Acceleration
Page 23
1. (a) 20.0 km/h/s
   (b) 3.00 m/s^2
2. 2.00 km/h/s
3. -15 km/h/s
   (Car is decelerating, so $a < 0$.)
Page 31
1. Slope = 14.0 m/s^2
   (a) Equation is: $v_f = 20.0$ m/s + 14.0 m/s$^2 t$
   (b) $v_f = 14.0$ m/s$^2 t$
   (c) a = Slope = 14.0 m/s^2
   (d) a = 14.0 m/s^2
   (e) Observers were at different locations. The
       aircraft was already moving when observer (a)
       recorded data.
2. (a) 10. m/s^2
   (b) $a = 0$
   (c) - 7.5 m/s^2
Page 34
1. (a) 15.0 m/s
   (b) k = 4.00 m/s^2
   (c) acceleration
   (d) v_f = 15.0 m/s + (4.00 m/s^2)t

2. (a) 5.0 m/s
   (b) 9.8 m/s^2
   (c) 17 m/s.

3. (a) 5.5 m/s
   (b) - 7.9 m/s^2
   (c) v_f = 5.5 m/s - (7.90 m/s^2)t
4. (a) 6.6 m/s
   (b) - 2.2 m/s^2
   (c) 3.0 s

Page 38
1. (a) 4.0 m/s
   (b) 10. m
2. (a) 25.6 m/s
   (b) 84.6 m
3. - 36 m/s^2
4. t = 3.0 s
5. (a) 3.00 m/s^2
   (b) 45.0 m/s
   (c) d = 3.38 x 10^2 m
6. d = 0.40 m/s^2
7. a = -1.2 m/s^2
8. (a) 4.9 m
   (b) 14.7 m
9. (a) 196 m/s^2
   (b) -9.8 m/s^2
   (c) 196 m/s^2
   (d) At B, because v_y = 0 at peak of the flight.
   (e) As soon as the ball leaves the pitcher's
       hand, the only force is gravity, which
       means a = g = -9.8 m/s^2.
   (f) *Direction is important, as well as speed.*
   (g) d = $\bar{v} t$ = ½(39.2 m/s)(4.20 s) = 82.3 m
   (h) d = 82.3 m
   (i) Average *velocity* = **Displacement**/time
       = 0! (Ball returns to its original place!)

Page 40   Chapter Review Questions
4. When no change in direction occurs.
5. (a) 8.00 m/s^2
   (b) 40.0 m/s
   (c) 2.00 x 10^2 m
   (d) v_f= 20.0 m/s + (8.0 m/s^2)t
6. 70. m/s or 2.5 x 10^2 km/h
7. (a) -12.0 m/s^2
   (b) v_f = 60.0 m/s - (12.0 m/s^2)t
   (c) $\bar{v}$ = $\dfrac{60.0 \text{ m/s} + 0}{2}$ = 30.0 m/s
   (d) d = $\bar{v} t$ = (30.0 m/s)(5.0 s) = 1.5 x 10^2 m
   (e) Area = ½ height x base
       = ½(60.0 m/s)(5.0 s) = 1.5 x 10^2 m
   Note! ½ height x base = average speed x time
   (Same as (d)!)
8. 4.0 m/s
9. 77.3 s
10. d ≅ 167 m or 1.7 x 10^2 m
11. 1.0 x 10^1 s
12. 9.0 x 10^{15} m/s^2
13. 66 m/s
14. 49 m
15. (a) 16 m/s

(b) t = 6.7 s
(c) 6.4 s
16. 0.10 s to pass the window.
17. (a) Graph of d vs t is a parabola.
    (b) Graph of d vs t^2 is a straight line, with a
        slope of k = 2.5 cm/s^2. So d = kt^2.
        Since d = ½at^2, the slope k must equal ½a.
        Therefore, a = 2k = 5.0 cm/s^2.

Chapter 3 Forces
Page 49
1. 0.750 cm/N
2. y = (0.750 cm/N)F
3. (a) 3.0 cm
   (b) 2.7 N
4. k = 0.75 cm/N

Page 56
1(a) steering, axles, chain, sprocket. Lubricants.
(b) brakes, tires/road

2. (a) μ = $\dfrac{F_f}{F_N}$; (b) The units cancel. (c) 0.480

3. 2.45 x 10^3 N
4. Friction force is independent of surface area of
   contact. The force remains the same.

Page 62 Chapter Review Questions
1. electrical and magnetic forces.
2. The graph of F vs x is a straight line.
   (a) Slope = $\dfrac{\Delta F}{\Delta x}$ = $\dfrac{8.30 \text{ N}}{2.00 \text{ cm}}$ = 4.15 N/cm
       F_g = (4.15 N/cm)x
   (b) F_g = (4.15 N/cm)(1.50 cm) = 6.23 N
   (c) 1.56 cm (≅1.6 cm)
3. 0.105
4. F_f = μF_N. If F_N (which in this case = F_g) is
   doubled, F_f will double to 448 N. If side by
   side, the F_f is the same as stacked, since the
   friction force is independent of surface area of
   contact.
5. 100 N
6. (a) (i) 1/4 F_g (ii) 1/9 F_g (iii) 4F_g (iv) 9 F_g
   (b) (i) 2 F_g (ii) 2 F_g (iii) 4 F_g (iv) F_g
   (c) (i) 9.80 x 10^2 N (ii) 1.62 x 10^2 N
       (iii) 1.4 x 10^{-11} N
7. (a) k = 5.0 Nm^2
   (b) F_E = (5.0 Nm^2) $\dfrac{1}{d^2}$
   (c) F_E is inversely proportional to the square
       of the distance between the two spheres.
8. Water adheres to the rod.
9. Water coheres to the wet string.

Chapter 4
Newton's Laws of Motion
Page 75
1. 25 N
2. (a) 2.5 m/s^2
   (b) 5.1 x 10^3 m/s

3. 6.0×10^1 kg
4. (a) 5.0×10^1 m/s^2
   (b) 6.0 N
   (c) Thrust = F_g + net upward Force = 7.2 N
5. (a) 1.3 m/s^2
   (b) As fuel is expelled, mass decreases, so acceleration will increase. Also, gravitational field strength g decreases with altitude.
6. 0.11

Page 77
1. 9.8×10^{-3} N
2. 9.790 N/kg
3. 80.6 kg
4. 3.6 N/kg or 3.6 m/s^2 Fraction = 0.37
5. (a) % Difference = 0.510%
   (b) 600.0 N + 0.51% of 600.0 N = 603.0 N
   (c) Mass does **not** change.

Page 83
1. 0.20 kgm/s
2. 5.5×10^{-2} Ns
3. - 12 m/s
4. 0.88 m/s
5. 25.8 N
6. 18 m/s
7. (a) -13.1 kgm/s, or -13.1 Ns
      (Ball reverses direction.)
   (b) - 1.31×10^4 N

Page 84 Chapter Review Questions
1. If the car stops suddenly, and you are not 'attached' to it, your inertia will cause you to keep moving at the same speed and in the same direction, until you collide with the windshield and/or steering wheel. A seatbelt attaches you to the vehicle, and you accelerate at the same rate as the vehicle.
2. In an inertial frame of reference ($\Sigma F = 0$), if there are no unbalanced forces acting on a mass, it will not accelerate. It will continue moving at the same speed and in the same direction. If $F=0$, then $a = 0$.
3. 3.0×10^3 N
4. 2.0×10^{-2} m/s^2
5. 5.0×10^2 kg
6. 2.0 m/s-2
7. (a) 443 N   (b) 9.80 m/s^2
8. See text. (Weight is the force of gravity on a mass.)
9. Newton's Third Law tells you that the force exerted along the rope is 500 N. The rope will not break.
12. (b) 2.8 kgm/s, or 2.8 Ns   (c) 5.6×10^3 N
13. 3.4 m/s
14. Measure acceleration of baby when pulled by a steady force. Calculate mass from $m = F/a$.
15. The mutual force between the ground and the feet of the competitors is what wins the match.

16. The reaction force on the rifle accelerates it into one's shoulder.
17. - 3.6 m/s
18. 3.0 m/s

Chapter 5   Vectors
Page 90
1. (a) 503.0 m
   (b) 290.0 m.

Page 93
1. (a) 1.0×10^2 m
   (b) 7.5×10^1 m
   (c) 1.3×10^2 m
2. (a) 8.5 m/s, $\theta = 21°$ to the right
   (b) 13 s
   (c) 38 m
   (d) 1.1×10^2 m
3. $\theta = 22°$ $v_R = 7.4$ m/s directed upstream
   $t = 13.5$ s $\cong 14$ s

Page 94
1. 130.0 N, $\theta = 22.6°$ E of S.
2. (a) 1.25×10^3 N
   (b) 1.39×10^3 N
   (c) 720 N

Page 97
1. $F_R = 720$ N + (- 480 N) = 240 N *down*.
2. The third ant's force is 37 mN, in a direction 19° west of south (or 71° south of west.)
3. F_R is 170 N, 61.9° W of N, or 28.1° N of W.

Page 102
1. 0.997 km North
2. Displacement from golfer to hole = 227 m
   To clear the ditch, she must hit the ball 219 m. Yes! She should 'go for it'!
3. 1.1 m/s sideward
4. 3.3 m/s
5. 24 N
6. Decreasing the angle will increase F_x.

Page 103 Chapter Review Questions
3. 122 m/s, 9.46° east of north
4. 997 km/h west
5. 24.0 cm/s (down)
6. 25.0 N (74° west of north)
7. 6.93 m/s^2
8. 1.39×10^3 N

9. PUSHING: Your force is pushing the mower into the surface.(Top diagram)
   PULLING: Your force is helping to LIFT the mower up the hill. This is the easier way. (Bottom diagram)

Chapter 6
Mechanical Energy
Page 107
1. 1.1×10^2 J
2. 1.72×10^4 J, or 17.2 kJ
3. $W = F \times 0 = 0!$
4. 4.9×10^2 J
5. 1.3×10^3 J
Page 111
1. 73 W
2. 5.4×10^5 J/h
3. Total Energy = 1.08×10^6 J
   Light energy: 5% of 1.08×10^6 J
   = 5.4×10^4 J
   Heat energy: 95% of 1.08×10^6 J
   = 1.03×10^6 J
4. Effort force (b) will only be 1/8 of the load.
5. With the following pulley arrangement,
   mechanical advantage is 1/2. The load is 1/2
   the effort. (So, the effort is twice the load!)

Page 115
1. (a) 5.2 m/s
   (b) 7.4 m/s
2. 0.32 m
3. 3.14×10^4 J
4. $E_k = \frac{1}{2} mv^2$
   Doubling mass will double kinetic energy, but
   doubling speed will *quadruple* kinetic energy.
5. Loss of potential energy = $mgh_o - mgh_1$
   = mg (2.0 m) - mg (1.6 m)
   = (0.40m) mg
   (a loss of 20%) The energy is used to warm
   the floor and the ball.
6. 3.8×10^3 J
7. Without considering friction,
   $\frac{1}{2}mv^2 = mgh$.
   $$h = \frac{v^2}{2g} = \frac{(25 \text{ m/s})^2}{2(9.8 \text{ m/s}^2)} = 32 \text{ m}$$
   With friction, the vertical height will be less.
8. $E_k = \frac{1}{2}$ (2.6 kg)(2.0 m/s)(2.0 m/s) = 5.2 J
   This energy is momentarily stored as spring
   potential energy, E_p.
   $\overline{F}x$ = 5.2 J
   $\overline{F}$ = 5.2 J / 0.12 m = 43 N.
   The actual force will vary from 0 N to 86 N!
Page 116 Chapter Review Questions
1. (a) 9.8 J
   (b) zero

2. 1.3×10^2 J
3. (a) 4 (b) 60 N (c) 11.2 m (d) 4.2×10^2 W
4. The 60 kg student moves. The MA is 2 for pulling
   him, but only 1 for pulling the 40 kg student.
5. 5.4×10^6 J
6. 3.6×10^6 J, or 3.6 MJ
7. 8.8×10^2 W; 1.2 HP
8. 0.17 m (or 17 cm)
9. $h = 2 \times$ radius, or 20.0 cm.
10. 0.288 m
11. 320 m

Chapter 7 Thermal Energy
Page 122
2. (a) 293 K (b) (i) 586 K (ii) 313°C
3. (a) water (b) nail (c) Nail loses heat to water
   (d) (i) water (ii) neither
Page 127
1. convection 2. (a) (i) Breeze toward shore (ii)
Breeze away from shore (b) Early morning breeze
goes out to sea.
Page 130
1. Vacuum stops conduction, convection. Silvered
walls reflect radiant heat back into the bottle. Rubber
or plastic stopper slows heat transfer by all three
methods. 2. Glass wool, Styrofoam™, wool, fur,
cotton, feathers, etc.
3. Dirty snow absorns more radiant heat. 4. Body
heat is reflected back to the body. Hypothermia
victims require warming from the outside, and the
suit would prevent this.   5 (a) radiation (b)
convection
(c) conduction (d) convection (e) conduction and
convection

Page 131
1. 2.3×10^7 J, or 23 MJ
2. 39°C
3. 4.0×10^6 J, or 4.0 MJ
4. Water has a very high heat capacity.
5. $c = 3.9 \times 10^2$ J/kg/C°
6. 5.0×10^4 J, or 50. kJ
7. 1.5×10^5 J, or 150 kJ
Page 134
1. 90%
2. 960 W
3. 5% of 60 W is 3.0 W.
4. 12% efficient
Page 135 Chapter Review Questions
1. (a) 523 K (b) 100°C 2. 323°C 4. The metal knob
conducts heat from your hand better than the wood
door does. 5. Convection. Warm water is less dense
than cold water. 6. (a) convection, conduction (b)
conduction, radiation
(c) radiation, conduction 7. Insulation *slows down*
heat transfer. 8. Black vanes absorb more radiant

energy than the white vanes, so they become warmer. It is presumed that the few air molecules that collide with the black surface will gain some kinetic energy, and rebound with greater speed and momentum than air molecules that rebound from the white surfaces. Newton's Third Law tells us that if molecules leave the surface with a certain impulse, they will give an equal and opposite impulse to the vanes. The black vanes receive a harder 'kick' from the rebounding air molecules than the white vanes do. 9. Igloo traps air inside it. Snow insulates because of the air trapped inside it. White walls reflect radiant heat. 10. See text. 11. Water gives off 10 times as much heat. 12. $\cong 36°C$
13. Large bodies of water warm slowly and cool slowly because of the high specific heat of water.
14. 7.2×10^5J, or 720 kJ
15. Efficiency = 93%
16. 92%
17. Three times as much light is emitted by the fluorescent light bulb.

Chapter 8   Waves
Page 142
1. (a) 1.25 Hz (b) 0.800 s
2. (a) 256 Hz (b) 3.91×10^{-3} s
3. 0.25 Hz 4. 0.40 m
5. $T = 1/f$; If f is tripled, period = 1/3 T.
Page 147
1. (a) If f doubles, λ is halved, since $\lambda f = v$.
   (b) If f is halved, λ doubles.
2. 200. Hz
3. 1.5 m
4. 10. Hz
5. 5.0×10^{14} Hz (orange)
6. 1.0×10^{-2} m, or 1.0 cm.

Page 162
1. 588 nm [nm = nanometre]
2. 0.250 m, 1320 Hz
3. (a) 6.348×10^{-3} m, or 6.35 mm
   (b) CD = 4.70 mm
   (c) CD = 4.20 mm
   (d) CD = 3.97 mm
Page 162 Chapter Review Questions
5. (a) 2.5 Hz (b) 0.40 s
8. 5.0×10^6 m, or 5000 km!
9. 0.645 m
15. 400 nm.

Chapter 9   Sound
Page 169
1. The speed of sound in a vacuum is zero!
2. Use a radio. Speakers and microphones must be inside spacesuits where there is some air.

3. (a) 1.0×10^{-5} s (b) 0.50 s (c) 9.1 s
4. 3.0 s
5. Sound does not travel in a vacuum!
6. 0.50 s, delay of 1.77 s
7. There is a about a 1 s delay. Sound reaches them 'late'.
8. $\cong 2600$ km/h
Page 178
1. 5 Hz
2. 5.0 Hz   Frequency of second fork is 256 Hz ± 5 Hz (Either 251 Hz or 261 Hz.)
3. You hear alternating maximum and minimum volume, due to interference of sound waves from the two tines of the fork.
Page 181 Chapter Review Questions
4. (a) 1.65 km (b) 26.0 km (c) 7.50 km
   (d) 30.0 km
5. (a) 332 m/s (b) 353 m/s 7. 165 m
8. 3300 km/h   12. 10^{10} 19. 2 Hz
20. 264 Hz ± 0.50 Hz   24. 335 m/s

Chapter 10   Light
Page 184
1. Sound and light signals are transmitted by microwaves to your receiver, at the speed of light. The light from the TV screen reaches your eyes faster that the sound from the speaker, but the distance is so short you cannot detect the slight delay in sound.
2. 0.133 s, 7.5 trips around earth in 1 s.
3. 9.5×10^{12} km/year
4. It will be 8 years before he sees himself. He will be 18 a. He will still look 10 a old.

Page 195
1. No light reaches the mirror. 2. 3.0 m/s
3. Arrange them at 90°. Three mirrors mutually at right angles will reflect any incoming beam back the way it came.
4. (a) 5 (b) 7 (c) 23 (d) 35 (e) 359
5. You need a mirror 1/2 your own height. (90 cm)
Page 198
1. 1.53
2 $\angle r = 4.11°$
3. $\angle r = 19.5° \cong 20°$
   Light enters the glass at 30° from the normal, then refracts within the glass at 20° from the normal. When it leaves the glass and goes back into air, it will be at 30° from the normal again.
4. Prism. Violet refracts most.
Page 201
1. $i_c = 24.4°$ 2. $i_c = 41.8°$ 3. n = 1.27
4. Incident angle is 70°, which is greater than the critical angle, so this particular ray will reflect

back into the water. Some rays will refract out at other angles and reach the fisher's eyes.

5. (a) below

(b) Aim at what your see. The laser light refracts, too!

6.

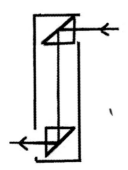

7.

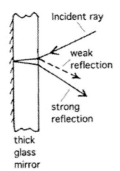

8.

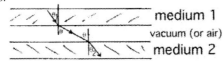

Snell's Law: For the situation above, where light travels from medium1 into a vacuum and then into medium 2,

$$\frac{\sin\theta}{\sin\theta_1} = n_1 \text{ and } \frac{\sin\theta}{\sin\theta_2} = n_2$$

$$\frac{n_1}{n_2} = \frac{\sin\theta}{\sin\theta_1} \times \frac{\sin\theta_2}{\sin\theta} = \frac{\sin\theta_2}{\sin\theta_1}$$

or, $n_1\sin\theta_1 = n_2\sin\theta_2$

Page 211

1. Yes. 2. No. 3. The filter blocks light that is not polarized in the same plane as the filter is aligned to let pass. 5. prism, diffraction grating. 6. (a) Yes (b) No. It is already one wavelength. 7. Water is pure, light is coming from a vacuum or air, and the

frequency is for 'average' visible light. 8. white; use red or green. 9. refraction, dispersion and total internal reflection. 10. All the same speed in a vacuum. Red is fastest in glass.

11. 2.0×10^8 m/s

12. 1.24×10^8 m/s

13. 1.54

14. 489 nm(blue) (*Frequency* is what determines colour.)

Page 215 Challenges

1. Ozone absorbs it. 2. If the ozone layer is lost, excess ultraviolet light reaches us, which can cause cancer, sunburn. 3. Sky would be red. Sunrise and sunset would be blue-violet.

4. Water absorbs red light very weakly. You see what is left---mainly blue-green. At great depths, red has been absorbed by water, and red objects appear black.

Page 215 Chapter Review Questions

1. 1.97×10^4 s (330 minutes, or 5.5 h)

4. 0.8 m 5. 3.0 m 6. (a) 3 (b) 7

7. $\angle r = 21°$

The beam will leave the glass at 35°.

8. use the ratio of $\angle i / \angle r$.

9. $\angle i_c = 41.1°$

10. $n = 1/\sin45° = 1.41$

12. Waves vibrate in a vertical plane. Only waves can be polarized. Particles cannot.

13. Different colours of light have different indices of refraction.

17. 1.5×10^8 m/s

28. Reflection of the sky makes it look wet.

Chapter 11 Optics

Page 226

2(a) real, diminished, inverted

(b) real, same size, inverted

(c) real, enlarged, inverted

Page 230

1. 100. cm

2. $D = 2f$.

3. 13.3 cm

4. $D_i = -30.0$ cm. The image is virtual, and appears to be behind the mirror.

5. concave, convex, convex, concave

6. (a) No (b) No

Page 242

1. 50.5 mm

2. 100.0 mm (or, 10.0 cm)

3. 20 mm

4. - 50 cm (a virtual image)

5. 19.0 mm

6. Use similar triangles.

7. $H_i = 1.7$ cm
8. Magnification is 2.00,
   The image is *real*, because $D_o > f$.
9. $D_i = -3.75$ cm (virtual image)

$$\frac{H_i}{H_o} = \frac{D_i}{D_o} = \frac{3.75cm}{10.00cm} = 0.375$$

(Image is diminished.) $H_i = 1.9$ cm.
Image is on the same side of the lens as object.

Page 248
1. You need an aperture 4 times as large, Use f/3.5.
2. You need an aperture 4 times as large. Use f/8.

Page 252 Chapter Review Questions
1. wide angle of view 2. Rays from centre of curvature are reflected back the way they came, then go out through condenser lens, through the slide to the focussing lens, and then to the screen. 3. Place the filament between f and $2f$.
4. At the focus. 5. D_o is less than f.
6. 1.7 m (real image)
7. 60.0 cm
8. 2.0 m
11. A short-sighted person needs *concave* corrective lenses, which *diverge* light.
12. Change either shutter speed or aperture.
13. (a) D_o is greater than 2f.
    (b) D_o is between f and $2f$.
    (c) $D_o = 2f$
    (d) D_o is much less than f.
14. Move the lens out 0.80 mm from its 'normal' position.
15. 135 mm
24. Use a shutter speed 4x as fast. (1/250s).

Chapter 12 Static Electricity
Page 260
1. Charge an electroscope negatively, and see if your comb repels it. If not, charge an electroscope positively and see if your comb repels it. Your comb has the same charge as the electroscope it repels. 2. negative 3. repel
4. neutral (none) 5. electron (-), proton (+), and neutron (0).
6. (a) Thomson, (b) Rutherford, (c) Chadwick

Page 266 (top)
1. The neutral ball is attracted to the positively charged rod. Electrons are attracted to the side of the ball nearer the rod. When the ball touches the rod, some electrons are conducted over to the rod, and the ball becomes positively charged. The rod is still positively charged, so repulsion occurs.
2. The positive strip attracts electrons to the nearer sphere. If the far sphere is pulled away, it will be left with a positive charge, while the nearer sphere will have a negative charge.

Page 266 (bottom)
Electrons from ground would be attracted to the small sphere through your hand. The small sphere would be charged negatively by induction.

Page 266   Chapter Review Questions
1. Du Fay 2. Franklin 3. Gilbert
4. Rutherford 5. Thomson 6. Chadwick
7. Glass loses electrons to the silk. Charge is conserved. 8. Your comb is negative. 9. Free electrons 10. No free electrons 11. Induction. No permanent transfer of electrons occurs.
12. (a) Touch it with acetate (conduction).
    (b) Hold the acetate near the can, and ground the can by touching it with your finger (induction).
13. Connecting to a large conducting surface such as the earth.

Chapter 13
Current Electricity
Page 272
1. (a) 0.540 A (b) 0.021 A (c) 1.500 A
   (d) 1.2×10^{-3} A (e) 5.6×10^{-5} A
   (f) 3.50×10^{-4} A
2. (a) 2.4 mA (b) 2.5×10^3 mA (c) 78 mA
   (d) 490 mA (e) 0.68 mA
3. (a) 5.6 μA (b) 48 μA
Page 282
1. 3.0×10^2 C
2. 1.0×10^1 A
3. 2.7×10^{23} electrons/hour.
4. 23 days
5. 1.8 g of Cu were transferred.
6. 4.026 g of silver
Page 287
1. yellow, violet, red
2. (a) $21\Omega \pm 5\%$ (b) $100\Omega \pm 10\%$
   (c) 5 M$\Omega \pm 10\%$ (d) 1.0 M$\Omega \pm 5\%$
   (e) 10 k$\Omega \pm 10\%$
3. Each of the four 1-m pieces will have a resistance of 4.0 Ω. If they are bundled into one cable, the cross-sectional area is increased by four times, so the resistance will decrease to one-quarter of what it was. The final resistance is 1 Ω.
4. 5.1 Ω.
5. 65.4 cm
6. 26 Ω
7. 1.4 mm
Page 288
1. 4.0 kΩ
2. 7.2 V
3. 5.0 A
4. 2.4×10^{-8} Ωm. The metal is gold.
5. 1.5×10^3 Ω, or 1.5 kΩ
6. 12.0 A
7. 25 V

Page 296 Chapter Review Questions

5. (a) 3.4×10^{-3} A   (b) 0.450 A
   (c) 6.52×10^{-4} A   (d) 2.1×10^{-6} A
6. (a) 4.4 mA   (b) 11 mA   (c) 44 mA
   (d) 2.2 mA   (e) 2.2 A
7. 4.0×10^1 A
8. 2.7×10^{24} electrons
9. 24.7 g of Ag
10-12. See textbook
13. brown, black, orange
14. 55 Ω ± 10%
15. 1 Ω
16. 0.29 Ω   17-18. See textbook.
19. (a) 15 V   (b) 120 V
20. 30 kΩ   21. 8.0×10^1 V

Chapter 14 Circuit Theory
Page 300
1. 1.20 V
2. $r = 0.030$ Ω
3. 5.0 A
Page 305
1. (a) 60 Ω   (b) 25 mA
2. (a) 1.5 Ω   (b) 2.0 A   (c) 0.60 A
3. (a) 11.0 Ω (b) 4.0 kΩ (c) 4.0 Ω (d) 20 kΩ
4. 9.0 A
5. (a) 10.0 Ω (b) 1.2 A (c) 0.40 A (d) 2.4 V
   (e) Decrease to 0.86 A
Page 308
1. 240 Ω
2. (a) 24 Ω
   (b) 2.2×10^5 J   (or, 220 kJ)
3. 22 V   4. 60 W   5. 144 Ω   6. 12.5 A
7. 1500 W   8. 1800 W   9. (a) 17.5 A (b) Yes
Page 309
1. (a) 6.48×10^7 J (b) 18 kWh, $1.08
2. $7.20   3. 20.5 kWh
Page 309 Chapter Review Questions
1. 1.29 V
2. 0.75 Ω
3. (i) (a) 20.0 kΩ, 1.0 mA
       (b) 100 Ω, 0.033 A
       (c) 8.0 Ω, 0.25 A
   (ii)   8.0 V
   (iii) 10.0 V (same as source)
   (iv)   3.0 V.
4. $P = IV = I^2R = V^2/R$
5. 1.00×10^3 W
6. ≅ 21 A   7. 24 Ω
8. 35 kWh   Cost = $2.45
9. 6 Ω, 8 Ω, 12 Ω, 16 Ω, 24 Ω, 32 Ω,
   36 Ω, 48 Ω, 60 Ω, 72 Ω, 96 Ω
10. 33 V

Chapter 15
Special Relativity
Page 313
1. (a) 10 km/h (b) 15 km/h
2. (a) 25 km/h (b) 0 km/h (c) 5 km/h 3. 0 km/h 4. 10
km/h 5. Assigning a positive value to velocities to
the right in the figure:
wind + 20 km/h; bird: - 5 km/h boat: - 15 km/h;
earth: 0 km/h river: - 5 km/h
Page 315
1. zero, which is constant!
2. same as **Figure 15.4**, but the parabola is elongated.
Page 319
1. (a) 6.6 s
   (b) 10. s
   (c) 50. s
   (d) 1.1×10^2 s

Page 321
1. (a) 78 m
   (b) 50. m
   (c) 4.5 m

Page 322
1. (a) 0.10 mc (b) 0.50 mc (c) 0.87 mc
   (d) 0.9999 mc (e) mc
2. (a) ≅ 0.10 mc
   (b) 0.58 mc
   (c) 1.8 mc
   (d) 71 mc
   (e) p approaches infinity $(p \rightarrow \infty)$
3. $F = \Delta p/\Delta t$
   $F \rightarrow \infty$ since $\Delta p \rightarrow \infty$.

Page 324 Chapter Review Questions
2. Speed = c.
3. (a) 13 a
   (b) 38.0 m
4. $v = 0.87c$
5. To see if it is possible, $t = \dfrac{t_o}{\sqrt{1 - \dfrac{v^2}{c^2}}}$

$$500\ a = \frac{50\ a}{\sqrt{1 - \dfrac{v^2}{c^2}}}$$

Solving for v gives $v = 0.995c!$

6. 9×10^{10} J!

Answer Key for
Test Yourself!

Chapter 1

1. (a) 16.2 cm
   (b) 77.7 mL
   (c) 338 m^2
   (d) 18 g/mL
2. 60.0 s^{-1}, or 60.0 Hz
3. 1.67 x 10^{-2} s
4. 6.2 x 10^2 km/h
5. (a) 1.3 x 10^2 s
   (b) 2.2 min
6. 114 km/h
7. 1.0 x 10^{-2} mm/s
8. 3.84 x 10^5 m
9. 0.5%
10. (a) Graph is a parabola,
    starting at (0,0).
    (b) $L \cong$ 9.5 cm
    (c) $L \cong$ 38 cm
    (d) approximately 4 times

Chapter 2

1. (a) 4.0 cm/s
   (b) 1.0 cm/s^2
   (c) v = 4.0 cm/s + (1.0 cm/s^2)t
2. (a) 4.00 m/s^2
   (b) 9.0 s
3. 2.4 x 10^2 m
4. 10.4 s
5. (a) 24.6 m/s
   (b) 88.5 km/h
6. -20.0 m/s^2
7. 8.2 s
8. (a) 3.50 m/s
   (b) -0.25 m/s^2
   (c) 24.5 m
   (d) v = 3.5 m/s - (0.25 m/s^2)t

Chapter 3

1. (a) k = 0.050 cm/N
   (b) y = (0.050 cm/N)F_g
   (c) 4.00 cm
   (d) 60.0 N
2. 5.0 x 10^1 N
3. 1.8 x 10^2 N

Multiple Choice Questions

1. C	6. C
2. A	7. A
3. D	8. C
4. D	9. D
5. D	10. E

Chapter 4

1. If a vehicle stops suddenly, an
   'unattached' occupant will, because of
   inertia, tend to continue moving forward
   at the same speed and in the same
   direction, until stopped by the steering
   wheel or windshield.
   A seatbelt 'unites' the occupant with the
   vehicle, and he or she will accelerate with
   the massive vehicle.
2. 20.0 m/s^2
3. 147 N
4. 12.0 kg
5. (a) 3.9 N
   (b) 12 N
   (c) 16 N
6. (a) 60.0 N
   (b) 0.500 m/s^2
7. 1.0 kg m/s
8. 43 m/s
9. 2.0 x 10^2 m/s
10. - 0.36 m/s
11. 1.3 m/s
12. See Text.

Multiple Choice Questions

1. D	11. D
2. D	12. B
3. C	13. B
4. A	14. C
5. C	15. D
6. B	16. B
7. D	17. D
8. A	18. C
9. D	
10. B	

Chapter 5

Multiple Choice Questions

1. D
2. B
3. D

Word Problems

1. (a) 1100 m
   (b) 500 m
2. (b) 1.0 m/s
   (c) 37° east of vertical
3. 1130 km/h
4. (a) 141 N
   (b) 28°
5. As $\theta \rightarrow 180°$, $T \rightarrow \infty$. The rope *has* to break!

Chapter 6

---

1. (a) 1.2×10^2 J
   (b) 0
2. 8.6×10^4 J
3. 375 J
4. (a) 5
   (b) 120.0 N
   (c) 7.2×10^2 J
   (d) 6.0 m
   (e) 7.2×10^2 J
5. (a) 5
   (b) 0.70 m
6. (a) 16
   (b) 4800 N
7. 4.9×10^3 W
8. 4.32×10^6 J

9. (a) 6.9×10^3 W
   (b) 9.3 HP
10. The ramp reduces effort force at the expense of effort distance, which increases. The ramp does *not* save you work!
11. 9.9 m/s
12. (a) MA = 12
    (b) 2.40 m
    (c) 168 J
    (d) 168 J

Multiple Choice Questions

1. A
2. D
3. C
4. A
5. C
6. B

Chapter 7

---

1. 14.7 MJ
2. 200 J/kg/C°
3. 83%
4. (a) 0.0455 C°/s (b) 95.6 W (c) 100 W
5. 90%
6. 18.6°C

Multiple Choice Questions

1. D	7. C
2. A	8. D
3. C	9. B
4. B	10. B
5. A	11. C
6. B	12. C

Chapter 8

---

1. The phenomenon is reflection. Waves reflect from the barrier with a curvature as if the centre of curvature was a point *behind* the mirror at a distance equal to the distance of the source from the barrier.
2. Diffraction occurs. Circular waves come from the opening.

3. (a) 0.20 Hz

   (b) 5.0 s

4. 1.8 s

5. Circular waves, originating at the focus, reflect from the first mirror as straight, parallel waves that travel to the second mirror, reflect as circular waves with a centre at the focus of the second mirror, where the match is.

6. 1.33 m

7. 4.9×10^{14} Hz

Multiple Choice Questions

1. D
2. B
3. B
4. D
5. B

Chapter 9

Multiple Choice Questions

1. A
2. A
3. B
4. D
5. C
6. A
7. E
8. C

Open-ended Questions

1, 2. See Text.

3. 6.0 s

Chapter 10

Multiple Choice Questions

1. C	14. D
2. D	15. C
3. B	16. A
4. A	17. C
5. D	18. D
6. B	19. E
7. A	20. D
8. A	21. D
9. A	22. B
10. B	23. B
11. C	24. C
12. C	25. A
13. A	

Open-ended Questions

1. 39.3°

2. 600 nm

3. 1.24×10^8 m/s

4. (a) The graph is a straight line through (0,0).

   (b) slope is 1.50. (n = 1.50)

   (c) 41.8°

Chapter 11

1. Inverted, diminished, real image forms between C and F.

2. E (at 5)

3. 22.5 cm

4. Inverted, enlarged, real image forms beyond C.

5. 12 mm

6. Use f/5.6.

Chapter 12

Multiple Choice Questions

1. D
2. B
3. C
4. A
5. B
6. B
7. B

Open-Ended Question

(a) Rub the vinyl with wool to give the vinyl
   a negative charge. Touch the can with
   the vinyl.
(b) Rub the vinyl with wool to give the vinyl
   a negative charge. Hold the vinyl *near*
   the can, while you touch the can with
   your finger. Remove both your finger
   and the vinyl. The can is now positively
   charged.

Chapter 13

1. A	6. A
2. D	7. C
3. D	8. B
4. B	9. A
5. C	10. D

Chapter 14

1. 0.25 V
2. 7.5 V
3. 1/16 R
4. (a) 9.0 Ω
   (b) 2.0 kΩ
   (c) 314 Ω
5. (a) 60 kWh
   (b) $4.20

Chapter 15

1. See Text.
2. $1.15t_o$
3. 0.866 c $\cong$ 0.9 c
4. (c) It takes time for the light to
   travel from the star to you.
5. See Text.
6. (a) 4.1 x 10^{15} J
   (b) 2.0 x 10^5 years!

Index